MATH FOR PHYSICS

M000287139

MATH FOR PHYSICS

Richard Dalven

Department of Physics
University of California at Berkeley

McGraw-Hill Book Company

New York St. Louis San Francisco Auckland Bogotá Caracas Colorado Springs
Hamburg Lisbon London Madrid Mexico Milan Montreal New Delhi Oklahoma City
Panama Paris San Juan São Paulo Singapore Sydney Tokyo Toronto

This book was set in Times Roman by Automated Composition Service, Inc.
The editors were John Zumerchik and Scott Amerman;
the production supervisor was Louise Karam.
The cover was designed by Albert M. Cetta.
R. R. Donnelley & Sons Company was printer and binder.

MATH FOR PHYSICS

2 3 4 5 6 7 8 9 0 DOC DOC 8 9 4 3 2 1 0 9

ISBN 0-07-015212-8

Library of Congress Cataloging-in-Publication Data

Dalven, Richard.
    Math for physics/Richard Dalven.
    p.   cm.
    Based on author's Calculus for physics. c1984.
    1. Mathematical physics.   2. Mathematics.   I. Dalven,
Richard.
    Calculus for physics.   II. Title.
    QC20.D28   1989
    530.1′55—dc19   88-38486

THIS ONE IS FOR GAIL

CONTENTS

TO THE READER

This book has two aims. The first is to "bridge the gap" between the calculus you've learned in your mathematics classes and the calculus used in your introductory physics courses. The second is to introduce you to vectors and their uses in physics.

Concerning the first aim, it has been my experience, based on several years of teaching physics, that many students who are reasonably familiar with the techniques of calculus are not familiar with the meanings of the derivative, differential, and integral when applied to physics. The book concentrates on explaining the meanings and the uses of the key concepts of calculus as applied to elementary physics. However, its aim is not to teach physics itself, and the physics used is kept as simple as possible. The emphasis is on the derivative as a rate of change, the use of differentials as small quantities, and the integral as a sum, all in the context of physics. The book assumes that you have taken, or are taking, a course in calculus, so it reviews the definitions and techniques of differentiation and integration but does not attempt to teach them from the beginning. It is also assumed that you are familiar with elementary algebra and trigonometry, but a brief review of this material is given in Chapter 1. This book is designed essentially for self-study by a student who is beginning to learn physics. I would suggest that you work through the material fairly slowly, using your calculus book to refresh your memory, if necessary, on mathematical points. Most sections of the text conclude with a few exercises. These are designed to reinforce the concepts just presented and to give you practice in using them. The exercises are not meant to be a challenge and are both straightforward and moderate in number so you may realistically do them all. I suggest that you try the exercises as you work through the book. Detailed solutions (not just answers) to the exercises are given in the back of the book and should be consulted after you've given the problems a try.

The second aim of the book is an introduction to vectors and their use in introductory physics. Chapter 5 discusses these topics, and here my approach is different from that used in dealing with calculus. I assume that the reader has had little or no exposure to vectors, so this material is presented from the very beginning and in some detail. It has also been my experience that vectors and vector calculus are used quite early in the study of mechanics in the usual introductory physics course for scientists and engineers. Frequently, however, these subjects are not covered until the end of the student's concurrent mathematics course. My book is an attempt to provide a useful discussion of vector analysis for the beginning student of physics. Again, the exercises (and their solutions) are an integral part of the presentation.

I've made a real effort to explain the concepts clearly. In fact, you may sometimes think that I'm overexplaining. However, repetition is a useful tool in teaching, and I'd rather say too much about an important topic than say too little. In the same vein, I've tried to write in an informal tone, just as if I were lecturing to a small class. I've also tried to keep this book short by concentrating on material I believe to be really important and useful for physics students in their courses.

This book is the outgrowth of my earlier book *Calculus for Physics*, and my debts to those who helped me with that book remain outstanding. My new debts include those to Glenn Fletcher, David Shucker, William S. Smith, and Robert Zako, who commented on part of the manuscript, and to Rita Jones, who typed the manuscript with great skill and patience, and to all of whom I extend my sincere thanks. It is, as always, a pleasure to thank John Clarke for his generous hospitality at the Lawrence Berkeley Laboratory.

Richard Dalven

CHAPTER
1

REVIEW OF ALGEBRA AND TRIGONOMETRY

INTRODUCTION

The aim of this chapter is to review some topics in precalculus mathematics that will be useful later. Since this is a review, it is assumed that you have seen this material before but may be rusty in its use.

SOLVING LINEAR EQUATIONS IN ONE VARIABLE

We consider first the familiar first-degree (that is, linear) equation in one variable,

$$ax + b = 0 \qquad (1.1)$$

where a and b are constants. An example is

$$5x - 10 = 0 \qquad (1.2)$$

a case for which $a = 5$, $b = (-10)$. Since the highest power of the variable x appearing in Eq. (1.1) is the first power, these equations are of the first degree. To "solve" an equation such as (1.1) or (1.2), we seek a value of x which, on substitution into the equation, gives an identity in

1

which the same quantity appears on both sides of the "equals" sign. We know that an equation is unchanged if we do the same thing to both sides of the equation, so in Eq. (1.2), we add 10 to both sides of the equation and get

$$5x = 10 \qquad (1.3)$$

Next, we divide both sides of the equation by 5, obtaining

$$x = 2 \qquad (1.4)$$

The value of x given by Eq. (1.4) is the solution to Eq. (1.2) because, on substituting $x = 2$ into Eq. (1.2), we get

$$5(2) - 10 = 0 \qquad (1.5)$$

$$0 = 0 \qquad (1.6)$$

the requisite identity which tells us that $x = 2$ is a solution of Eq. (1.2). One also says that the value $x = 2$ "satisfies" Eq. (1.2).

We can also solve Eq. (1.1), where we don't know the values of the constants a and b. We add the constant $(-b)$ to both sides of Eq. (1.1) and get

$$ax = -b \qquad (1.7)$$

Then we divide both sides of Eq. (1.7) by the constant a and obtain

$$x = -\frac{b}{a} \qquad (1.8)$$

Equation (1.8) says that the solution of Eq. (1.1) is the value $x = (-b/a)$, and Eq. (1.8) is the solution of Eq. (1.1) for any and all values of the constants a and b. For example, in Eq. (1.2) $a = 5$ and $b = -10$, so the solution of Eq. (1.2) is

$$x = \frac{-(-10)}{5} = 2 \qquad (1.9)$$

just the same result that we obtained before.

SOLVING QUADRATIC EQUATIONS

We consider next the quadratic equation in one variable

$$ax^2 + bx + c = 0 \qquad (1.10)$$

where a, b, and c are constants. Since the highest power of the variable x that appears is 2, Eq. (1.10) is also called an *equation of the second degree*. Since the equation involves x^2, there are two values of x which satisfy Eq. (1.10). If we denote the two values of x which satisfy Eq.

(1.10) by x_1 and x_2, then these values are

$$x_1 = \frac{(-b) + (b^2 - 4ac)^{1/2}}{2a} \tag{1.11}$$

and

$$x_2 = \frac{(-b) - (b^2 - 4ac)^{1/2}}{2a} \tag{1.12}$$

One sometimes sees the two values x_1 and x_2 combined in a single equation as

$$x_1, x_2 = \frac{(-b) \pm (b^2 - 4ac)^{1/2}}{2a} \tag{1.13}$$

where use of the plus (+) sign in Eq. (1.13) gives x_1 and use of the minus (−) sign gives x_2. The values x_1 and x_2 which satisfy Eq. (1.10) are often called the "roots" of Eq. (1.10), so we say that a second-degree equation has two roots.

As an example, consider the equation

$$x^2 + x - 2 = 0 \tag{1.14}$$

for which the coefficients in Eq. (1.10) are $a = 1$, $b = 1$, and $c = (-2)$. Using Eq. (1.11), we find

$$x_1 = \frac{-1 + (1 + 8)^{1/2}}{2} = \frac{(-1) + 3}{2} = 1 \tag{1.15}$$

Similarly, use of Eq. (1.13) yields $x_2 = (-2)$, so the two values of x satisfying Eq. (1.14) are $x_1 = 1$ and $x_2 = (-2)$.

Note also that the presence of the square root

$$(b^2 - 4ac)^{1/2} \tag{1.16}$$

in the solution (1.13) means that b^2 must be larger than the magnitude $|4ac|$ when $(4ac)$ is positive, if Eq. (1.10) is to have real (and unequal) roots. If $(4ac)$ is positive and equal to b^2, then, from Eqs. (1.11) and (1.12), the two roots x_1 and x_2 are both equal to $(-b/2a)$.

SOLVING TWO (OR MORE) EQUATIONS IN TWO (OR MORE) UNKNOWNS

A second useful algebraic technique is the solution of two equations in two unknowns, denoted by x and y. Suppose we have the equations

$$5x - 3y - 1 = 0 \tag{1.17a}$$

$$2x + y - 7 = 0 \tag{1.17b}$$

and wish to solve them for x and y. By "solving" in this context, we mean finding values of x and y which simultaneously satisfy both Eqs. (1.17a) and (1.17b). In order to do this, we must reduce the two equations in the two unknowns to a single equation in one unknown which we can then solve. A way to do this is to solve one of the equations for one variable in terms of the other. Thus we can solve Eq. (1.17b) for y in terms of x as

$$y = -2x + 7 \tag{1.18}$$

We can thus substitute this expression [Eq. (1.18)] for y into Eq. (1.17a), thereby eliminating y from the equation. We obtain from Eq. (1.17a) the result

$$5x - 3(-2x + 7) - 1 = 0$$
$$5x + 6x - 21 - 1 = 0 \tag{1.19}$$
$$11x - 22 = 0$$

Equation (1.19) can then be solved for x to give the result $x = 2$. To find the value of y which satisfies Eqs. (1.17a) and (1.17b), we substitute the value $x = 2$ into either Eq. (1.17a) or (1.17b) and solve for y. We find, say, from Eq. (1.17b) with $x = 2$, that

$$2(2) + y - 7 = 0 \tag{1.20}$$
$$y = 3$$

so $y = 3$ satisfies the two equations (1.17a) and (1.17b). The complete solution of Eqs. (1.17a) and (1.17b) is thus $x = 2$, $y = 3$.

In general, if we have N equations in N unknowns, the equations can be solved for the N unknowns. For example, suppose we have three equations in three unknowns x, y, and z. To solve these, take any two of the equations and, as done above, eliminate one of the three unknowns, say, x. This results in an equation in two unknowns, y and z. Next, take a different pair of the original three equations and eliminate x, giving a second equation in the two unknowns y and z. This procedure thus results in two equations in the two unknowns y and z which can be solved. Knowing the values of y and z, we can substitute these values into any one of the three original equations and thus find the value of the third unknown, x.

As a rather complicated example, consider the four equations in four unknowns,

$$-T + mg = ma \tag{1.21}$$

$$\tau = RT \tag{1.22}$$

$$\tau = (1/2)MR^2\alpha \tag{1.23}$$

$$a = R\alpha \tag{1.24}$$

where m, g, M, and R are constants; the unknowns are T, a, α, and τ. (These equations come from a mechanics problem in which a mass m hangs from a cord from a rotating disk of mass M and radius R. The tension in the cord is T, and α is the angular acceleration of the disk.) We want to solve Eqs. (1.21) to (1.24) for the unknown α in terms of the constants. We multiply Eq. (1.24) by m to get

$$ma = mR\alpha \tag{1.25}$$

which, combined with Eq. (1.21), gives

$$-T + mg = mR\alpha \tag{1.26}$$

To obtain an expression for α in terms of the constants of the problem, we must eliminate the unknown T from Eq. (1.26). Combining Eqs. (1.22) and (1.23) gives, on dividing by R,

$$T = (1/2)MR\alpha \tag{1.27}$$

Using Eq. (1.27) to eliminate T from Eq. (1.26) gives

$$-(1/2)MR\alpha + mg = mR\alpha \tag{1.28}$$

leading to the final result

$$\alpha = \frac{mg}{R(m + \frac{1}{2}M)} \tag{1.29}$$

for the desired unknown α. In a similar way, one can solve Eqs. (1.21) to (1.24) for the other unknowns a, τ, and T.

EXERCISES

1.1. Solve the equation

$$4x + 6 = 2x + 10$$

for x.

1.2. Solve the equation

$$2x - y = 0$$

for y in terms of x. Can this equation be solved for separate values of the unknowns x and y?

1.3. Solve the equation $z^2 - z - 2 = 0$ for the two roots z_1 and z_2.

1.4. Solve the following equations for x, y, and z:

$$2x - y = 0$$
$$x - 2z = -10$$
$$y + z = 10$$

TRIGONOMETRY

We review first the basic trigonometric functions, defined by Fig. 1.1, which shows a right triangle ABC, in which θ is the angle BAC. The trigonometric functions of the angle θ are defined as

$$\sin \theta \equiv \frac{\overline{BC}}{\overline{AB}} = \frac{a}{c} \tag{1.30}$$

$$\cos \theta \equiv \frac{\overline{AC}}{\overline{AB}} = \frac{b}{c} \tag{1.31}$$

$$\tan \theta \equiv \frac{\overline{BC}}{\overline{AC}} = \frac{a}{b} \tag{1.32}$$

From basic inequalities about the lengths of the sides of triangles, one can show that the sine and cosine of any angle have magnitudes between zero and one, and values between $(+1)$ and (-1), so we have

$$0 \leq \left|\sin \theta\right| \leq 1; \quad (-1) \leq \sin \theta \leq 1 \tag{1.33}$$

$$0 \leq \left|\cos \phi\right| \leq 1; \quad (-1) \leq \cos \phi \leq 1 \tag{1.34}$$

where θ and ϕ are any angles and $\left|\sin \theta\right|$ denotes the magnitude (or absolute value) of $\sin \theta$, and so forth.

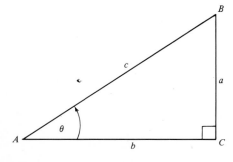

FIGURE 1.1
Right triangle used to define the trigonometric functions. The lengths $\overline{AB} \equiv c$, $\overline{AC} \equiv b$, and $\overline{BC} \equiv a$.

The other three basic trigonometric functions are the reciprocals of the sine, cosine, and tangent, so we have

$$\text{secant } \theta = \sec \theta \equiv \frac{1}{\cos \theta} \tag{1.35}$$

$$\text{cosecant } \theta = \csc \theta \equiv \frac{1}{\sin \theta} \tag{1.36}$$

$$\text{cotangent } \theta = \text{ctn } \theta \equiv \frac{1}{\tan \theta} \tag{1.37}$$

The functions (1.35) to (1.37) do not occur as frequently in introductory physics as do the sine, cosine, and tangent.

There are a number of useful relations between the trigonometric functions which are true for any value of the angle θ; these are trigonometric identities. First, from Eqs. (1.30) and (1.31), we see that

$$\tan \theta = \frac{a}{b} = \left(\frac{a}{c}\right)\left(\frac{c}{b}\right) = \frac{\sin \theta}{\cos \theta} \tag{1.38}$$

a very useful identity relating the sine, cosine, and tangent of any angle. From Eq. (1.38) and the relations (1.33) and (1.34), we can see that the value of $\tan \theta$ ranges from $(+\infty)$ to $(-\infty)$ and its magnitude, from ∞ to zero. Second, from the definitions (1.30) and (1.31), we have

$$\sin^2 \theta + \cos^2 \theta = \frac{a^2 + b^2}{c^2} = \frac{c^2}{c^2} = 1 \tag{1.39}$$

since, applying the pythagorean theorem to the right triangle ABC in Fig. 1.1, it is true that $a^2 + b^2 = c^2$. Equation (1.39) establishes the important identity

$$\sin^2 \theta + \cos^2 \theta = 1 \tag{1.40}$$

true for any value of the angle θ.

The following is a brief list of useful trigonometric identities. (Very extensive lists of such identities may be found in *Mathematical Handbook of Formulas and Tables*, by M. R. Spiegel, McGraw-Hill, 1968, or in *Tables of Integrals and Other Mathematical Data*, by H. B. Dwight, 4th ed., Macmillan, 1961.) These identities are true for any values of the angles θ and ϕ:

$$\sin (\theta + \phi) = \sin \theta \cos \phi + \cos \theta \sin \phi \tag{1.41}$$

$$\cos (\theta + \phi) = \cos \theta \cos \phi - \sin \theta \sin \phi \tag{1.42}$$

$$\sin (\theta - \phi) = \sin \theta \cos \phi - \cos \theta \sin \phi \tag{1.43}$$

$$\cos(\theta - \phi) = \cos\theta \cos\phi + \sin\theta \sin\phi \qquad (1.44)$$

$$\sin\theta + \sin\phi = 2 \sin\tfrac{1}{2}(\theta + \phi) \cos\tfrac{1}{2}(\theta - \phi) \qquad (1.45)$$

$$\sin\theta - \sin\phi = 2 \sin\tfrac{1}{2}(\theta - \phi) \cos\tfrac{1}{2}(\theta + \phi) \qquad (1.46)$$

$$\cos\theta + \cos\phi = 2 \cos\tfrac{1}{2}(\theta + \phi) \sin\tfrac{1}{2}(\theta - \phi) \qquad (1.47)$$

$$\cos\theta - \cos\phi = 2 \sin\tfrac{1}{2}(\theta + \phi) \cos\tfrac{1}{2}(\theta - \phi) \qquad (1.48)$$

$$\sin 2\theta = 2 \sin\theta \cos\theta \qquad (1.49)$$

$$\cos 2\theta = 2 \cos^2\theta - 1 \qquad (1.50)$$

As an example of the utility of these trigonometric identities, consider the following. Suppose we know sin A, where A is some angle (less than 90°). What is the value of the sine of the angle $(180° - A)$, that is, $\sin(180° - A)$? Using Eq. (1.43) with $\theta = 180°$, $\phi = A$, we have

$$\sin(180° - A) = \sin 180° \cos A - \cos 180° \sin A \qquad (1.51)$$

Recalling that $\sin 180° = \sin 0° = 0$, and $\cos 180° = -1$, we obtain

$$\sin(180° - A) = (0)(\cos A) - (-1)(\sin A) = \sin A \qquad (1.52)$$

showing that $\sin(180° - A) = \sin A$. Thus, for example, $\sin 162° = \sin(180° - 18°) = \sin 18° = 0.309$.

We should also mention the *inverse* trigonometric functions. If

$$y = \sin x \qquad (1.53)$$

an equation that says that y is the sine of the angle x, we may solve (1.53) for x in terms of y, writing

$$x = \sin^{-1} y \qquad (1.54)$$

an equation that is read "x is the angle whose sine is y." As an example,

$$0.707 = \sin 45° \qquad (1.55)$$

$$45° = \sin^{-1}(0.707) \qquad (1.56)$$

Note that x in (1.54) is a many-valued function of y; more than one value of x corresponds to a single value of y. For example, in addition to (1.56), it is also true that

$$135° = \sin^{-1}(0.707) \qquad (1.57)$$

There are also other inverse trigonometric functions. If

$$y = \cos x \qquad (1.58)$$

then its inverse is

$$x = \cos^{-1} y \qquad (1.59)$$

and if

$$y = \tan x \qquad (1.60)$$

its inverse is

$$x = \tan^{-1} y \qquad (1.61)$$

Another notation is also used for inverse trigonometric functions, namely,

$$x = \text{arc sin } y \equiv \sin^{-1} y \qquad (1.62)$$

Both notations in (1.62) mean the same thing, namely, "x is the angle whose sine is y."

Finally, there are two useful relations between the sides and angles of a triangle. Figure 1.2 shows a triangle ABC (not necessarily a right triangle, whose sides are of lengths a, b, and c, and whose interior angles are denote by α, β, and γ). The first relation, the Law of Sines, states that

$$\frac{a}{\sin \alpha} = \frac{b}{\sin \beta} = \frac{c}{\sin \gamma} \qquad (1.63)$$

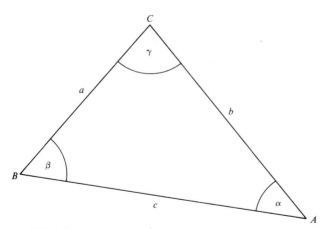

FIGURE 1.2
Triangle ABC used to define the Law of Sines and Law of Cosines.

The second relation, the Law of Cosines, says

$$c^2 = a^2 + b^2 - 2ab \cos \gamma \qquad (1.64)$$

$$b^2 = a^2 + c^2 - 2ac \cos \beta \qquad (1.65)$$

$$a^2 = b^2 + c^2 - 2bc \cos \alpha \qquad (1.66)$$

These relations permit calculation of the magnitudes of the sides and/or angles of a triangle from a knowledge of the magnitudes of the remaining sides and/or angles. For example, if $a = 1$ meter, $b = 2$ meters, $\gamma = 60°$, then, from Eq. (1.64), we obtain

$$c^2 = 1 + 4 - 2(1)(2) \cos 60° = 3 \qquad (1.67)$$

so

$$c = \sqrt{3} \text{ meters} = 1.73 \text{ meters} \qquad (1.68)$$

Using the result (1.68) and the Law of Sines (1.63), we have, with $a = 1$ meter, $c = \sqrt{3}$ meters, $\gamma = 60°$,

$$\frac{1}{\sin \alpha} = \frac{\sqrt{3}}{(\sqrt{3}/2)} = 2 \qquad (1.69)$$

yielding the value $\sin \alpha = (1/2)$, so $\alpha = 30°$. Since the sum of the interior angles of a triangle is $180°$, and $(\alpha + \gamma) = 90°$, $\beta = 90°$, the triangle in this example is a right triangle.

EXERCISES

1.5. Use Eq. (1.43) to prove that $\sin(-\phi) = -\sin \phi$; use Eq. (1.44) to prove $\cos(-\phi) = \cos \phi$. Both of these results are true for any value of ϕ.

1.6. Solve the following equation for a value of x less than $90°$:

$$x = \tan^{-1} 1$$

1.7. Prove that the identity

$$\sec \theta = (1 + \tan^2 \theta)^{1/2}$$

is valid by showing both sides of the identity are the same.

1.8. Use the Law of Cosines to prove that each of the interior angles of an equilateral triangle is $60°$.

CHAPTER
2

VARIABLES, FUNCTIONS, AND GRAPHS

INTRODUCTION

The aim of this chapter is to introduce much of the terminology we will use in the later chapters and to review some of the basic concepts you have learned in your calculus course. These are variables, functions, and graphs. The point of view, however, will be that of the physicist, not the mathematician. The concepts we will discuss here are things we will use frequently as we progress.

VARIABLES AND FUNCTIONS

A *variable* is a quantity which may take on different values in the course of the discussion of some question. An example might be the radius r of a circle during a discussion of geometry. The idea of a variable should be contrasted with that of a *constant*, which is a quantity having a fixed value. Examples of constants are the numbers 6, 21, π, etc. The variable (or variables) under consideration in some situation will be denoted by appropriate and convenient symbols; an example is the symbol r for the radius of a circle.

Suppose x and y are both variables. A *function* is a rule connecting the two variables x and y such that, if the value of one variable (say, x) is given, the value of the other variable is determined. For example, suppose

$$y = x^2 \tag{2.1}$$

Equation (2.1) tells us that the value of the variable y is equal to the square of the value of the variable x. Equation (2.1) therefore tells us that y is a function of x because, if we know the value of the variable x, the value of the variable y is determined. For example, if $x = 2$, $y = 4$, we say that Eq. (2.1) gives the variable y as a function of the variable x, or, more simply, Eq. (2.1) gives y as a function of x. In Eq. (2.1), assigning a value to x determines the value of y. We call x the *independent variable* in the function $y = x^2$ given in Eq. (2.1). The variable y is called the *dependent variable*, since the value of y depends on the value of x. In discussing Eq. (2.1), we say that y is a function of x, or that there exists a *functional relationship* between the variables y and x.

The function $y = x^2$ in Eq. (2.1) is such that only a single value of the dependent variable y corresponds to each value of the independent variable x. Such a function is called *single-valued*. Functions for which there are more than one value of the dependent variable for each value of the independent variable are called *many-valued* functions. An example of a many-valued function is $y = \pm \sqrt{x}$, in which there are two values of y for each value of x. When we indicate a square root, as in $\sqrt{x}$, or $(1-x)^{1/2}$, we mean the positive square root; the negative square root would be indicated explicitly, as $-\sqrt{x}$, or $-(1 - x)^{1/2}$. Most of the functions we will encounter will be single-valued.

Given the existence of a functional relationship between the variables y and x, then the set of values which the independent variable x may take on is called the domain of the function. The set of values which the dependent variable y may take on is called the range of the function.

Consider a second example. The familiar relation between the area A of a circle and its radius r is given by Eq. (2.2). Equation (2.2),

$$A = \pi r^2 \tag{2.2}$$

expresses the area A as a function of the radius r; π is a constant. From Eq. (2.2), if the value of the independent variable r is specified, then the value of the dependent variable A is determined according to the function (2.2) which gives A as a function of r.

In physics, the variables with which we deal are almost always quantities with a physical meaning and are things that can be measured.

For example, the variables A and r in Eq. (2.2) are the area and radius of a circle, both of which are quantities with a physical meaning and which can be measured if we wish. We may contrast the case of Eq. (2.2) with that of Eq. (2.1), in which the variables x and y are mathematical symbols, whose physical meanings (if any) are not specified. In dealing with physical problems, it is helpful to keep in mind the meanings of the symbols with which we deal. In physics, we will constantly be working with functions which give a dependent variable of physical interest in terms of an independent variable (or variables) which will also be physically interesting and measurable quantities.

As a final example of a function, recall the familiar result from elementary physics that "distance equals rate times time" for a body moving with constant rate or speed. If the symbol s is used for distance, v for speed or rate, and t for time, our familiar result is expressed by

$$s = vt \qquad (2.3)$$

Equation (2.3) gives the distance s (the dependent variable) as a function of the time t (the independent variable) in the case in which the speed v is constant, so v is not a variable in this situation. Equation (2.3) introduces us to a most important independent variable in physics—the time. Much of physics is concerned with how different quantities vary with time, so physics is often concerned with equations, like Eq. (2.3), giving some quantity *as a function of time*.

EXERCISES

2.1. Consider the variables w and u connected by the function

$$w = 7u^2 + 6u + 3$$

Which is the independent variable? Which is the dependent variable?

2.2. Equation (2.1) gives y as a function of x. Use Eq. (2.1) to obtain an equation giving x as a function of y. In the functional relation you obtained, identify the dependent and independent variables.

2.3. A familiar geometric relation is that between the circumference C and the radius r of a cricle, which says that the circumference is the constant 2 times the constant π times the radius of the circle. Write the equation giving C as a function of r. In the functional relation between C and r, which is the dependent and which is the independent variable?

FUNCTIONAL NOTATION

We now discuss a few points concerning the notation used to express functions and functional relationships between variables.

The existence of a general functional relationship between two variables x and y may be indicated by writing

$$y = f(x) \qquad (2.4)$$

an equation which tells us that the dependent variable y is some function f of the independent variable x, but we are not told what the specific function is. Equation (2.4) does tell us, however, that y is a function of x, so y depends on x. If the specific function f is known, then that information may also be given. For example, in the example in Eq. (2.1) in which $y = x^2$, the specific function f is given, so we may write

$$y = f(x) = x^2 \qquad (2.5)$$

Equation (2.5) says that the dependent variable y is a function $f(x)$ of the independent variable x, and that the specific function $f(x)$ is x^2.

A situation often encountered in physics is the following. Suppose y is some function f of x, so

$$y = f(x) \qquad (2.6)$$

and the variable x is itself a function g of another variable t, so

$$x = g(t) \qquad (2.7)$$

Equation (2.6) says y is a function $f(x)$ of the variable x; Eq. (2.7) says x is a function $g(t)$ of the variable t. One can combine Eqs. (2.6) and (2.7) by writing

$$y = f[g(t)] \qquad (2.8)$$

Equation (2.8) says that the variable y is a function f of the function $g(t)$ of the variable t, so the dependent variable y is ultimately a function of the dependent variable t. One also describes the situation in Eq. (2.8) by saying that y is a function f of the function g of t.

As an example, suppose we have the relations

$$y = f(\theta) = \sin \theta \qquad (2.9)$$

$$\theta = g(t) = \omega t \qquad (2.10)$$

where, in Eq. (2.10), ω is a constant. Equation (2.9) says that the variable y is a function (the sine) of the variable θ, while θ is a function of the variable t. We may combine Eqs. (2.9) and (2.10), using Eq. (2.8), to give

$$y = \sin \omega t \qquad (2.11)$$

showing that y is a function of t.

Finally, one sometimes sees notation like the following. Suppose y

is a function of x; one may write this functional relationship as

$$y = y(x) \tag{2.12}$$

simply to conserve symbols (which, surprisingly, are sometimes in short supply). Equation (2.12) says that y is some (unspecified) function of x, so Eq. (2.12) conveys the same information as Eq. (2.6) but uses fewer symbols to do so. In physics, one frequently sees the relations like

$$x = x(t) \tag{2.13}$$

$$y = y(t) \tag{2.14}$$

saying that x is a function of t and y is a (different) function of t, so, in Eqs. (2.13) and (2.14), t is the independent variable in both equations.

FUNCTIONS OF SEVERAL VARIABLES

In the preceding sections, we discussed a function

$$y = f(x) \tag{2.15}$$

in which y depends on the single variable, x. The function $f(x)$ in Eq. (2.15) is a function of one independent variable. We may also consider functions of more than one variable, such as

$$w = g(x, y) \tag{2.16}$$

Equation (2.16) says that the dependent variable w is a function of the two independent variables x and y; if values of x and y are specified, then the value of w is determined. Note that the two independent variables x and y are *independent of each other*, so x and y are separate independent variables.

An example of a function of two variables of the type given in Eq. (2.16) is

$$w = g(x, y) = x^2 + y^2 \tag{2.17}$$

A second example is the expression

$$V = \pi r^2 h \tag{2.18}$$

for the volume V of a right circular cylinder of radius r and height h. In Eq. (2.18) V is a function of r and h, both of which are independent variables, so the volume V is a function $V(r, h)$ of r and h. Another example is the function

$$y = y(x, t) = A \sin(kx - \omega t) \tag{2.19}$$

where A, k, and ω are constants. The function in Eq. (2.19) gives y as a sinusoidal function of the two independent variables x and t.

While we will, in this book, usually restrict ourselves to dealing with functions of one variable, we will, on occasion, introduce functions of more than one variable.

VALUE OF A FUNCTION AT A POINT

Generally, the independent variable x in a function

$$y = f(x) \tag{2.20}$$

will take on a set of values called the domain of the function. What this set of values is will be determined by the particular function, the physical situation being discussed, etc. We will often wish to consider the value of the dependent variable y for some *particular* values of x. For example, if

$$y = f(x) = x^2 \tag{2.21}$$

then $y = 4$ when $x = 2$. We say the function $y = f(x) = x^2$ has the value 4 when $x = 2$, or, equivalently, that the function $y = 4$ at the point $x = 2$. (The use of the term *point* for a particular value of x refers to the point on the x axis, such as $x = 2$, corresponding to the value of x. Thus we refer to the value of a function at a point.)

If y is a function $f(x)$ of x, as in Eq. (2.20), then there is a common notation used to indicate the value of $f(x)$ for some particular value of x. It is usual to denote particular values of a variable by putting a subscript on the variable. Thus

$$x = x_1 \tag{2.22}$$

is an equation saying that the variable x has the particular value x_1. In the example above, we consider the case in which x has the value 2, so we were considering

$$x = x_1 = 2 \tag{2.23}$$

meaning that the variable x has the particular value $x_1 = 2$. If, at the same time, we wished to consider a different particular value of x we might call it x_2. For example, we might consider

$$x = x_2 = 5 \tag{2.24}$$

as a second particular value of x.

If we are considering a function

$$y = f(x) \tag{2.25}$$

and if the independent variable x has the value x_1 so

$$x = x_1 \tag{2.26}$$

then we indicate the value of the function $f(x)$ when x has the value x_1 by the notation

$$f(x_1) \tag{2.27}$$

Expression (2.27) stands for the value of the function $f(x)$ at the point $x = x_1$, or, saying it in another way, the value of the function $f(x)$ at the point $x = x_1$. As an example, let's return to the function

$$y = f(x) = x^2 \tag{2.28}$$

and find the value of the function (2.28) when x has the value 2, i.e., when

$$x = x_1 = 2 \tag{2.29}$$

Using the notation described above, we have

$$f(x_1) = (x_1)^2 = (2)^2 = 4 \tag{2.30}$$

Since $x_1 = 2$, we can (and will often) also write

$$f(2) \tag{2.31}$$

for the value of the function $f(x)$ when $x = 2$. Similarly, when $x = 5$, $f(5)$ is the value of the function $f(x)$ when $x = 5$.

To summarize, if y is a function $f(x)$ of x, so $y = f(x)$, then $f(x_1)$ is the value of the dependent variable y, and of the function f, when the independent variable x has the value x_1.

These ideas may be extended to a function of several variables. Suppose

$$w = f(x, y) \tag{2.32}$$

is a function of the two variables x and y. Then

$$f(x_1, y_1)$$

is the value of the function f when x has the value x_1 (i.e., $x = x_1$) and y has the value y_1 (i.e., $y = y_1$). For example, suppose

$$w = f(x, y) = x^2 + y^2 \tag{2.33}$$

What is the value of $f(0, 2)$, which is the value of the function f when $x = 0$ and $y = 2$? From Eq. (2.33),

$$f(0, 2) = (0)^2 + (2)^2 = 4 \tag{2.34}$$

Note that we may sometimes wish to consider a function like $f(x, y)$ for a particular value of one independent variable but for *any* value of the other independent variable. As an example consider the function f in Eq. (2.33) when $x = 0$; then we have

$$f(0, y) = y^2 \tag{2.35}$$

as the value of $f(x, y)$ when $x = 0$. In this case the "value" of $f(0, y)$ is itself a function (in this case the function y^2) and not just a number.

EXERCISES

2.4. Given the function

$$y = f(x) = 3x^2 + 2$$

Find (a) $f(2)$; (b) $f(0)$; (c) $f(-1)$.

2.5 Given the function

$$y(x, t) = A \sin(kx - \omega t)$$

where A, k, and ω are constants. Find expressions for the following: (a) $y(0, 0)$; (b) $y(0, t)$; (c) $y(x, 0)$

2.6 Given the function $y = f(x) = (1 - x^2)^{1/2}$. Find $f(x - a)$, where a is a constant. Note that $f(x - a)$ is obtained by replacing the independent variable x in $f(x)$ by the new variable $(x - a)$.

THE GRAPH OF A FUNCTION

When we are considering a function, it is usual in physics to display the functional relationship between the dependent and independent variables by means of a *graph* of the function. Suppose we are considering a function

$$y = f(x) \tag{2.36}$$

We can assign a series of values to the independent variable x, and, from the functional relationship in Eq. (2.36), obtain the corresponding values of the dependent variable y. For example, if the specific function under discussion were

$$y = f(x) = x^2 \tag{2.37}$$

we would obtain the table of values below for integral

x	0	1	2	3	4	5
y	0	1	4	9	16	25

values of x between 0 and 5. However, it is difficult from a table of values to "see" the behavior of the function $f(x)$ as x takes on various values. For this reason it is usual to construct a graph of the function.

The definition of a graph is as follows. The graph of the function $f(x)$ is the set of all points with rectangular coordinates $(x, f(x))$. Here the notation $(x, f(x))$ means the point whose abscissa (x coordinate) has the value x and whose ordinate (y coordinate) has the value $f(x)$. For our example in Eq. (2.37), the graph of the function $y = f(x) = x^2$ is the set of all points with coordinates (x, x^2). Six such points, $(0, 0)$, $(1, 1)$, $(2, 4)$, $(3, 9)$, $(4, 16)$, and $(5, 25)$ are seen in the table above. These six points are, of course, not *all* of the points forming the graph of the function $y = f(x) = x^2$; there are an infinite number of other points, such as $(2.5, 6.25)$, with the form (x, x^2).

If we plot, in two dimensions, all of the points of the form $(x, f(x))$, we obtain the graph of $f(x)$. For our example, we plot points of the form (x, x^2) and obtain the graph shown in Fig. 2.1. In that figure, we plot $y = f(x) = x^2$ vertically (ordinate) and x horizontally (abscissa) and obtain the curve shown in the figure. The graph is the set of all points whose coordinates (x, y) satisfy the functional relation $y = x^2$ given in Eq. (2.37). Therefore, any point on the graph (or *curve*, as it is also

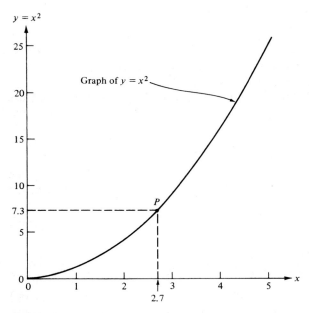

FIGURE 2.1
Graph of the function $y = f(x) = x^2$ for $0 \le x \le 5$.

called) has coordinates (x, y) such that $y = x^2$. The point P, for example, has coordinates $(2.7, 7.29)$. From the figure, we can "see" how the function $y = f(x) = x^2$ varies with x.

In general, then, if we have the graph of the function $y = f(x)$ plotted as a function of x, we may find the value of the function for any value $x = x_1$ of x by reading it off the graph. The point $(x_1, f(x_1))$ will be a point on the graph, so, knowing the value of x_1 determines the value of $f(x_1)$. In Fig. 2.1, in which $f(x) = x^2$, we considered the point $x_1 = 2.7$ on the x axis; the y coordinate of point P can be read to be $f(x_1) \cong 7.3$, as shown on the curve in the figure. Note that we can read the value of $f(x_1) = f(2.7)$ off the graph in Fig. 2.1 only approximately. From the graph, we read $f(2.7) \cong 7.3$, which may be compared with the exact value $f(2.7) = (2.7)^2 = 7.29$. (It should be pointed out that, in physics, the reading of graphs in this manner is frequently necessary for graphs of experimental data for which the functional relationship is not known. In such cases, the reading of values is necessarily approximate.)

There are a number of functions of one variable whose graphs are frequently encountered in physics. One is the parabola, an example of which is seen in the graph of $y = x^2$ in Fig. 2.1. From analytic geometry, we know that the general quadratic equation

$$y = f(x) = ax^2 + bx + c \qquad (2.38)$$

where a, b, and c are constants, has as its graph a parabola whose axis is parallel to the y axis. In our example above, in Eq. (2.37), $y = x^2$ is the special case of Eq. (2.38) for which $a = 1$ and $b = c = 0$.

A second important function in physics is of the form

$$y = f(x) = mx + b \qquad (2.39)$$

where m and b are constants. Equation (2.39) shows a function whose graph is a straight line of slope m which passes through the point whose coordinates are $y = b$, $x = 0$. We recall that the slope m of the straight line (2.39) is defined as the tangent of the angle the line makes with the positive direction of the x axis. The point $(0, b)$ is called the y intercept of the line. As an example, consider the function

$$y = f(x) = 2x + 1 \qquad (2.40)$$

whose graph is shown in Fig. 2.2 for values of x between 0 and 3. Comparison of the function in Eq. (2.40) with the general form of the straight line given in Eq. (2.39) shows that the y intercept is at the point $(0, 1)$ so $b = 1$ in Eq. (2.39). In Fig. 2.2, θ is the angle between the straight line and the x axis. Then, from the definition of the slope, we

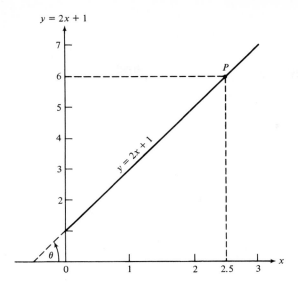

FIGURE 2.2
Graph of $y = f(x) = 2x + 1$ for $0 \leq x \leq 3$.

have from Eq. (2.39) that

$$m = \tan \theta = 2 \tag{2.41}$$

leading to the value $\theta = \tan^{-1} 2 = 63.4° = 1.11$ radians (radian measure of angles is discussed below). Any point, such as P in Fig. 2.2, on the graph of the function in Eq. (2.40) has coordinate $(x, (2x + 1))$. For example, if $x = 2.5$, $y = 2x + 1 = 6$, we have point P whose coordinates are $(2.5, 6)$.

EXERCISES

2.7 Consider the function

$$y = f(x) = x - 2x^2$$

(a) Calculate the value of y for values of x from $x = 0$ to $x = 0.5$ in increments of 0.05. (b) Using graph paper, draw the graph of $f(x)$ as a function of x. (c) What is the name of this curve? (d) From your graph, determine the value of y when $x = 0.32$. (e) For what values of x does $y = 0$?

2.8 (a) What is the equation of a straight line of slope 2 passing through the origin? (b) What angle does this line make with the x axis? (c) Make a graph of this function for values of x from 0 to 2.

2.9 In Exercise 2.6 (above), you were given $y = f(x) = (1 - x^2)^{1/2}$ and found the new function $y = f(x - a) = [1 - (x - a)^2]^{1/2}$. (a) On graph paper, make a careful graph of $f(x - a)$ as a function of x for the value of the constant $a = 0$. Use values of x between $x = 1$ and $x = -1$ (inclusive) at intervals of 0.2. (b) Repeat the graph of $f(x - a)$ for $a = 4$ for values of x between $x = 3$ and $x = 5$ (inclusive), also at intervals of 0.2. Consider only positive values of y in making your tables and graphs.

GRAPHS OF TRIGONOMETRIC FUNCTIONS. RADIAN MEASURE

The graphs of the trigonometric functions sin x and cos x are often encountered in physics. In order to discuss these functions, it is necessary to introduce the measurement of angles in *radians*. Figure 2.3 shows a circle of radius r with two points, A and B, on its circumference; radii are drawn from the center O to points A and B. The distance along the circumference between A and B is denoted by s and is called the *arc length* between A and B; θ is the angle between the radii OA and OB. With this notation, the magnitude of the angle θ, in radians, is given by the equation

$$\theta = \frac{s}{r} \text{ (radians)} \tag{2.42}$$

From Eq. (2.42), we can see that the angle θ has the value 1 radian when the arc length s subtended by the angle θ is equal to the radius r of the circle. [Note that, from Eq. (2.42), the quantity (s/r) is dimensionless because it is the ratio of two lengths. The radian is thus really a number of geometric significance and is not a "unit" in the sense in which we use the term in physics.] We recall that the circumference C of a circle is related to its radius r by the relation

$$C = 2\pi r \tag{2.43}$$

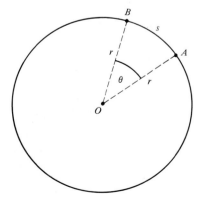

FIGURE 2.3
Circle used in defining radian measure.

so the arc length of the entire circumference of a circle of radius r is equal to $2\pi r$. If we set the arc length s equal to $2\pi r$ in Eq. (2.42), we obtain

$$\theta = \frac{2\pi r}{r} = 2\pi \text{ (radians)} \qquad (2.44)$$

Equation (2.44) says that the number of radians in a complete circle of 360° is 2π radians. Since 360° is equal to 2π radians,

$$1 \text{ radian} = \frac{360°}{2\pi} \cong 57.3° \qquad (2.45)$$

so 1 radian is (approximately) equal to 57.3°. In physics, angles are very frequently measured in radians, and some common angles are given below in radians.

$$45° = (\pi/4) \text{ radian}$$
$$90° = (\pi/2) \text{ radians}$$
$$180° = \pi \text{ radians} \qquad (2.46)$$
$$360° = 2\pi \text{ radians}$$

As a final point on radian measure, we note that Eq. (2.42) can be rewritten as

$$s = r\theta \qquad (2.47)$$

Equation (2.47) gives the arc length s along a circle of radius r in terms of the angle θ subtended by that arc length. For example, in a circle of radius 1 meter an angle of 0.1 radian would subtend an arc length $s = (1)(0.1) = 0.1$ meter. It is important to keep in mind in using Eqs. (2.47) and (2.42) that the angle θ must be expressed in radians.

We now consider the graph of the important trigonometric function

$$y = f(x) = \sin x \qquad (2.48)$$

As with any other graph of a function $f(x)$, every point on the graph of the function in Eq. (2.48) will have a coordinate of the form $(x, f(x))$, so points comprising the graph of $\sin x$ will have coordinates $(x, \sin x)$, where x is an angle in radians. Figure 2.4 shows the graph of $y = \sin x$ as a function of x; as is customary, the angle x (in radians) is plotted in multiples of π. Examining the graph of $\sin x$ in Fig. 2.4, we see that $\sin x$ is positive for values of x between $x = 0$ and $x = \pi$ radians, and that $\sin x$ is negative for values of x between π and 2π radians. Each point on the graph has coordinates $(x, \sin x)$; for example, point P has coordinates $((3\pi/4), 0.707)$.

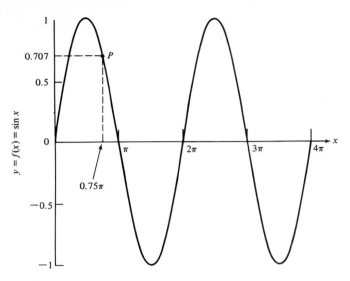

FIGURE 2.4
Graph of $y = f(x) = \sin x$ for $0 \le x \le 4\pi$.

Let us describe the variation of $y = \sin x$ as x increases from 0 to 2π radians. When $x = 0$, $y = 0$; as x increases, y increases and reaches its maximum value of unity (i.e., 1) when $x = (\pi/2)$ radians. As x increases further, y decreases, reaching the value zero when $x = \pi$ radians; y continues to decrease with increasing x until y reaches its minimum value of (-1) when $x = (3\pi/2)$ radians. As x increases beyond $(3\pi/2)$ radians, y increases from (-1), reaching the value zero when $x = 2\pi$ radians. We have just described the variation of $y = \sin x$ as x varies from zero to 2π radians. This variation is often referred to as one *cycle* of the sine function because, as x increases beyond 2π radians, the variation shown in Fig. 2.4 is repeated for values of x between 2π and 4π radians. The variation of $\sin x$ with x is thus repetitive, or *periodic*, with a period of 2π radians. One refers to the set of values of x over which $\sin x$ varies through one cycle as the *period* of the sine function; the period of the sine function is thus 2π radians.

As a last point, we may mention the following useful fact. If θ is a small angle and is expressed in *radians*, then

$$\theta \cong \sin \theta \cong \tan \theta \qquad (2.49)$$

Equation (2.49) says that, for a small angle θ expressed in radians, the numerical value of θ is approximately equal to the sine of θ, which is approximately equal to the tangent of θ. For example, suppose $\theta =$

$(\pi/100)$ radian, so θ is $1.8°$. Then $\theta = 0.03142$ radian, $\sin\theta = 0.03141$, $\tan\theta = 0.03143$, and we can see that the relation in Eq. (2.49) is satisfied to within about 1 part in 3000, or about 0.03 percent. The smaller the angle θ, the more accurate is relation (2.49), which is usually called the *small-angle approximation*. For how large a value of θ is Eq. (2.49) valid? The answer depends on how accurately you wish Eq. (2.49) to be satisfied. For example, if $\theta = (\pi/20)$ radian $= 0.1571$ radian (about $9°$), then $\sin\theta = 0.1564$ and $\tan\theta = 0.1584$. Thus, for this larger angle, the relation in Eq. (2.49) is valid to only about 1 percent. The small-angle approximation is often used to deal with the trigonometric functions of small angles.

EXERCISES

2.10 Calculate the number of degrees in the following angles: (a) $(\pi/8)$ radian; (b) $(3\pi/4)$ radians; (c) 3π radians; (d) $(31\pi/32)$ radians.

2.11 (a) Make a table giving values of $\cos x$ for values of x from 0 to 4π radians, inclusive. Calculate values at intervals of $(\pi/8)$ radian. (b) Using graph paper, make a graph of $\cos x$ as a function of x for $0 \le x \le 4\pi$ radians. (c) What are the maximum and minimum values of $\cos x$? (d) Is the function $f(x) = \cos x$ periodic with x? Give the reason for your answer. (e) What is the period of function $\cos x$? (f) How many cycles of the function $\cos x$ are there on the graph in part (b)? (g) Using your graph, find the value of $\cos(39\pi/16)$ and compare the value you read from the graph with the value from your calculator. (*Note*: This rather tedious exercise gives you practice in a number of useful skills, including the use of radian measure, making graphs, interpreting graphs, and calculating trigonometric values.)

PATH OF A MOVING PARTICLE

An important type of graph in physics is the path or trajectory of a particle (or any other kind of body) as it moves through space. This path is the set of points in space successively occupied by the particle as it moves with increasing time. Generally, the path of a moving particle is denoted by specifying the equation of the mathematical curve composed of the set of points occupied by the moving particle. For example, suppose that a particle is moving in a circular path, of radius r, in a horizontal plane. Let us define that horizontal plane as the xy plane and let us choose the origin of coordinates at the center of the circular path. Then the path traced out by the particle as it moves is a circle of radius r centered at the origin, so every point on the path satisfies the equation

$$x^2 + y^2 = r^2 \tag{2.50}$$

This means that every point, with coordinates (x, y), that the particle passes through as it moves will have x and y values which satisfy Eq. (2.50). We recall that Eq. (2.50) is the equation of a circle of radius r, centered at the origin, in the xy plane. When, in physics, we speak of a particle moving in a path given by some particular equation, the idea above is what is meant.

It is usual, however, to find that information on the path of a moving particle is given in a form different from Eq. (2.50). Equation (2.50) gives the equation of the path of the particle in space. It is more useful in many situations to have information on the position of a moving particle as a function of time. This is generally given by specifying the coordinates, such as the rectangular coordinates (x, y, z), of the particle as functions of time, as

$$x = f(t); y = g(t); z = h(t) \qquad (2.51)$$

Equation (2.51) says that the x coordinate of the moving particle is a function $f(t)$ of the time t, etc. With equations of the type in Eq. (2.51), one can calculate the coordinates (x, y, z) of the particle at any value of the time t. Equations of the form in Eq. (2.51) are called *parametric* equations because they give x, y, and z as functions of another variable t, where t is called the parameter.

As an example, let's consider again the particle moving in the xy plane in a horizontal circle of radius r, now adding for convenience the stipulation that the velocity v of the particle is constant. (The velocity v is the tangential velocity of the particle, not its angular velocity.) In analytic geometry it is shown that the parametric equations of the circle in Eq. (2.50) are

$$x = r \cos \theta \qquad (2.52)$$

$$y = r \sin \theta \qquad (2.53)$$

which can be seen to be true by verifying that substitutions of Eqs. (2.52) and (2.53) satisfy Eq. (2.50). In your physics course, you will find out that the parameter θ in Eqs. (2.52) and (2.53) is given by

$$\theta = \frac{vt}{r} \qquad (2.54)$$

where v is the particle's velocity, r is the radius of the circular path, and t is the same time. Substituting Eq. (2.54) into Eqs. (2.52) and (2.53) gives us

$$x = r \cos (vt/r) \qquad (2.55)$$

$$y = r \sin (vt/r) \qquad (2.56)$$

as the parametric equations, of the form in Eq. (2.51), of the circular path of the particle. The important thing about Eqs. (2.55) and (2.56) is that they give us the x and y coordinates of the particle as functions of time. This enables us to calculate the coordinates (x, y) of the position of the particle at any instant of time we like.

For example, suppose the velocity $v = 10$ meters per second and the radius $r = 10$ meters. Then Eqs. (2.55) and (2.56) become

$$x = 10 \cos t \qquad (2.57)$$

$$y = 10 \sin t \qquad (2.58)$$

Let us calculate the coordinates (x, y) of the position of the particle when the time $t = 1$ second. Then

$$x = 10 \cos 1 = 10(0.540) = 5.40 \text{ meters} \qquad (2.59)$$

where, in Eq. (2.59), the angle is in radians, so we are taking the cosine of 1 radian. Similarly,

$$y = 10 \sin 1 = 10(0.841) = 8.41 \text{ meters} \qquad (2.60)$$

so the coordinates of the moving particle at the instant $t = 1$ second are

$$(x = 5.40 \text{ meters}, y = 8.41 \text{ meters})$$

You will frequently encounter paths of moving particles in physics, and they will often be given in parametric form like Eqs. (2.55) and (2.56). One of the most important examples will be the parametric equations of the two-dimensional parabolic path of the projectile, giving the projectile's coordinates (x, y) as functions of time.

PLANE-POLAR COORDINATES

In addition to rectangular or cartesian coordinates (x, y), there is another two-dimensional coordinate system frequently used in introductory physics. Those coordinates are plane-polar coordinates (r, θ), shown in Fig. 2.5. In that figure, P is a point in the xy plane, where OP is the line from the origin O to point P. The line OP makes an angle θ with the positive x axis, and r is the distance $\overline{OP}$ from O to P. The location of point P is thus specified by giving the values of its plane-polar coordinates r and θ. In Fig. 2.5, if $r = 1$ unit, then the plane-polar coordinates of point P are $(r = 1, \theta = 45°)$ or $(r = 1, \theta = (\pi/4)$ radian$)$.

If, in Fig. 2.5, we know the rectangular coordinates (x, y) of point

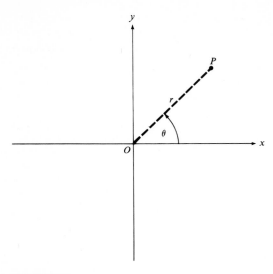

FIGURE 2.5
Plane-polar coordinates (r, θ) in the xy plane. The distance $\overline{OP}$ is equal to r, and θ is the angle made by the line OP with the positive x axis.

P, there is a relation between the polar coordinates (r, θ) and (x, y). From the drawing, we see that this relation is

$$x = r \cos \theta \qquad (2.61)$$

$$y = r \sin \theta \qquad (2.62)$$

from elementary trigonometry. Further, from Eqs. (2.61) and (2.62), we have

$$x^2 + y^2 = r^2 \qquad (2.63)$$

as a relation between the rectangular coordinates (x, y) of point P and the polar coordinate r.

While they are not used a great deal in introductory physics, it is worth noting that plane curves have equations in polar coordinates which are different from their more familiar equations in rectangular coordinates. For example,

$$x^2 + y^2 = a^2 \qquad (2.64)$$

is the equation of a circle of radius a, centered at the origin (0, 0), in rectangular coordinates. In polar coordinates, the equation of the circle (2.64) is

$$r = a \qquad (2.65)$$

with the angle θ understood to take all values between $\theta = 0$ and $\theta = 360° = 2\pi$ radians. Equation (2.65) can be seen to be intuitively reasonable, since it describes all points at a constant distance a from the origin ($r = 0$, $\theta = 0$) of polar coordinates.

EXERCISES

2.12. Given the equation $y = mx + b$ in rectangular coordinates of a straight line of slope m and intercept $(0, b)$, use Eqs. (2.61) and (2.62) to express the polar coordinates (r, θ) of a point P on this line in terms of the rectangular coordinates (x, y) of point P. Do you think polar coordinates are as convenient to describe a straight line as they are to describe a circle? For this reason, polar coordinates are especially useful in physical problems involving motion in a circle.

CHAPTER
3

DERIVATIVES
AND DIFFERENTIALS

INTRODUCTION

The aim of this chapter is to review some topics in differential calculus and to describe some applications to physics. In particular, the idea of the derivative as a rate of change is emphasized because of its central importance in physics. Special attention is given to dealing with functions of time. The notion of the differential, sometimes neglected in calculus courses, is also given emphasis because of its frequent use in elementary physics. Finally, some applications of the geometric interpretation of the derivative and series expansions of functions are considered.

REVIEW OF THE DEFINITION OF THE DERIVATIVE

We begin by *reviewing* the definition of the derivative on the assumption that you have already studied this material in your calculus course. If your notion of a *limit* is vague, this would be a good point at which to refresh your memory by reviewing limits in your calculus text.

Suppose we have a function $f(x)$ of the independent variable x. We will tacitly assume that the function $f(x)$ is a "well-behaved" function, which we will, rather casually, take to mean that all of the relevant limits exist and that $f(x)$ exhibits no cusps, discontinuities, or other exceptional features which may cause difficulty. Consider the value

$$f(x_1) \tag{3.1}$$

of the function at some point $x = x_1$ and consider also the value

$$f(x_1 + \Delta x) \tag{3.2}$$

at a second point $x = (x_1 + \Delta x)$. The quantity Δx is called the *increment* in the variable x and is the amount of change in the variable x when x varies from the value x_1 to the value $(x_1 + \Delta x)$. (Keep in mind that Δx is really a single symbol, read "delta-x," and is *not* the product of Δ and x.)

Next, we form the quotient

$$\frac{f(x_1 + \Delta x) - f(x_1)}{\Delta x} \tag{3.3}$$

and consider what happens when the increment Δx gets very small. The process of Δx getting very small (as small as we wish) is symbolized by writing

$$\Delta x \to 0 \tag{3.4}$$

an expression which is read "Δx approaches zero." To define the *derivative* of the function $f(x)$, we examine what happens to the expression in Eq. (3.3) as Δx gets very small. The limit of expression (3.3) as Δx gets very small is written

$$\lim_{\Delta x \to 0} \frac{f(x_1 + \Delta x) - f(x_1)}{\Delta x} \tag{3.5}$$

and will be assumed to exist in the cases of physical interest which we will consider. The limit given in Eq. (3.5) is defined as the derivative of the function $f(x)$ at the point $x = x_1$ and is written

$$f'(x_1) \tag{3.6}$$

an expression which is read "f prime at x_1" or "f prime of x_1."

To summarize so far, the derivative $f'(x_1)$ of the function $f(x)$ at the point $x = x_1$ is defined as

$$f'(x_1) = \lim_{\Delta x \to 0} \frac{f(x_1 + \Delta x) - f(x_1)}{\Delta x} \tag{3.7}$$

again assuming that the limit exists at the point $x = x_1$. For the functions we will consider in our physics examples, we will assume that the appropriate limit in Eq. (3.7) exists for *all* values of x under consideration.

Thus the point x_1 can be *any* point x in the set of values which the independent variable x may take on. We may therefore replace x_1 in Eq. (3.7) by x since x_1 can be any value of x. Doing this, Eq. (3.7) becomes

$$f'(x) = \lim_{\Delta x \to 0} \frac{f(x + \Delta x) - f(x)}{\Delta x} \qquad (3.8)$$

Equation (3.8) defines the derivative $f'(x)$ of the function $f(x)$.

As an example which will illuminate the definition, let us calculate the derivative of a simple function using the definition (3.8). Suppose the function f is

$$f(x) = 2x^2 \qquad (3.9)$$

Then

$$f(x + \Delta x) = 2(x + \Delta x)^2 \qquad (3.10)$$

is the value of the function f at the point $(x + \Delta x)$. Evaluating the expression in Eq. (3.10) gives us

$$f(x + \Delta x) = 2(x^2 + 2x(\Delta x) + (\Delta x)^2)$$
$$= 2x^2 + 4x(\Delta x) + 2(\Delta x)^2 \qquad (3.11)$$

so we obtain next

$$f(x + \Delta x) - f(x) = 2x^2 + 4x(\Delta x) + (\Delta x)^2 - 2x^2$$
$$= 4x(\Delta x) + (\Delta x)^2 \qquad (3.12)$$

Dividing expression (3.12) by the quantity Δx gives

$$\frac{f(x + \Delta x) - f(x)}{\Delta x} = \frac{4x(\Delta x) + (\Delta x)^2}{\Delta x} = 4x + (\Delta x) \qquad (3.13)$$

The next step in applying the definition (3.8) of the derivative is to take the limit of the expression (3.13) as $\Delta x \to 0$, so we have

$$\lim_{\Delta x \to 0} \frac{f(x + \Delta x) - f(x)}{\Delta x} = \lim_{\Delta x \to 0} (4x + \Delta x) = 4x \qquad (3.14)$$

From the result in Eq. (3.14), we have

$$f'(x) = 4x \qquad (3.15)$$

as the derivative of the function $f(x) = 2x^2$. [It should be pointed out that the step of taking the limit as $\Delta x \to 0$ is not usually as simple as the one in Eq. (3.14); see your calculus text for details, techniques, and examples.] We note also that, in Eq. (3.15), the derivative $f'(x)$ is itself a function of x.

In summary, the definition of the derivative $f'(x)$ of the function $f(x)$ is given by

$$f'(x) \equiv \lim_{\Delta x \to 0} \frac{f(x + \Delta x) - f(x)}{\Delta x} \qquad (3.8)$$

We will see in later sections how this definition is useful in describing physical (and geometric) situations.

We conclude with a few remarks about the nomenclature and notation for the derivative $f'(x)$. Since we are finding the derivative of a function $f(x)$ of the variable x, $f'(x)$ is often referred to as the derivative of f *with respect to* x and the process of calculating $f'(x)$ is often called differentiation with respect to x. (It may seem overly precise to specify the variable, e.g., x, with respect to which we are calculating the derivative, but this usage focuses attention on the independent variable involved. Furthermore, in dealing with functions of more than one variable, it is essential to specify which variable is involved in the derivative.)

While the notation $f'(x)$ is very common, there are others, some of which are particularly useful in physics. Another notation for the derivative of $f(x)$ is

$$\frac{df}{dx} \qquad (3.16)$$

Formally, we may define the expression (3.16) by the relation

$$\frac{df}{dx} \equiv f'(x) \qquad (3.17)$$

which simply says that the symbol (df/dx) means the derivative $f'(x)$. [Incidentally, the symbol (df/dx), written on a line, is identical to the form in expressions (3.16) and (3.17). Writing it (df/dx) simply saves space in the text.] Similarly, if the dependent variable y is related to the function $f(x)$ by

$$y = f(x) \qquad (3.18)$$

we may write the derivative of the function f as y', so

$$y' \equiv f'(x) \qquad (3.19)$$

Still another notation is often used. When y is a function of x, as in Eq. (3.18), the derivative $f'(x)$ is sometimes written as

$$\frac{dy}{dx} \qquad (3.20)$$

which you may also see written on a line as (dy/dx) to save space. The meaning of the expression (3.20) is defined by the relation

$$\frac{dy}{dx} \equiv f'(x) \tag{3.21}$$

Equation (3.21) simply says that, if $y = f(x)$, then the symbol (dy/dx) means the derivative $f'(x)$. The expression (dy/dx) is read "the derivative of y with respect to x."

Keep in mind that (at least for now) the symbols (df/dx) and (dy/dx) are *not* to be considered as quotients. It is especially important to realize that, in calculus, the symbol dy does *not* ever mean a quantity d times a quantity y. The same is true for df; in calculus, it *never* means d times f. Among other things, this means that it is wrong and without meaning to attempt to "cancel" the d's in (dy/dx) or (df/dx). For now, we will consider the symbols (dy/dx) and (df/dx) as single symbols for the derivative $f'(x)$.

As a last point in this section, suppose we know that y is some function of x, so

$$y = f(x) \tag{3.22}$$

a functional relationship in which y is the dependent and x is the independent variable. If we were to solve Eq. (3.22) for x as a function of y, we would obtain

$$x = g(y) \tag{3.23}$$

where Eq. (3.23) is the function *inverse* to Eq. (3.22). In Eq. (3.23), x is the dependent variable and y is the independent variable. A useful theorem relates (dy/dx), the derivative of y with respect to x, and (dx/dy), the derivative of x with respect to y, where

$$(dy/dx) \equiv f'(x) \qquad (dx/dy) \equiv g'(y) \tag{3.24}$$

in our usual notation. The theorem states as its result that

$$f'(x) = \frac{1}{g'(y)} \tag{3.25}$$

or, alternatively,

$$\frac{dy}{dx} = \frac{1}{\dfrac{dx}{dy}} \tag{3.26}$$

The result in Eq. (3.25) or Eq. (3.26) is often useful in the calculation of derivatives. Note that this result assumes that $g'(y)$ is not equal to zero.

EXERCISES

3.1. Using the definition in Eq. (3.8), find the derivative $f'(x)$ of the function $f(x) = x^3$. The aim of this exercise is not so much to obtain the derivative itself, but to see how the definition leads to the derivative.

3.2. Using the definition in Eq. (3.8), find the derivative $f'(x)$ of the function $f(x) = (1/x)$, where $x \neq 0$. Again, the aim of the exercise is to illustrate the definition of the derivative.

CALCULATING DERIVATIVES—A REVIEW

In your calculus course, you learned how to calculate the derivatives of various kinds of functions; it is assumed you have seen them before in your calculus course. Some of the derivatives are reviewed in this section. It will be useful to introduce another common notation at this point. One often sees the symbols

$$\frac{d}{dx}\left[f(x)\right] = f'(x) \tag{3.27}$$

used for the derivative $f'(x)$. The left-hand side of Eq. (3.27) is used to indicate the *operation or process* of calculating the derivative $f'(x)$ of the function $f(x)$. One would read Eq. (3.27) by saying "the operation of taking the derivative of the function $f(x)$ yields $f'(x)$." As an example of this notation, consider the function $f(x) = 2x^2$ given in Eq. (3.9); in Eq. (3.15), we found the derivative $f'(x) = 4x$. In the notation of Eq. (3.27), we would write

$$\frac{d}{dx}\left[2x^2\right] = 4x \tag{3.28}$$

Equation (3.28) says that the operation or process of calculating the derivative of the function $2x^2$ produces $4x$, where $f'(x) = 4x$ is the derivative of the function $f(x) = 2x^2$. Another example would be

$$\frac{d}{dx}\left[x^3\right] = 3x^2 \tag{3.29}$$

Equation (3.29) says that the derivative of the function x^3 is $3x^2$. This notation will be used in the review of derivatives below. All of the following derivatives follow directly from the definition in Eq. (3.8) and can be obtained (albeit with some difficulty) in the same way as were the examples in Exercises 3.1 and 3.2.

If c is a constant, then the derivative of c is zero. This is expressed in the equation

$$\frac{d}{dx}[c] = 0 \tag{3.30}$$

where Eq. (3.30) states that the derivative of any constant is zero.
Suppose

$$u = u(x)$$

and

$$v = v(x)$$

are two functions of the independent variable x. Then the derivative of
the *sum* of the two functions is the sum of the derivatives, so we have

$$\frac{d}{dx}[u + v] = \frac{du}{dx} + \frac{dv}{dx} = u'(x) + v'(x) \tag{3.31}$$

In Eq. (3.31), we exhibit two different notations, (du/dx) and $u'(x)$, for
the derivative of the function $u(x)$ with respect to x, and the same for the
derivative of $v(x)$.

If we consider the derivative of a constant c times a function $u = u(x)$, we have that

$$\frac{d}{dx}[cu] = c\frac{du}{dx} = cu'(x) \tag{3.32}$$

Equation (3.32) says that the derivative of a constant times a function is
equal to the constant times the derivative of the function.

As an example of the use of these results, consider the functions

$$u(x) = 6x^3 \qquad v(x) = \frac{2}{x}$$

and find the derivative of the function $(6x^3 + (2/x))$. Then

$$\frac{d}{dx}\left[6x^3 + \frac{2}{x}\right] = \frac{d}{dx}[6x^3] + \frac{d}{dx}\left[\frac{2}{x}\right]$$

from Eq. (3.31). From Eq. (3.32), we have

$$\frac{d}{dx}[6x^3] = 6\frac{d}{dx}[x^3]$$

$$\frac{d}{dx}\left[\frac{2}{x}\right] = 2\frac{d}{dx}\left[\frac{1}{x}\right] \tag{3.33}$$

The derivatives of x^3 and $(1/x)$ were found in Exercises 3.1 and 3.2 as $3x^2$ and $(-1/x^2)$, respectively, so the final answer is

$$\frac{d}{dx}\left[6x^3 + \frac{2}{x}\right] = 6(3x^2) + 2\left(\frac{-1}{x^2}\right) = 18x^2 - \frac{2}{x^2} \quad (3.34)$$

We now review the derivatives of some of the elementary functions commonly encountered in physics.

The derivative of a power n of a variable x is given by

$$\frac{d}{dx}[x^n] = nx^{n-1} \quad (3.35)$$

An example would be

$$\frac{d}{dx}[x^4] = 4x^3 \quad (3.36)$$

The derivative of the exponential function e^x is

$$\frac{d}{dx}[e^x] = e^x \quad (3.37)$$

The derivatives of two important trigonometric functions are as follows.

$$\frac{d}{dx}[\sin x] = \cos x \quad (3.38)$$

$$\frac{d}{dx}[\cos x] = -\sin x \quad (3.39)$$

Next, we consider derivatives of the product and quotient of two functions $u(x)$ and $v(x)$. The derivative of the product uv is given by

$$\frac{d}{dx}[uv] = u\frac{dv}{dx} + v\frac{du}{dx} = u(x)v'(x) + v(x)u'(x) \quad (3.40)$$

As an example of the use of Eq. (3.40), suppose that

$$u(x) = x^2 \qquad v(x) = e^x$$

and we wish to find the derivative of the function $x^2 e^x$. Then

$$\frac{d}{dx}[x^2 e^x] = x^2\frac{d}{dx}[e^x] + e^x\frac{d}{dx}[x^2]$$

Using Eqs. (3.37) and (3.35) we have

$$\frac{d}{dx}[e^x] = e^x \qquad \frac{d}{dx}[x^2] = 2x$$

so

$$\frac{d}{dx}[x^2 e^x] = x^2[e^x] + e^x[2x] = e^x(x^2 + 2x) \qquad (3.41)$$

The derivative of the quotient (u/v) is given by

$$\frac{d}{dx}\left[\frac{u}{v}\right] = \left(\frac{1}{v^2}\right)\left[v\frac{du}{dx} - u\frac{dv}{dx}\right] = \left(\frac{1}{v^2}\right)[v(x)u'(x) - u(x)v'(x)]$$

$$(3.42)$$

To illustrate the use of Eq. (3.42), let us calculate the derivative of tan x by using the trigonometric identity

$$\tan x = \frac{\sin x}{\cos x}$$

Then

$$\frac{d}{dx}[\tan x] = \frac{d}{dx}\left[\frac{\sin x}{\cos x}\right] \qquad (3.43)$$

We evaluate Eq. (3.43) by using Eq. (3.42) with $u(x) = \sin x$ and $v(x) = \cos x$, so we obtain

$$\frac{d}{dx}\left[\frac{\sin x}{\cos x}\right] = \left(\frac{1}{\cos^2 x}\right)\left[\cos x \frac{d}{dx}[\sin x] - \sin x \frac{d}{dx}[\cos x]\right] \qquad (3.44)$$

Using Eqs. (3.38) and (3.39) for the derivatives of sin x and cos x, Eq. (3.44) becomes

$$\frac{d}{dx}\left[\frac{\sin x}{\cos x}\right] = \left(\frac{1}{\cos^2 x}\right)[\cos x(\cos x) - \sin x(-\sin x)]$$

$$= \frac{1}{\cos^2 x}[\cos^2 x + \sin^2 x] = \frac{1}{\cos^2 x} = \sec^2 x \qquad (3.45)$$

on using the trigonometric identity $\sin^2 x + \cos^2 x = 1$. Our final result, combining Eq. (3.43) with Eq. (3.45), is

$$\frac{d}{dx}[\tan x] = \sec^2 x \qquad (3.46)$$

a result which is probably familiar to you from your calculus course.

Finally, the derivative of the natural logarithm function ln x is

$$\frac{d}{dx}[\ln x] = \frac{1}{x} \qquad (3.47)$$

EXERCISES

3.3. Calculate the derivative of the function

$$f(x) = e^x \sin x$$

3.4. Calculate the derivative of the function $f(x) = \cot x$ using the trigonometric identity

$$\cot x = \frac{\cos x}{\sin x}$$

3.5. Use Eq. (3.35) to calculate the derivatives of x^3 and x^{-1}; compare these results with those you obtained in Exercises 3.1 and 3.2 and note that they are the same.

THE CHAIN RULE. THE SECOND DERIVATIVE

Suppose a variable y is a function g of a variable u, and, further, u is itself a function f of another variable x. In equations,

$$y = g(u) \qquad u = f(x) \tag{3.48}$$

Then the *chain rule* allows us to calculate the derivative $y'(x)$ of y with respect to x. The chain rule states that

$$y'(x) = g'(u) u'(x) \tag{3.49}$$

Equation (3.49) says that the derivative $y'(x)$ of y with respect to x is equal to the derivative $g'(u)$ of g *with respect to u* times the derivative $u'(x)$ of u with respect to x.

Let's consider an example in which

$$y = g(u) = \sin u \tag{3.50}$$

$$u = f(x) = 2x \tag{3.51}$$

so the function

$$y(x) = \sin 2x \tag{3.52}$$

We want to calculate $y'(x)$, the derivative of $y(x) = \sin 2x$ with respect to x. According to the chain rule in Eq. (3.49), we need to know

$$g'(u) = \cos u \tag{3.53}$$

and

$$u'(x) = 2 \tag{3.54}$$

so the chain rule in Eq. (3.49) gives us

$$y'(x) = \frac{d}{dx}[\sin 2x] = (\cos u)(2) \qquad (3.55)$$

Since, from Eq. (3.51), $u = 2x$, we obtain from Eq. (3.55) the result that

$$y'(x) = \frac{d}{dx}[\sin 2x] = 2\cos 2x \qquad (3.56)$$

for the derivative of $y(x) = \sin 2x$ with respect to x.

We can see that the chain rule enables us to find the derivative of "a function of a function." Equation (3.52) says that the variable y is a function (the sine) of the function $2x$, and, using the chain rule, we found its derivative given in Eq. (3.56).

A second example is the following, in which we find $y(x)$, take its derivative directly, and compare it with the result of using the chain rule. Suppose

$$y = g(u) = 4u^2 \qquad (3.57)$$

$$u = f(x) = 2x - 1 \qquad (3.58)$$

so

$$y(x) = 4(2x - 1)^2 = 16x^2 - 16x + 4 \qquad (3.59)$$

Taking the derivative directly, we have

$$y'(x) = 32x - 16 \qquad (3.60)$$

Let's use the chain rule to obtain the same result. From Eqs. (3.57) and (3.58)

$$g'(u) = 8u$$

$$u'(x) = 2$$

so Eq. (3.49) for the chain rule gives us

$$y'(x) = g'(u)u'(x) = 16u \qquad (3.61)$$

Since $u = 2x - 1$, we obtain from Eq. (3.61) the result that

$$y'(x) = \frac{d}{dx}[4(2x - 1)^2] = 16(2x - 1) = 32x - 16 \quad (3.62)$$

in agreement with the result in Eq. (3.60) of calculating the derivative directly.

Another example is the function

$$y(x) = \cos(6x^2) \qquad (3.63)$$

so we have, in the notation of Eqs. (3.48) to (3.49),

$$y = g(u) = \cos u$$
$$u = f(x) = 6x^2$$

From Eq. (3.49) for the chain rule,

$$y'(x) = \frac{d}{dx}\left[\cos (6x^2)\right] = g'(u)\,u'(x)$$

where

$$g'(u) = -\sin u$$
$$u'(x) = 12x$$

so

$$\frac{d}{dx}\left[\cos (6x^2)\right] = (-12x)\sin (6x^2) \qquad (3.64)$$

As a last example, consider the exponential function

$$y(x) = e^{ax} \qquad (3.65)$$

where a is a constant. Here $y = g(u) = e^u$ and $u = ax$, so

$$y'(x) = \frac{d}{dx}\left[e^{ax}\right] = g'(u)\,u'(x) = (e^u)(a)$$

so

$$\frac{d}{dx}\left[e^{ax}\right] = ae^{ax} \qquad (3.66)$$

is the derivative of e^{ax} with respect to x.

As a final point on the chain rule, it is instructive to rewrite Eq. (3.49) in a different notation as

$$\frac{dy}{dx} = \left(\frac{dy}{du}\right)\left(\frac{du}{dx}\right) \qquad (3.67)$$

where, as before in Eq. (3.48),

$$y = g(u) \qquad (3.48)$$
$$u = f(x)$$

saying y is a function g of the variable u and u is a function f of the variable x. Then Eq. (3.67), which is equivalent to Eq. (3.49), says that the derivative (dy/dx) of y with respect to x is equal to the product of the derivative (dy/du) of y, with respect to the variable u, times the derivative (du/dx) of u with respect to x. Equations (3.67) and (3.49) both say the same thing and both express the chain rule.

The last topic we will review here is the second derivative of a function $f(x)$. Consider the derivative $f'(x)$, where, from Eq. (3.27),

$$f'(x) = \frac{d}{dx}[f(x)] \qquad (3.27)$$

We saw, in numerous examples earlier, that the derivative $f'(x)$ is often a function of x, so we may take the derivative of the derivative $f'(x)$. We symbolize this process by

$$\frac{d}{dx}[f'(x)] = f''(x) \qquad (3.68)$$

where the symbol $f''(x)$ stands for the derivative, with respect to x, of the derivative $f'(x)$. The quantity $f''(x)$ is called the *second derivative* of the function $f(x)$. The derivative $f'(x)$ is often called the *first derivative* of $f(x)$.

As an example, consider the function

$$y = f(x) = x^4 \qquad (3.69)$$

whose first derivative is

$$f'(x) = 4x^3 \qquad (3.70)$$

Since $f'(x)$ is itself a function of x, we may take its derivative, obtaining the second derivative

$$f''(x) = 12x^2 \qquad (3.71)$$

[We could also differentiate $f''(x)$ and obtain the third derivative $f'''(x) = 24x$, but derivatives of order higher than the second are not of great importance in elementary physics.]

We noted earlier that, given a function

$$y = f(x) \qquad (3.72)$$

the symbols

$$\frac{dy}{dx} = \frac{d}{dx}[f(x)] = \frac{df}{dx} = f'(x) \qquad (3.73)$$

all are used to represent the first derivative $f'(x)$. Similarly, the second derivative $f''(x)$ of the function given by Eq. (3.72) is often represented by the symbols

$$f''(x) = \frac{d}{dx}\left[\frac{dy}{dx}\right] = \frac{d^2y}{dx^2} \qquad (3.74)$$

or

$$f''(x) = \frac{d}{dx}\left[\frac{df}{dx}\right] = \frac{d^2f}{dx^2} \qquad (3.75)$$

All of the symbols in Eqs. (3.74) and (3.75) mean the same thing, namely, the second derivative of the function $y = f(x)$ with respect to x. In fact, one also sees the symbol

$$\frac{d^2}{dx^2}[f(x)] = f''(x) \qquad (3.76)$$

where the symbol

$$\frac{d^2}{dx^2} \qquad (3.77)$$

indicates the operation of taking the second derivative of the function $f(x)$, just as the symbol

$$\frac{d}{dx} \qquad (3.78)$$

in Eq. (3.27) indicated the operation of taking the first derivative.

We can illustrate the notation using our previous example

$$y = f(x) = x^4 \qquad (3.69)$$

where

$$\frac{d^2y}{dx^2} = \frac{d^2f}{dx^2} = 12x^2 \qquad (3.79)$$

is the second derivative of x^4 with respect to x. You will see in your physics course that the second derivative occurs in many important equations of physics.

This concludes our review of the definition of the derivative and of calculation of derivatives of various functions. We now move on to the central topic of this chapter, the meaning of the derivative as applied to physics.

EXERCISES

3.6. Calculate the derivative of the function

$$y(x) = e^{-2x^2}$$

3.7. Calculate the derivative of the function

$$y(x) = (x^2 + 3x - 2)^4$$

3.8. Calculate the derivative of the function

$$y(x) = \sin[e^{x^2}]$$

3.9. Given the function $y = e^x \sin x$. Calculate $f''(x)$.

RATE OF CHANGE

Let us consider a function $f(x)$ of the independent variable x where y is the dependent variable, so

$$y = f(x) \tag{3.80}$$

Since the functional relationship in Eq. (3.80) assigns a value of y to every value of x, we expect that a change in the value of x will produce a change in the value of y. Suppose that x has the value x_1, so

$$x = x_1 \tag{3.81}$$

and that x changes, by an amount Δx, to the value

$$x = x_1 + \Delta x \tag{3.82}$$

In Eq. (3.82), the amount Δx by which x changes is called the increment in x, just as it was in the earlier discussion of Eq. (3.2). When $x = x_1$, the function f has the value $f(x_1)$; when $x = (x_1 + \Delta x)$, the function f has the value $f(x_1 + \Delta x)$. Thus, when x changes from the value x_1 to the value $(x_1 + \Delta x)$, the function f changes by the amount

$$f(x_1 + \Delta x) - f(x_1) \tag{3.83}$$

Since, from Eq. (3.80), $y = f(x)$, the expression (3.83) is the change in the variable y when x changes from x_1 to $(x_1 + \Delta x)$. We will use the symbol Δy for this change in y, so

$$\Delta y = f(x_1 + \Delta x) - f(x_1) \tag{3.84}$$

Keep in mind that the symbol Δy, called the increment in y, is a single symbol (like the symbol Δx) and is not the product of Δ and y. Equation (3.84) thus gives the change in the variable y when the variable x changes, by an amount Δx, from x_1 to $(x_1 + \Delta x)$. We next form the ratio of Δy to Δx.

$$\frac{\Delta y}{\Delta x} = \frac{f(x_1 + \Delta x) - f(x_1)}{\Delta x} \tag{3.85}$$

In Eq. (3.85), the ratio $(\Delta y/\Delta x)$ is called the *average rate of change* of y with respect to x. The average rate of change $(\Delta y/\Delta x)$ gives the change in y per unit of change in x, meaning that *each unit* of change in x results in a change $(\Delta y/\Delta x)$ in y. Stated again, when x changes by one unit, y

changes by $(\Delta y/\Delta x)$ units. Keep in mind that we are referring only to what occurs to y when x changes by Δx over the interval from x_1 to $(x_1 + \Delta x)$, and that $(\Delta y/\Delta x)$ is the average rate of change in that interval.

Let's consider an example. Suppose

$$y = f(x) = 2x \tag{3.86}$$

is the function f, and suppose x changes from the value

$$x_1 = 2.00 \tag{3.87}$$

to the value

$$x_1 + \Delta x = 2.01 \tag{3.88}$$

so the increment in x is $\Delta x = 0.01$. We want to calculate first the increment Δy in y. Since $f(x) = 2x$, we have

$$f(x_1) = 2(2.00) = 4.00$$

$$f(x_1 + \Delta x) = 2(2.01) = 4.02 \tag{3.89}$$

$$\Delta y = f(x_1 + \Delta x) - f(x_1) = 4.02 - 4.00 = 0.02$$

Forming the ratio $(\Delta y/\Delta x)$, we obtain

$$\frac{\Delta y}{\Delta x} = \frac{f(x_1 + \Delta x) - f(x_1)}{\Delta x} = \frac{0.02}{0.01} = 2 \tag{3.90}$$

Equation (3.90) gives the value of $(\Delta y/\Delta x)$, the average rate of change of y with respect to x over the interval $\Delta x = 0.01$ from $x = 2.00$ to $x = 2.01$. We can rewrite Eq. (3.90) as

$$\Delta y = 2(\Delta x) \tag{3.91}$$

an equation which tells us that the increment or change Δy in y is twice the increment or change Δx in x. Thus we see again the meaning of the rate of change $(\Delta y/\Delta x)$ in Eq. (3.90); it gives the change in y per unit of change in x. When x changes by one unit, y changes by two units, so the rate of change of y with respect to x has the value 2.

We can use these results to calculate, for example, the change Δy in y when x changes from $x_1 = 2.000$ to $(x_1 + \Delta x) = 2.005$, so $\Delta x = 0.005$. Since $(\Delta y/\Delta x) = 2$ is the average rate of change of y with respect to x for values of x between 2.00 and 2.01, we can use the value $(\Delta y/\Delta x) = 2$ to find Δy when $\Delta x = 0.005$. Using Eq. (3.91), we have

$$\Delta y = 2(\Delta x) = 2(0.005) = 0.01 \tag{3.92}$$

so y changes by the increment $\Delta y = 0.01$ when x changes by the increment $\Delta x = 0.005$ when x changes from 2.000 to 2.005.

So far we haven't specified any *physical meaning* to the variables x

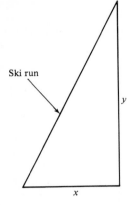

Ski run

y

x

FIGURE 3.1
Vertical distance y and horizontal distance x for a ski run.

and y connected by the functional relation $y = f(x)$ in Eq. (3.80). They can just be considered as mathematical variables, but, for concreteness, let's consider a physical example. Suppose x is a horizontal distance, measured in meters, and y is a vertical distance, also in meters, and suppose further that y is a function of x as in Eq. (3.86), which says

$$y = f(x) = 2x \qquad (3.86)$$

The variables x and y might be related to a ski run whose constant steepness is such that, as in Fig. 3.1, the vertical distance y is twice the horizontal distance x. Then, as we found before,

$$\frac{\Delta y}{\Delta x} = 2 \qquad (3.93)$$

is the average rate of change of y (vertical distance) with respect to x (horizontal distance). Skiing down the run, the skier would move a vertical distance (in meters) of $(\Delta y / \Delta x) = 2$ for each meter of horizontal distance moved. Since

$$\Delta y = 2(\Delta x) \qquad (3.94)$$

the skier would, for instance, move a vertical distance $\Delta y = 10$ meters while moving a horizontal distance $\Delta x = 5$ meters.

EXERCISES

3.10. Given the function $y = 6x + 2$, (a) calculate the average rate of change of y with respect to x over the interval from $x = 1.00$ to $x = 1.01$; (b) calculate the change Δy in y when x changes from 1.00 to 1.01.

CONNECTION BETWEEN THE DERIVATIVE AND RATE OF CHANGE

In the preceding section, the quantity

$$\frac{\Delta y}{\Delta x} = \frac{f(x_1 + \Delta x) - f(x_1)}{\Delta x} \tag{3.95}$$

was introduced as the average rate of change of y, with respect to x, over the interval Δx from x_1 to $(x_1 + \Delta x)$. We now let Δx become very small and take the limit

$$\lim_{\Delta x \to 0} \frac{f(x_1 + \Delta x) - f(x_1)}{\Delta x} = f'(x_1) \tag{3.96}$$

using the definition of the derivative in Eq. (3.7). Equation (3.96) is the derivative $f'(x_1)$ of the function $f(x)$ at the point $x = x_1$. Since the expression in Eq. (3.95) is a rate of change, it is reasonable to expect that the derivative $f'(x_1)$ given by Eq. (3.96) will also be a rate of change.

Since the quantity given by Eq. (3.95) is the average rate of change of y with respect to x, and since also

$$y = f(x) \tag{3.97}$$

we may say also that the quantity

$$\frac{f(x_1 + \Delta x) - f(x_1)}{\Delta x} \tag{3.98}$$

is the average rate of change of the function $f(x)$, with respect to x, over the interval Δx from x_1 to $(x_1 + \Delta x)$. When the limit as $\Delta x \to 0$ is taken in Eq. (3.96), we are essentially finding the average rate of change of $f(x)$ over smaller and smaller intervals of size Δx from x_1 to $(x_1 + \Delta x)$. We know, from the definition of the derivative in Eq. (3.96), that the limit approached by Eq. (3.98) is $f'(x_1)$, the derivative at $x = x_1$. As we take the limit of expression (3.98) as $\Delta x \to 0$, the *average* rate of change of the function $f(x)$ approaches $f'(x_1)$ as its limiting value. We call this limiting value $f'(x_1)$ the *instantaneous* rate of change of $f(x)$, with respect to x, at the point $x = x_1$.

We may restate this conclusion for emphasis. As the limit as $\Delta x \to 0$ is taken, the average rate of change of $f(x)$, given by Eq. (3.98), approaches $f'(x_1)$, the value of the derivative at $x = x_1$. The derivative $f'(x_1)$, at $x = x_1$, is the instantaneous rate of change of $f(x)$, with respect to x, at the point $x = x_1$.

Let's consider again the example in the previous section. We recall that the function was

$$y = f(x) = 2x \qquad (3.86)$$

and we found in Eq. (3.90) that the average rate of change of y, or f, was, for $x_1 = 2$,

$$\frac{f(x_1 + \Delta x) - f(x_1)}{\Delta x} = 2 \qquad (3.90)$$

From Eq. (3.86), we calculate that

$$f'(x) = \frac{d}{dx} (2x) = 2 \qquad (3.99)$$

is the derivative of $f(x) = 2x$, with respect to x, for *any* value of x, including, of course, $x = x_1 = 2$. The derivative $f'(x)$ thus has the value 2 for $x = x_1 = 2$, so

$$f'(x_1) = f'(2) = 2 \qquad (3.100)$$

is the value of the derivative of $f(x) = 2x$ for $x = 2$. The value of the *instantaneous* rate of change of the function $f(x) = 2x$ therefore has the value 2 for all values of x.

As another example, consider

$$y = f(x) = 2x^2 \qquad (3.101)$$

so

$$f'(x) = 4x \qquad (3.102)$$

The derivative $f'(x)$ in Eq. (3.102) is itself a function of x, so the value of $f'(x)$ will vary with the value of x. When x has the value x_1, the derivative has the value

$$f'(x_1) = 4x_1 \qquad (3.103)$$

From the preceding discussion, we see that $f'(x_1) = 4x_1$ is the value of the instantaneous rate of change of the function $f(x) = 2x^2$ at the value $x = x_1$. For example, if $x_1 = 3$, the value of the derivative is

$$f'(x_1) = f'(3) = 4(3) = 12 \qquad (3.104)$$

so the instantaneous rate of change of $f(x) = 2x^2$, with respect to x, is the value $f'(3) = 12$ when $x = 3$.

What does the word ''instantaneous'' mean when we say ''instantaneous rate of change of $f(x)$ with respect to x''? The dictionary definition of instantaneous is ''occurring or present at a specific instant of time.''

Since time is not involved here (that will come later), we will take "instantaneous" to mean "for a particular value of the independent variable." Thus, the derivative $f'(x_1)$ is the instantaneous rate of change of the function $f(x)$ for the value $x = x_1$ of the independent variable x. As an example, consider the function $f(x) = 2x^2$, given in Eq. (3.101), for which the derivative $f'(x) = 4x$ is the instantaneous rate of change. This means that the instantaneous rate of change of the function $f(x) = 2x^2$ is the quantity $f'(x) = 4x$, which itself depends on x. Hence, in this case, the value of the instantaneous rate of change depends on the value of the independent variable x. As shown in Eq. (3.104),

$$f'(3) = 4(3) = 12 \qquad (3.105)$$

is the value of the instantaneous rate of change of $f(x) = 2x^2$ for the value $x = 3$ of the independent variable x. For, say, $x = 4$,

$$f'(4) = 4(4) = 16 \qquad (3.106)$$

so the instantaneous rate of change $f'(4)$ has the value 16 when $x = 4$.

We can visualize these results by making graphs of $f(x) = 2x^2$ and $f'(x) = 4x$; these are shown in Figs. 3.2 and 3.3, respectively. Figure 3.3 shows the derivative $f'(x) = 4x$ plotted as a function of x. We can read values of $f'(x)$ for any value of x off the graph. The values $f'(3) = 12$ for $x = 3$ and $f'(4) = 16$ for $x = 4$ are shown on the graph. Note that

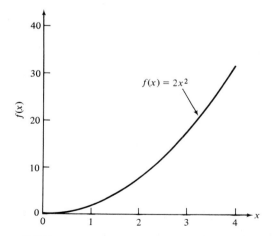

FIGURE 3.2
Graph of $f(x) = 2x^2$ as a function of x.

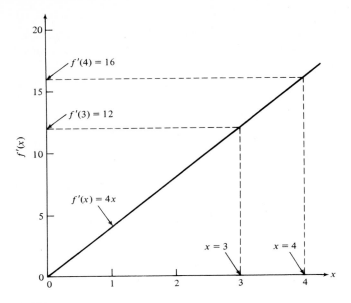

FIGURE 3.3
Graph of $f'(x) = 4x$ as a function of x.

the graph of the equation $f'(x) = 4x$ shows explicitly that the derivative is a function of x.

We may extend this idea as follows. Since $f'(x_1)$ is the instantaneous rate of change of $f(x)$ for $x = x_1$, and x_1 may be *any* value of x, the derivative $f'(x)$ is referred to as the *instantaneous rate of change of* $f(x)$ *with respect to* x. The derivative $f'(x)$ will usually be a function of x, so the value of the instantaneous rate of change will generally depend on x. Using our earlier example, if $f(x) = 2x^2$, the derivative $f'(x) = 4x$ is the instantaneous rate of change of $f(x)$ with respect to x. The value of $f'(x)$ depends on x and will have different values for different values of x. For example, $f'(4) = 16$ is the value of the instantaneous rate of change of $f(x) = 2x^2$ for the value $x = 4$ of the independent variable x.

It is useful to summarize briefly the results obtained so far. Given the function $f(x)$, the derivative $f'(x)$ is called the instantaneous rate of change of $f(x)$ with respect to x. The value $f'(x_1)$ of the derivative for $x = x_1$ is the value of that rate of change when $x = x_1$.

We defer the discussion of the *meaning* of the instantaneous rate of change to the next section.

EXERCISES

3.11. Given the function $y = f(x) = x^3$, (a) calculate the instantaneous rate of change of $f(x)$ with respect to x; (b) calculate the value of this rate of change when $x = 1$.

MEANING OF INSTANTANEOUS RATE OF CHANGE. FUNCTIONS OF TIME

The meaning of the instantaneous rate of change of a function is most clearly explained by considering functions which vary with the *time*. We are all familiar with quantities which are functions of time. Common examples are the temperature of the air and the distance moved by an automobile.

We will use the latter example in order to discuss in detail the meaning of the instantaneous rate of change of a function. Suppose we consider an auto starting from rest and moving in a straight line, and suppose further that we know the distance moved as a function of time. We will use the symbols s for distance and t for time, so we know distance s as a function of time t, which we write as

$$s = f(t) \tag{3.107}$$

In Eq. (3.107), s is the distance moved from the starting point and t is the elapsed time after the auto starts to move. Equation (3.107) allows us, in principle, to calculate the distance the auto has moved during any elapsed time. We will usually measure distance in meters and time in seconds.

It is useful to digress briefly here to explain in detail the precise meanings of distance and time as used in Eq. (3.107) or others like it. The symbol s refers to the distance moved, measured from the starting point. For example, if the car at some point on its path has moved 1000 meters from the starting position, we would say that $s = 1000$ meters. The position or point from which the distance is measured is often called the zero point or the zero of distance because it is the point at which $s = 0$. Since s is the distance *moved*, $s = 0$ at the starting point. The symbol t refers to elapsed time, as measured from the instant at which the motion begins. (Note that t is *not* a clock time like, say, 11:15 A.M.) For example, if we were considering an instant of time 30 seconds after the car starts moving, we would say that $t = 30$ seconds at that instant. Since t is the elapsed time, $t = 0$ at the instant the motion begins. To summarize these points, distance s is measured from the starting point of the motion and time t is measured from the starting time of the motion. At the instant at which the motion begins, $s = 0$ and $t = 0$, and both s and t increase as the motion proceeds with time.

We return to Eq. (3.107) giving the distance moved as a function of time,

$$s = f(t) \qquad (3.107)$$

The derivative of $f(t)$ is, from the definition,

$$\frac{ds}{dt} = f'(t) = \lim_{\Delta t \to 0} \frac{f(t + \Delta t) - f(t)}{\Delta t} \qquad (3.108)$$

In Eq. (3.108), $f(t)$ is the distance that has been moved at the instant of time t, $f(t + \Delta t)$ is the distance moved at the later instant of time $(t + \Delta t)$, and Δt is the length of the time interval between those two instants. Since the quantity

$$f(t + \Delta t) - f(t)$$

is the distance moved in the time interval of length Δt, we can see that

$$\frac{f(t + \Delta t) - f(t)}{\Delta t}$$

is the average rate of change of distance with time during the time interval of length Δt. When we take the limit, as $\Delta t \to 0$, in Eq. (3.108), we obtain the derivative $f'(t)$ of distance s with respect to time t. From our results in the preceding section, the derivative $(ds/dt) = f'(t)$ is the instantaneous rate of change of distance with respect to time. We will discuss this particular rate of change in detail as a way of introducing and illuminating the general idea of an instantaneous rate of change.

For concreteness, let us consider as an example the specific function

$$s = f(t) = 2t^2 \qquad (3.109)$$

giving the distance s moved by the auto as a function of time t. The derivative

$$\frac{ds}{dt} = f'(t) = 4t \qquad (3.110)$$

is the instantaneous rate of change of distance with respect to time when the distance is given as a function of time by Eq. (3.109).

The physical meaning of the rate of change of distance with respect to time is familiar to us as *velocity*. Velocity, commonly expressed in units like miles per hour or meters per second, means the distance moved in one unit of time, often called the distance moved per unit time. Each of the quantities given in Eq. (3.110) is the *instantaneous velocity* of the auto, meaning the auto's velocity at one instant of time. If distance s is expressed in meters and time in seconds in Eq. (3.109), then the instantaneous velocity will be in meters per second. Equation (3.110) therefore gives the instantaneous velocity, which is the instantaneous rate of change of distance with respect to time. We can write

$$v \equiv \frac{ds}{dt} = f'(t) \tag{3.111}$$

defining the instantaneous velocity v as the instantaneous rate of change of distance s with respect to time t. Since in this example, $f'(t) = 4t$, we have

$$v = \frac{ds}{dt} = f'(t) = 4t \tag{3.112}$$

an equation which gives the instantaneous velocity v as a function of time.

The velocity itself varies with time and we may, from Eq. (3.112), calculate v at any instant of time. For example, if we consider the instant of time 4 seconds after the auto starts, we are considering the instant at which

$$t = 4 \text{ seconds} \tag{3.113}$$

Substituting $t = 4$ seconds into Eq. (3.112), we obtain

$$v = f'(4) = 4(4) = 16 \text{ meters per second} \tag{3.114}$$

giving the value $v = 16$ meters per second of the instantaneous velocity v at the particular instant of time $t = 4$ seconds.

We digress briefly again here to consider the notation used to indicate the value of the derivative at a particular instant or value of the time. Considering a function $f(x)$ of x, we have been using the notation $f'(x_1)$ to indicate the value of the derivative $f'(x)$ at the particular point $x = x_1$. There is another common notation in use. If (dy/dx) is the derivative of $y = f(x)$ with respect to x, then the symbol

$$\left(\frac{dy}{dx}\right)_{x=x_1} \tag{3.115}$$

is also used to indicate the value of the derivative at the point $x = x_1$. One might also see

$$\left(\frac{df}{dx}\right)_{x=x_1} \tag{3.116}$$

for the same derivative evaluated at $x = x_1$. All three notations are equivalent, so if we consider a function $y = f(x)$, it is true that

$$\left(\frac{dy}{dx}\right)_{x=x_1} = \left(\frac{df}{dx}\right)_{x=x_1} = f'(x_1) \tag{3.117}$$

all of which mean the value of the derivative at the point $x = x_1$. Applying this notation to functions of time, we indicate the value of the derivative $f'(t)$ when $t = 4$ seconds by any of the following symbols:

$$\left(\frac{ds}{dt}\right)_{t=4} = \left(\frac{df}{dt}\right)_{t=4} = f'(4) \tag{3.118}$$

all of which mean the same thing: the derivative of distance s, with respect to time t, evaluated at the particular instant of time $t = 4$ seconds.

Returning to our consideration of the derivative of distance wtih respect to time, we note particularly the use of the term ''instantaneous'' in the discussion of velocity. We earlier defined the instantaneous rate of change as the rate of change for a particular value of the independent variable. Thus $f'(x)$ is the instantaneous rate of change of $f(x)$ for some particular value of x. In treating velocity, we are dealing with distance as a function of the independent variable time. The instantaneous velocity is the instantaneous rate of change of distance, with respect to time, for some particular value of time, so $v = (ds/dt) = f'(t)$ is the value of the velocity for a particular value of the time.

We can visualize how the instantaneous velocity changes with time by making a graph of Eq. (3.112) giving v as a function of time. Figure 3.4 shows a graph of the equation

$$v = f'(t) = 4t \tag{3.119}$$

as a function of time, for times from 0 to 5 seconds. The instantaneous velocity v is plotted in meters per second and time t is in seconds. We can see from the graph that the instantaneous velocity v increases with time from the value $v = 0$ when $t = 0$ (the auto starts from rest at $t = 0$) to the value $v = 20$ meters per second when $t = 5$ seconds.

Since the velocity is the instantaneous rate of change of distance with respect to time, the graph in Fig. 3.4 shows clearly that *the rate of change is itself changing with time*. The instantaneous rate of change is just the value of the rate of change at some particular instant of time. On the graph is shown the value $v = 16$ meters per second of the instantaneous rate of change (velocity), at the instant $t = 4$ seconds, as given by the relations in Eq. (3.114).

We may now summarize our results concerning the instantaneous

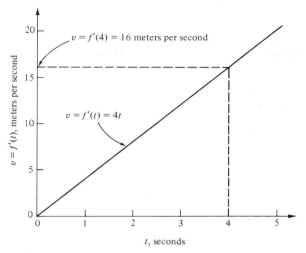

FIGURE 3.4
Instantaneous velocity $v = f'(t)$ as a function of time t when $v = f'(t) = 4t$.

velocity. Given the distance s moved as a function of elapsed time t, as

$$s = f(t) \qquad (3.120)$$

Then the instantaneous rate of change of distance with respect to time t is called the instantaneous velocity v, so

$$v = \frac{ds}{dt} = f'(t) \qquad (3.121)$$

In general, the velocity v will vary with time, so the rate of change $f'(t)$ is itself a function of time and varies with time. The instantaneous velocity v, or instantaneous rate of change $f'(t)$, is then the value at some particular value of t, i.e., at some particular instant of time.

We can now see the general meaning of an instantaneous rate of change. Given a function $f(x)$, then $f'(x)$ is the instantaneous rate of change of $f(x)$ with respect to x. In general, the rate of change $f'(x)$ will itself be a function of the independent variable x. The instantaneous rate of change thus specifies the rate of change for some particular value of x. While we have illustrated the idea of an instantaneous rate of change with the example of velocity, there are many other quantities in physics whose rates of change with respect to some independent variable are of interest. Often the independent variable of interest in physics is the time, but that is not always the case. We now examine some examples of rates of change, including one with respect to a variable other than the time.

As an example of a rate of change, let's consider the familiar phenomenon of the variation of the temperature of some object with time. Suppose a sample of water is heated and the temperature T [in kelvins (sometimes abbreviated K)] is measured as a function of time t (in seconds). Suppose further that the temperature as a function $f(t)$ of time is found to be

$$T = f(t) = 0.5t + 300 \qquad (3.122)$$

an equation in which the temperature T is the dependent variable and the time t is the independent variable. Then the derivative $f'(t)$ is the instantaneous rate of change of the temperature T with respect to time t. Differentiating T with respect to t in Eq. (3.122) yields

$$f'(t) = \frac{dT}{dt} = 0.5 \qquad (3.123)$$

Equation (3.123) gives us (dT/dt), the instantaneous rate of change of temperature with respect to time as 0.5 kelvin per second. This rate of change is the change in temperature per unit of change in time. In this example, the rate of change is 0.5 kelvin in 1 second and the rate of change is constant and does not itself vary with the time.

Let us consider as a second example one in which the rate of change is *not* with respect to time. Consider the situation shown in Fig. 3.5, in which we have a thin rod of metal with its length oriented parallel to the x axis. Let us choose the origin $x = 0$ at the left-hand end (1) of the rod; then, if the rod is of length 1 meter, the right-hand end (2) will be at the point $x = 1$ meter on the x axis. Suppose that the left-hand end (1) is heated, so heat flows along the rod from end 1 to end 2. Suppose also that we have measured the temperature T at many points between $x = 0$ and $x = 1$, so we know the temperature as a function $f(x)$ of position along the rod between $x = 0$ and $x = 1$. As an equation, we have

$$T = f(x) \qquad (3.124)$$

giving the dependent variable T as a function of distance x (measured from $x = 0$ at end 1 of the rod) along the rod. As a concrete example,

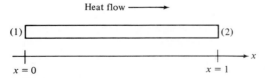

FIGURE 3.5
Rod, of length 1 meter, placed parallel to the x axis. The direction of heat flow is as shown.

suppose

$$T = f(x) = 400 - 100x \qquad (3.125)$$

where T is in kelvins and x is in meters. Since the temperature varies along the length of the rod, there will be a rate of change of temperature T *with respect to distance x* along the rod. The derivative $f'(x)$ of T with respect to x is the instantaneous rate of change (in kelvins per meter) of temperature with respect to distance. Calculating the derivative $f'(x)$ from Eq. (3.125) gives the result

$$f'(x) = \frac{dT}{dx} = -100 \qquad (3.126)$$

Equation (3.126) gives (dT/dx), the instantaneous rate of change of temperature, with respect to distance, as -100 kelvins per meter. The negative sign means that the temperature is decreasing with increasing distance, meaning that the temperature is lower at points further away from the left-hand end of the rod at $x = 0$. The rate of change is the change in temperature per unit of change of distance. In this example, that rate of change is (-100) kelvins in one meter, and, again, the rate of change is constant and does not itself vary with distance along the rod. The derivative (dT/dx) is called the temperature gradient along the length of the rod.

EXERCISES

3.12. It is found in a certain physics experiment that the distance s moved by a body is directly proportional to the cube of the time t the body moves. (a) Using the symbol B for the constant of proportionality, write the equation giving s as a function of t. (b) Use your result in part (a) to find the rate of change of distance with respect to time. (c) Write down an expression for the velocity of the body as a function of time.

3.13. Starting from rest, a block of ice slides down a chute in such a way that the distance s that it moves is given as a function of time t by the relation

$$s = 2.4t^2$$

where s is in meters if t is in seconds. (a) Find the equation giving the rate of change of distance with respect to time. (b) Is the rate of change found in part (a) a function of time? (c) Calculate the velocity of the ice block 1 second after it begins to move.

3.14. The circumference C of a circle is given as a function of its radius r by the equation

$$C = 2\pi r$$

(a) Find the equation giving the rate of change of the circumference of the circle with respect to its radius. (b) Express in your own words the meaning of the rate of change in (a).

THE SECOND DERIVATIVE AND ACCELERATION

We have seen that the physical meaning of the derivative $f'(x)$ of a function $f(x)$ is the rate of change of the function $f(x)$ with respect to x. We now examine the meaning of the *second* derivative of a function. We consider again a function $f(t)$, of the time t, whose first derivative is $f'(t)$. Then the second derivative may be written in the various equivalent ways:

$$f''(t) = \frac{d}{dt}\left[f'(t)\right] = \frac{d}{dt}\left[\frac{df}{dt}\right] \tag{3.127}$$

Equation (3.127) says that the second derivative $f''(t)$ is the derivative, with respect to time, of the derivative $f'(t)$. Since $f'(t)$ is the rate of change of $f(t)$ with respect to time, the second derivative $f''(t)$ is the rate of change, with respect to time, of the rate of change. In short, the second derivative is the rate of change of the rate of change.

We can illustrate this with a physical example by considering the velocity, given by Eq. (3.111) as

$$v = \frac{ds}{dt} = f'(t) \tag{3.111}$$

where the distance s is a function $f(t)$ of the time. If we take the derivative with respect to time of v in Eq. (3.111), we obtain

$$\frac{dv}{dt} = \frac{d}{dt}\left(\frac{ds}{dt}\right) = \frac{d^2s}{dt^2} = f''(t) \tag{3.128}$$

Equation (3.128) says that the second derivative (d^2s/dt^2) of the distance, with respect to time, is equal to the rate of change of the velocity v with respect to time. Since we have seen that the velocity is itself the rate of change of distance with respect to time, the quantity (dv/dt) is the rate of change of the rate of change of distance with respect to time. The rate of change (dv/dt) is called the *acceleration*, so acceleration is the rate of change of velocity with respect to time. An equivalent is that the second derivative of distance, with respect to time, is equal to the acceleration.

Let's discuss a specific example. Suppose we consider a body falling vertically from rest under the influence of gravity without any air resistance. Then it is known experimentally that the vertical distance s the body falls in time t is given by

$$s = 4.9t^2 \tag{3.129}$$

Equation (3.129) gives s in meters if t is in seconds. As before, t is measured from the instant at which the body starts to fall and s is measured from the starting point. Since Eq. (3.129) gives distance as a function of time, we may calculate the velocity by differentiating s with respect to t, obtaining

$$v = \frac{ds}{dt} = 9.8t \tag{3.130}$$

Equation (3.130) gives the velocity v as a function of the time and shows that the velocity itself varies with the time. Since s is in meters and t is in seconds, v in Eq. (3.130) is in meters per second.

Since the acceleration is the rate of change of velocity with respect to time, we may find the acceleration (denoted by the symbol a) by differentiating v with respect to time. Using Eq. (3.130), the result is

$$a = \frac{dv}{dt} = \frac{d}{dt}\left(\frac{ds}{dt}\right) = \frac{d^2s}{dt^2} = 9.8 \tag{3.131}$$

Equation (3.131) says that the acceleration a has the constant value 9.8, which is in units of meters per second per second since the velocity is in meters per second. The unit of acceleration "meters per second per second" emphasizes that acceleration is the rate of change of velocity with time. The statement of Eq. (3.131) that

$$a = \frac{dv}{dt} = 9.8 \text{ meters per second per second} \tag{3.132}$$

says that the velocity is changing with time at the constant rate of (9.8 meters per second) per second. Note that in this example the acceleration has a constant value and does not vary with the time.

Let's consider another example, one in which a particle moves along the x axis starting from the origin ($x = 0$) when the time $t = 0$. Although we have generally been using the symbol s for the distance moved, we will use x for the distance from the origin in this example. (This common usage is because the motion is confined to the x axis.) Suppose x is given as a function of time t by the equation

$$x = A \sin \omega t \tag{3.133}$$

where A and ω are constants. Thus Eq. (3.133) gives x, the distance of the particle from the origin at the time t, that is, after an elapsed time t. The velocity v of the particle is the rate of change of distance x with respect to time t, so

$$v = \frac{dx}{dt} = A\omega \cos \omega t \qquad (3.134)$$

Equation (3.134) gives the velocity v of the particle as a function of time t; v is equal to the constant $(A\omega)$ times the cosine of ωt. We see that the velocity varies cosinusoidally with the time. Next, the acceleration a of the particle is the rate of change of velocity with respect to time, so

$$a = \frac{dv}{dt} = \frac{d}{dt} [A\omega \cos \omega t] = -A\omega^2 \sin \omega t \qquad (3.135)$$

Equation (3.135) gives the acceleration a of the particle as a function of time t: a is equal to the constant $(-A\omega^2)$ times the sine of ωt. Thus the acceleration varies sinusoidally with the time. Note that, in contrast to the preceding example, the acceleration in this case is not constant and does vary with time. The motion described by Eqs. (3.133)–(3.135) is called *simple harmonic motion* and is very common in physics.

To summarize, the second derivative is the rate of change of the rate of change. An important physical example is the acceleration, which is the second derivative of distance with respect to time. The acceleration is thus the rate of change, with respect to time, of velocity, which is itself the rate of change of distance with respect to time.

EXERCISES

3.15. Using your results obtained in solving Exercise 3.12, calculate the acceleration of the moving body.

DIFFERENTIALS

We now consider the differential, a concept that is used frequently in physics and which is assumed to have been discussed, but probably not extensively, in your calculus course. Suppose we have a function

$$y = f(x) \qquad (3.136)$$

of the independent variable x. We introduce the symbol dx, called the *differential of* x. (Note that dx is a single symbol; it does *not* mean d times x.) The differential dx may be any real number, although (as we will see later) it is usually considered to be a very small number in situations of interest in physics.

We next introduce the differential of the function $f(x)$, denoted by the symbol df, and defined by the equation

$$df \equiv f'(x)\, dx \qquad (3.137)$$

where, as usual, $f'(x)$ is the derivative of $f(x)$ with respect to x. Equation (3.137) says that the differential df of the function $f(x)$ is equal to the product of the derivative $f'(x)$ and the differential dx of the independent variable x. Since, from Eq. (3.136), $y = f(x)$, the differential of the function $f(x)$ is also denoted by the symbol dy, so Eq. (3.137) may also be written

$$dy = f'(x)\, dx \qquad (3.138)$$

The quantity dy is a single symbol and is called the *differential of y*. Note that, from Eq. (3.138), the differential dy is a function of both x and dx, meaning that dy depends on the two quantities, x and dx.

As an example, consider the function

$$y = f(x) = x^3 \qquad (3.139)$$

Then the differential of y is given by

$$dy = f'(x)\, dx = (3x^2)\, dx \qquad (3.140)$$

where the parentheses in Eq. (3.140) are used to emphasize the fact that the differential dy is equal to the product of the function $3x^2$ and the differential dx. Since $y = f(x)$, we could equally well have written the result in Eq. (3.140) as

$$df = f'(x)\, dx = (3x^2)\, dx \qquad (3.141)$$

an equation which has the same content as Eq. (3.140). We will use whichever of the equivalent symbols dy or df is the more convenient in a given situation.

If we divide the differential dy as given by Eq. (3.138) by the differential dx, we obtain, assuming dx is not zero,

$$\frac{dy}{dx} = \frac{f'(x)\, dx}{dx} = f'(x) \qquad (3.142)$$

Equation (3.142) is very important. It says that the derivative $f'(x)$, of the function $y = f(x)$, is equal to the quotient of the differential dy, of y, divided by the differential dx. As an example, we take dy for the function $y = x^3$ given by Eq. (3.140) and divide it by dx, obtaining

$$\frac{dy}{dx} = \frac{(3x^2)\, dx}{dx} = 3x^2 \qquad (3.143)$$

Equation (3.143) says that the ratio of dy to dx is equal to the quantity $3x^2$, which is, of course, the derivative of x^3.

The fact that the derivative $f'(x)$ can be expressed as the ratio of the differentials dy and dx is much used in physics. Differentials may be manipulated just like numbers and may be added, subtracted, multiplied, and divided (whenever not equal to zero). A useful instance is afforded by the chain rule which was discussed earlier. There we considered two functions

$$y = g(u) \qquad u = f(x) \tag{3.144}$$

and the chain rule gives the derivative $y'(x)$ of y with respect to x as

$$y'(x) = g'(u)\,u'(x) \tag{3.145}$$

Equation (3.145) says that the derivative $y'(x)$ is equal to the derivative $g'(u)$ of g with respect to u times the derivative $u'(x)$ of u with respect to x. This can be written in alternative notation as

$$\frac{dy}{dx} = \left(\frac{dy}{du}\right)\left(\frac{du}{dx}\right) \tag{3.146}$$

since $g'(u) = (dy/du)$ and $u'(x) = (du/dx)$. Equation (3.146) says that the derivative (dy/dx) is the product of the derivative (dy/du) and the derivative (du/dx). If we regard the derivatives in Eq. (3.146) as ratios of differentials, we may write the product

$$\left(\frac{dy}{du}\right)\left(\frac{du}{dx}\right) \tag{3.147}$$

and then "cancel" the differential du in the numerator and denominator, treating du just like a number. The result of "canceling" the differential du in Eq. (3.147) is shown in Eq. (3.148),

$$\left(\frac{dy}{\cancel{du}}\right)\left(\frac{\cancel{du}}{dx}\right) = \frac{dy}{dx} \tag{3.148}$$

where the diagonal lines through the differentials du indicate "cancellation." Equation (3.148) is a statement of the chain rule for the functions involved and shows the utility of the approach using differentials.

As a specific example of the use of differentials, suppose we have the function

$$y = \sin x^3$$

so we then have

$$y = g(u) = \sin u$$
$$u = f(x) = x^3$$

and we want to find (dy/dx), the derivative of y with respect to x. We could do it directly with the chain rule in Eq. (3.146) by calculating the required derivatives, but let's do it instead with differentials. From the definition of the differential of a function given in Eq. (3.138), we have

$$dy = g'(u) \, du = (\cos u) \, du \qquad (3.149)$$

Let's divide both sides of Eq. (3.149) by the differential dx, obtaining

$$\frac{dy}{dx} = (\cos u)\left(\frac{du}{dx}\right) \qquad (3.150)$$

an equation that says the derivative (dy/dx) is equal to $\cos u$ times the derivative (du/dx). We can calculate (du/dx) from the differential du, given by

$$du = f'(x) \, dx = (3x^2) \, dx \qquad (3.151)$$

Then we divide both sides of Eq. (3.151) by the differential dx, obtaining

$$\frac{du}{dx} = \frac{(3x^2) \, dx}{dx} = 3x^2$$

Substituting $u = x^3$ and $(du/dx) = 3x^2$ into Eq. (3.150) gives the result

$$\frac{dy}{dx} = (3x^2)(\cos x^3)$$

for the required derivative (dy/dx). This result is, of course, the same as that obtained by applying the chain rule directly to the derivatives.

The differential can also be useful in finding rates of change of various sorts. An example would be a rate of change with respect to time. Consider the familiar equation

$$C = 2\pi r \qquad (3.152)$$

for the circumference C of a circle as a function of its radius r. Suppose we are interested in finding (dC/dt), the rate of change of the circumference with respect to time. Let us take the differential dC of C from Eq. (3.152), obtaining

$$dC = (2\pi) \, dr \qquad (3.153)$$

where dr is the differential of r. Next, we divide both sides of Eq. (3.153) by dt, the differential of t, the time. The result is

$$\frac{dC}{dt} = (2\pi)\frac{dr}{dt} \qquad (3.154)$$

Equation (3.154) tells us that the rate of change (dC/dt) of the circumference C with respect to time t is equal to the constant 2π times the rate of change (dr/dt) of the radius r with respect to time t.

This section is concluded with a brief list of differentials of common functions. In Eq. (3.149), we saw that, if $y = \sin u$, the differential dy is given by

$$dy = (\cos u)\, du \qquad (3.155)$$

The result exhibited in Eq. (3.155) is often expressed as

$$d[\sin u] = \cos u\, du \qquad (3.156)$$

Equation (3.156) is read "the differential of the sine of u is equal to the cosine of u times the differential du of u." Equations like Eq. (3.156) are frequentiy used to express the differential of some function. Just as the symbol

$$\frac{d}{dx}[f(x)]$$

was used earlier to indicate the *operation* of taking the derivative of the function f, the symbol

$$d[f(x)]$$

expresses the operation of taking the *differential* of the function f. Thus, in Eq. (3.156), $d[\sin u]$ indicates the operation of taking the differential of the function $\sin u$, and that that differential equals the cosine of u times the differential du.

This notation is used in the short list of differentials that follows; in the list u and v are functions, and a and n are constants

$$d[au] = a\, du \qquad (3.157)$$

$$d[u + v] = du + dv \qquad (3.158)$$

$$d[u^n] = (nu^{n-1})\, du \qquad (3.159)$$

$$d[e^u] = e^u\, du \qquad (3.160)$$

$$d[\ln u] = (1/u)\, du \qquad (3.161)$$

$$d[\sin u] = (\cos u)\, du \qquad (3.162)$$

$$d[\cos u] = (-\sin u)\, du \qquad (3.163)$$

$$d[uv] = u\, dv + v\, du \qquad (3.164)$$

EXERCISES

3.16. Given the function $y = f(x) = 6 \cos 6x^4$. Find the differential dy.

3.17. Given that the area A of a circle is πr^2, where r is the radius. Calculate the rate of change of the area with respect to time. Express the meaning of your result in words.

PHYSICAL APPLICATIONS OF DIFFERENTIALS

In physics, you will often see equations involving physical quantities written as differentials. In order to give a discussion involving concepts which are generally familiar to you, we recall the first law of thermodynamics, which you have probably studied in your chemistry course. Suppose a system undergoes a change, in the course of which heat energy enters or leaves the system and the system either does work on its surroundings or work is done on the system by its surroundings. Then the first law of thermodynamics, which is really a statement of the conservation of energy, is usually expressed by the equation

$$\Delta U = Q - W \tag{3.165}$$

In Eq. (3.165), Q is the energy added to the system by the transfer of heat, W is the energy given up by the system in doing work, and ΔU is the change in the internal energy of the system. Equation (3.165) simply says that the change ΔU in the internal energy of the system is equal to the heat energy entering the system minus the energy leaving the system as work done by the system.

Now suppose that the process or change undergone by the system is a *very small* one, by which is meant that the physical variables involved change only by very small amounts. In this example, the physical variables involved are the internal energy U, the heat energy Q, and the energy W appearing as work, so the internal energy, heat, and work will change only by very small amounts. It is customary in physics to indicate "a very small amount of . . ." by using the notation for differentials. Thus,

dQ means "a very small amount of heat energy."
dW means "a very small amount of work (energy)."
dU means "a very small amount of internal energy."

Note that each of the symbols dQ, etc., is a single symbol (just like the symbol for the differential dx) and does *not* mean "d times Q." Using the symbols above, we may write the first law of thermodynamics for a very small change undergone by the system as

$$dU = dQ - dW \tag{3.166}$$

Equation (3.166) is just the first law of thermodynamics stated for a very small change in a system. The equation says that the very small change dU in the internal energy is equal to the very small amount of energy dQ added to the system as heat minus the very small amount of work dW given up by the system in doing work.

The quantities dQ, etc., are also referred to as *infinitesimal quantities* or *differential quantities*. Thus dQ might be referred to as the infinitesimal quantity of heat energy, or the differential quantity of heat energy, entering the system. All of these terms for dQ, etc., signify the same physical meaning, namely, a very small amount of the quantity under discussion. Thus the symbol dA would in general mean "a very small amount of A," whatever physical quantity A may be.

Let's consider another example, this time from geometry, in Fig. 3.6, which shows the x axis. Suppose we consider a very short distance along the x axis, and give this very short length the symbol dx. Thus, dx means "a very small amount of distance along the x axis." It is customary to indicate such an "infinitesimal length" dx graphically as a short segment of the x axis, as shown in Fig. 3.6. This infinitesimal length dx might also be referred to as "an element of length" or the "differential distance" along the x axis.

We may discuss another example, this one involving the concept of *work*, which may already be familiar to you. If a force is applied to a body and moves it a distance in a direction parallel to the force, then the amount of work done is equal to the product of force times distance. Let's consider, as shown in Fig. 3.7, a force of constant magnitude F in a direction parallel to the x axis. Suppose that the force F moves a body a very small distance dx along the x axis. The amount of work done by the force on the body will be denoted by the symbol dW. Since work equals force times distance, we have

$$dW = F\,dx \qquad (3.167)$$

Equation (3.167) says that the infinitesimal (i.e., very small) amount of work dW done on the body is equal to the product of the force F and the infinitesimal distance dx moved by the body. (Once again, keep in mind that both dW and dx are single symbols and are *not* the products of d with W or x.) Equation (3.167) thus gives us the amount of work dW done in this infinitesimal process in which a force F moves a body an infinitesimal distance dx along the x axis. Note also that the force F is *not* considered

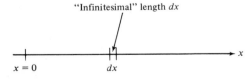

FIGURE 3.6
The x axis, showing an "infinitesimal" length dx.

FIGURE 3.7
Force F parallel to the x axis.

infinitesimal in magnitude; only the distance dx and the amount of work dW are considered as very small.

We now have the idea of very small or infinitesimal amounts of physical quantities, such as heat or distance. These quantities, denoted by symbols dQ or dx, may be manipulated by the rules for the manipulation of differentials. In other words, these very small quantities dQ, etc., may be treated just like the mathematical differentials we discussed in the previous section.

Let's consider an example of the value of differentials of physical variables using Eq. (3.167) for the infinitesimal amount of work dW. Consider the very short time necessary for the body to move the infinitesimal distance dx under the influence of the constant force F. We will denote this very small amount of time by the symbol dt. We now consider the quantities dW, dx, and dt to be mathematical differentials and manipulate them accordingly. Specifically, we will divide both sides of Eq. (3.167) by the infinitesimal time dt, obtaining

$$\frac{dW}{dt} = \frac{F\,dx}{dt} = F\frac{dx}{dt} \qquad (3.168)$$

Equation (3.168) says that the ratio (dW/dt) equals the force F times the ratio (dx/dt). Since we are treating dW, dx, and dt as differentials, the ratios (dW/dt) and (dx/dt) are derivatives and represent rates of change. The derivative (dW/dt) is the rate of change of work W done with respect to time t. The derivative (dx/dt) is the rate of change of distance x with respect to time t, so (dx/dt) is the velocity v. Substituting $v = (dx/dt)$ into Equation (3.168) gives us

$$\frac{dW}{dt} = Fv \qquad (3.169)$$

an equation which says that the rate of change of work done with respect to time is equal to the product of the force times the velocity of the body. [We assume in Eq. (3.169) that the force F and the velocity v are in the same direction.]

Another important application of the differential is geometric but is widely used in physics. This use is in differentials of the area or volume of a solid figure like a circle, sphere, or cylinder. Consider the area A of a circle of radius r, given by

$$A = \pi r^2 \tag{3.170}$$

The differential dA of the area A of a circle is, on taking the differential of both sides of Eq. (3.170), given by

$$dA = 2\pi r \, dr \tag{3.171}$$

where A is the dependent, and r the independent, variable.

Consider next, as shown in Fig. 3.8, a circular ring of width dr and radius r. We want to calculate the area dA of the circular ring. The area dA is just the difference between the area of a circle of radius $(r + dr)$ and the area of a circle of radius r. Thus

$$dA = \pi(r + dr)^2 - \pi r^2 = \pi r^2 + 2\pi r \, dr + \pi(dr)^2 - \pi r^2$$

$$dA = 2\pi r \, dr - \pi(dr)^2 \tag{3.172}$$

In Eq. (3.172), we have the term $\pi(dr)^2$, which includes $(dr)^2$, the *square* of the differential dr. Since r is the radius of the ring, we interpret dr as a very small length, and the quantity $(dr)^2$ is the *square* of a very small quantity. We conclude that $(dr)^2$ is negligibly small compared to $2\pi r \, dr$ in Eq. (3.172). Indeed, we conclude that in general we are justified in neglecting a differential raised to any power higher than the first. With this proviso, we have from Eq. (3.172) that

$$dA = 2\pi r \, dr \tag{3.173}$$

Equation (3.173) says that the area dA of a circular ring of radius r and width dr is equal to $2\pi r \, dr$. Note that the area dA given by Eq. (3.173) is the same as the differential dA of the area of a circle given by Eq. (3.171).

The same kind of result holds true for the volume. Consider a sphere of radius r, whose volume V is given by

$$V = \frac{4\pi}{3} r^3 \tag{3.174}$$

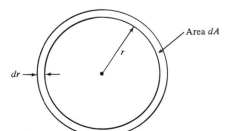

FIGURE 3.8
A circular ring of radius r and width dr. The area dA of the circular ring is equal to $2\pi r \, dr$.

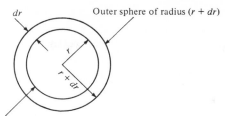

Outer sphere of radius $(r + dr)$

Inner sphere of radius r

FIGURE 3.9

A spherical shell of radius r and thickness dr is the volume contained between two concentric spheres, one of radius $(r + dr)$ and one of radius r. The volume dV of the shell is $4\pi r^2 \, dr$.

The differential dV of the volume of a sphere is, from Eq. (3.174),

$$dV = 4\pi r^2 \, dr \tag{3.175}$$

We now calculate the volume dV of the thin spherical shell, of radius r and thickness dr, shown in Fig. 3.9. The volume dV of this spherical shell is

$$dV = \frac{4\pi}{3} (r + dr)^3 - \frac{4\pi}{3} r^3$$

$$dV = \frac{4\pi}{3} \left(r^3 + 3r^2 \, dr + 3r(dr)^2 + (dr)^3 - r^3 \right) \tag{3.176}$$

Treating the terms containing $(dr)^2$ and $(dr)^3$ in Eq. (3.176) as negligible gives us

$$dV = 4\pi r^2 \, dr \tag{3.177}$$

for the volume of the spherical shell. Note again that this volume is equal to the differential dV of the volume of a sphere.

Differential elements of area and volume like Eq. (3.173) and Eq. (3.177) are widely used in setting up and solving physics problems involving geometric shapes. We will encounter them again when we discuss the applications of integrals to physics in Chap. 4.

As a final point on the physical interpretation of differentials, consider again the differential dy of a function $y = f(x)$, defined by the equation

$$dy = f'(x) \, dx \tag{3.178}$$

A common physical interpretation of Eq. (3.178) is as follows. Suppose the variable x changes by an infinitesimal amount dx. Then the corresponding change dy in y is given by Eq. (3.178) as the product of the derivative $f'(x)$ and dx. The basis for this interpretation lies in the fact that $f'(x)$ is the instantaneous rate of change of the function $f(x)$ with respect to x. That means that $f'(x)$ is the change in $f(x)$, or y, per unit of change in x, so $f'(x)$ times the change dx in x gives the total change dy in y. In physics, we generally consider the change dx to be very small, so the derivative $f'(x)$ can be considered as at least approximately constant in the interval of size dx over which x changes.

As an example, consider the function

$$y = f(x) = x^2$$

Suppose x changes from 1.00000 to 1.00001. What is the corresponding change in y? From Eq. (3.178),

$$dy = f'(x)\, dx = (2x)\, dx \qquad (3.179)$$

where the magnitude of the change dx in x is

$$dx = 0.00001$$

We now calculate the value of $f'(x) = 2x$. What value of x do we use? A reasonable choice is the value $x = 1.000005$, which lies halfway between the initial value $x = 1.00000$ and the final value $x = 1.00001$. We therefore take the value of $f'(x)$ in Eq. (3.179) as

$$f'(1.000005) = 2(1.000005) = 2.00001$$

Substituting this value of the derivative and the value $dx = 0.00001$ into Eq. (3.179) gives us

$$dy = (2.00001)(0.00001) \cong 0.00002 \qquad (3.180)$$

where the symbol "$\cong$" means "is approximately equal to." Equation (3.180) says that the function $y = x^2$ changes by an amount $dy \cong 0.00002$ when x changes from the value 1.00000 to the value 1.00001.

This procedure of calculating (at least approximately) with Eq. (3.178) the change dy in a function $y = f(x)$, when the independent variable x changes by dx, is often encountered in physics, and you will very probably see it used in your physics course.

This section illustrates how very small amounts of physical quantities (e.g., work) may be treated and manipulated as differentials. This approach is often used in physics, and you will encounter it frequently. Further, this idea of using differentials in physics will come up again, and in a very important way, when we consider the applications of integral calculus.

EXERCISES

3.18. Consider a particle moving with a constant velocity v in a straight line on the x axis for a very short time dt. Using the familiar notion that rate times time equals distance, write the equation for the very short (infinitesimal) distance dx moved by the particle in the time dt.

3.19. Given the definition that acceleration a is the rate of change of velocity v with time t, $a = (dv/dt)$. (a) Using this definition, calculate the differential dv of velocity in terms of a and dt. (b) Express in your own words the physical meaning of the equation you obtained as your result in (a).

3.20. Given the function $y = x^3$, calculate the change in y when x changes from 2.00000 to 2.00001.

3.21. Consider a physical process in which a small quantity dQ of heat produces a small temperature increase dT in a mass m of a substance. It is found that dQ is directly proportional to the product $m\,dT$. (a) Using the symbol c for the constant of proportionality, write the equation giving dQ in terms of c, m, and dT. The quantity c, called the specific heat of the substance, is not really a constant, but is generally itself a function $c(T)$ of the temperature. (b) Consider the equation you found in (a), and divide both sides of it by the differential dT. Your result gives the specific heat in terms of (dQ/dT), the derivative of the quantity of heat Q with respect to temperature T.

THE GEOMETRIC INTERPRETATION OF THE DERIVATIVE AND ITS PHYSICAL APPLICATIONS

While the most important interpretation of the derivative in physics is as a rate of change, we review here the geometric interpretation and discuss some of its applications. Given the function $f(x)$ of the variable x, consider the graph of $y = f(x)$ as a function of x shown in Fig. 3.10. We recall that, in discussing the definition of the derivative, we considered the ratio

$$\frac{f(x_1 + \Delta x) - f(x_1)}{\Delta x} \tag{3.181}$$

In Eq. (3.181), Δx is the increment in x, $f(x_1)$ is the value of the function f at the point $x = x_1$, and $f(x_1 + \Delta x)$ is the value of the function f at the point $x = (x_1 + \Delta x)$.

We now consider the meaning of the various quantities in Eq. (3.181) in terms of the graph of $y = f(x)$ in Fig. 3.10. The point A on the x axis is the point $x = x_1$; the point B is the point $x = (x_1 + \Delta x)$, so the distance **AB** (which equals the distance **CE**) along the x axis is equal to Δx. The distance **AC**, which equals the distance **BE**, is equal to the value $f(x_1)$ of the function $f(x)$ at point x_1. Similarly, distance **BD** is

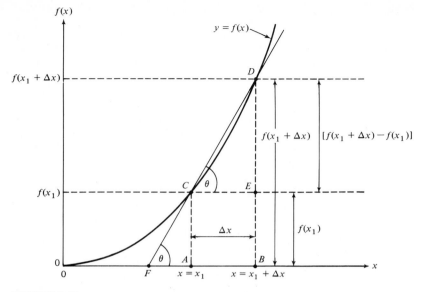

FIGURE 3.10
Graph of the function $f(x)$ as a function of x, showing the various quantities in Eq. (3.182).

equal to value $f(x_1 + \Delta x)$ of function $f(x)$ at the point $(x_1 + \Delta x)$. Distance **ED** is equal to the difference $[f(x_1 + \Delta x) - f(x_1)]$. Then, from Eq. (3.181), we have, since **AB** = **CE** = Δx, that

$$\frac{f(x_1 + \Delta x) - f(x_1)}{\Delta x} = \frac{\mathbf{ED}}{\mathbf{CE}} \tag{3.182}$$

As shown in Fig. 3.10, we will denote the angle DCE by the symbol θ. Since line CE is parallel to the x axis, angle DCE equals angle CFA, and both are denoted by θ. From elementary trigonometry, the tangent of the angle DCE is equal to the ratio of the length ED to the length CE. Thus it is true, from Eq. (3.182), that

$$\frac{f(x_1 + \Delta x) - f(x_1)}{\Delta x} = \tan \theta \tag{3.183}$$

where, as shown in Fig. 3.10, θ is the angle the straight line DCF makes with the x axis. By the definition of the *slope* of a straight line given in Chap. 2, Eq. (3.183) gives us the important result that the quantity

$$\frac{f(x_1 + \Delta x) - f(x_1)}{\Delta x} \tag{3.184}$$

is equal to the *slope* of the straight line DCF passing through the point C (at the point $x = x_1$) on the graph of the function $f(x)$.

Let us now take the limit, as the quantity Δx becomes smaller, of the quantity in expression (3.184). We can see what happens on the graph in Fig. 3.10 as Δx decreases. As Δx becomes smaller, the point D moves to the left along the curve $f(x)$ and approaches the point C. Eventually, as Δx becomes very small, the line DCF approaches (and becomes) the geometric tangent to the curve $f(x)$ at the point C where $x = x_1$. (Do not confuse the geometric tangent with the mathematical function $\tan \theta$.) Mathematically, we indicate the process of Δx becoming very small by writing $\Delta x \to 0$, and indicate the effect on the quantity in Eq. (3.184) by writing

$$\lim_{\Delta x \to 0} \frac{f(x_1 + \Delta x) - f(x_1)}{\Delta x} \tag{3.185}$$

We therefore conclude that, as $\Delta x \to 0$, the line DCF becomes the geometric tangent to the curve $f(x)$ at the point $x = x_1$. From Eq. (3.183), we conclude also that the value of the limit approached in Eq. (3.185) is equal to the value of the tangent of the angle θ, where θ is the angle made by the geometric tangent with the x axis.

Next, we see that the limit expression in Eq. (3.185) defines the derivative $f'(x_1)$, of $f(x)$ with respect to x, at the point $x = x_1$. We thus conclude that

$$\lim_{\Delta x \to 0} \frac{f(x_1 + \Delta x) - f(x_1)}{\Delta x} = f'(x_1) = \tan \theta \tag{3.186}$$

where θ is the angle made with the x axis by the geometric tangent to the curve of $f(x)$ at the point $x = x_1$. Since the quantity $\tan \theta$ in Eq. (3.186) is the slope of the geometric tangent, that equation says that

$$f'(x_1) = \tan \theta = \text{slope of geometric tangent at point } x = x_1 \tag{3.187}$$

Equation (3.187) says that the derivative $f'(x_1)$, at the point $x = x_1$, gives the slope of the geometric tangent to the curve at the point $x = x_1$. Figure 3.11 shows the graph of Fig. 3.10 redrawn to show the geometric tangent at the point C where $x = x_1$. The geometric tangent makes an angle θ with the x axis and the value of the angle θ is given by Eq. (3.187), meaning that a knowledge of the value of the derivative $f'(x_1)$ at the point $x = x_1$ gives us the value of $\tan \theta$, the tangent of the angle θ, which we can use to find the angle θ itself.

Let's consider a specific example of these ideas. Consider the function

$$y = f(x) = \tfrac{1}{4}x^2 + 1$$

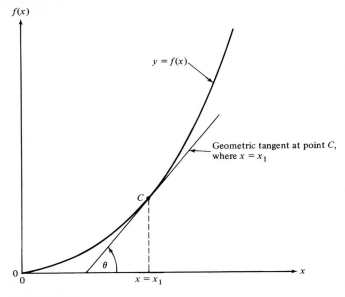

FIGURE 3.11
Graph of the function $f(x)$ as a function of x, showing the geometric tangent to the curve at the point C at which $x = x_1$. The slope $\tan \theta$ of the geometric tangent is equal to $f'(x_1)$, the value of the derivative at $x = x_1$.

whose derivative is

$$\frac{dy}{dx} = f'(x) = \frac{x}{2} \tag{3.188}$$

The graph of the function $y = f(x) = (1/4)x^2 + 1$ is shown in Fig. 3.12. Let's find the slope of the geometric tangent to the curve at the point C at which $x = 2$. From Eq. (3.188), the value of the derivative at $x = 2$ is

$$\left(\frac{dy}{dx}\right)_{x=2} = f'(2) = \frac{2}{2} = 1$$

so, from Eq. (3.187), we have

$$\tan \theta = 1 \tag{3.189}$$

where $\tan \theta$ is (by definition) the slope of the geometric tangent, so that the slope is equal to 1. To find the angle θ itself, we solve Eq. (3.189) for θ, obtaining

$$\theta = \tan^{-1} 1 = 45°$$

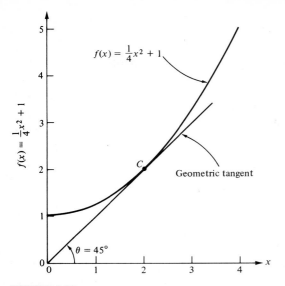

FIGURE 3.12
Graph of the function $y = (x^2/4) + 1$, showing the geometric tangent at the point $x = 2$. The slope of the geometric tangent has the value $\tan \theta = 1$, so the angle $\theta = 45°$. In this example, the geometric tangent happens to pass through the origin.

so the geometric tangent makes an angle of 45° with the x axis, as shown in Fig. 3.12.

Finally, we should note the following point of terminology. The slope $f'(x_1)$ of the geometric tangent to the curve $f(x)$ at $x = x_1$ is (by definition) called the *slope of the curve $f(x)$ at the point $x = x_1$*. In other words, the slope of the geometric tangent at a point is the slope of the curve itself at that point. In the future, we will use the term "slope of the curve" synonymously with "slope of the geometric tangent."

One of the most important uses in physics of the geometric interpretation of the derivative is in discussing graphs of position, velocity, and acceleration as functions of time. Suppose we return to Eq. (3.129)

$$s = f(t) = 4.9t^2 \qquad (3.129)$$

which gives the distance s moved by a body falling vertically from rest (without air resistance) as a function of time t. In Eq. (3.129), s is in meters and t is in seconds. Figure 3.13 shows a graph of s as a function of t from Eq. (3.129) for times from $t = 0$ to $t = 5$ seconds; the graph is a parabola passing through the origin.

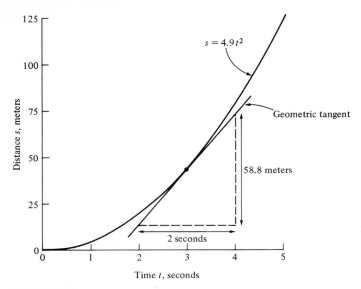

FIGURE 3.13

Graph of $s = 4.9t^2$ as a function of t, where s is the distance in meters and t is the time in seconds. Also shown is the geometric tangent (of slope 29.4 meters per second) at the point $t = 3$ seconds.

The derivative of s with respect to t is given by

$$\frac{ds}{dt} = f'(t) = 9.8t \tag{3.190}$$

and, since the velocity v is the rate of change of distance with respect to time, $v = (ds/dt) = f'(t)$, so we have

$$v = 9.8t \tag{3.191}$$

Equation (3.190) for $f'(t)$ gives the slope of the curve $s = f(t) = 4.9t^2$. Equation (3.191) gives the velocity as a function of time. Comparison of Eqs. (3.190) and (3.191) gives us the following useful result. The slope of the graph of distance as a function of time is the velocity. Thus if we calculate the slope of the curve of distance (as a function of time) at some value of the time, we have also calculated the value of the velocity at that value of the time.

As an example, consider the slope of the curve $s = 4.9t^2$ at the point $t = 3$ seconds. From Eq. (3.190), the slope is given by

$$\left(\frac{ds}{dt}\right)_{t=3} = f'(3) = (9.8)(3) = 29.4$$

which, from Eq. (3.191), is equal to the velocity, so

$$v = 29.4 \text{ meters per second}$$

at the instant of time $t = 3$ seconds. Figure 3.13 also shows the geometric tangent, of slope 29.4 meters per second, at the point $t = 3$ seconds. Note that, since the velocity is equal to the slope, the slope of the graph of distance (meters) as a function of time (seconds) is expressed in meters per second.

Using Eq. (3.191), we can also make a graph of the velocity v as a function of time. This is shown in Fig. 3.14 and is the graph of the equation $v = 9.8t$ for values of t from 0 to 5 seconds. As seen from the graph, the velocity increases linearly with increasing time, and we can find the velocity at any instant of time from the graph. For instance, when the time $t = 2$ seconds, $v = 19.6$ meters per second. Note that Fig. 3.14 is really a graph of the derivative $f'(t)$, given by Eq. (3.190), as a function of time. Thus Fig. 3.14 is a graph of the slope of the curve $s = 4.9t^2$, plotted as a function of time.

Last, we may consider the slope of the "curve" (which is a straight line) in Fig. 3.14. Since Fig. 3.14 is a graph of velocity as a function of

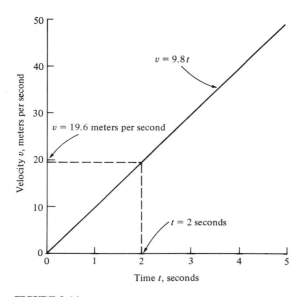

FIGURE 3.14
Graph of $v = 9.8t$ as a function of t, where v is the velocity in meters per second and t is the time in seconds.

time, the slope of the curve is given by

$$\frac{dv}{dt} = f''(t) = 9.8 \qquad (3.192)$$

on differentiating Eq. (3.191) with respect to time. Equation (3.192) says that the slope of the straight-line graph in Fig. 3.14 has the constant value 9.8, expressed in (meters per second) per second. Since the derivative (dv/dt) is the rate of change of velocity with respect to time, Eq. (3.192) gives us the acceleration a, where

$$a = 9.8 \text{ (meters per seconds) per second} \qquad (3.193)$$

From this example, we see the following important result. The slope of the graph of velocity as a function of time is the acceleration. In this example, the acceleration is constant and does not vary with time. This is shown in Fig. 3.15, which is a graph of the acceleration a given by Eq. (3.193). Since a is constant, its graph as a function of time is horizontal because it does not change with time. Note also that the result contained in Eq. (3.192) agrees with the result from analytical geometry that the slope of a straight line is constant.

We may conclude this section by summarizing some of our important conclusions about the geometric interpretation of the derivative. Given the graph of the function $f(x)$ as a function of x, the derivative $f'(x)$ gives the slope of the curve. The value $f'(x_1)$ of the derivative at the point $x = x_1$ gives the slope of the curve at that point. The slope (ds/dt) of a graph of distance s as a function of time t is equal to the velocity v. The

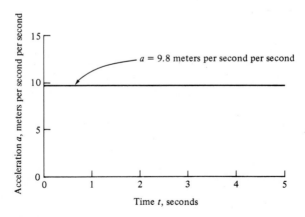

FIGURE 3.15
Graph of $a = 9.8$ as a function of time t, where a is the acceleration in (meters per second) per second. The acceleration is constant in this example and does not vary with time.

slope (dv/dt) of a graph of velocity v as a function of time t is equal to the acceleration a.

EXERCISES

3.22. (a) Calculate the slope of the geometric tangent to the curve $y = x^2 + 2$ at the point $x = 5$. (b) What angle θ does the geometric tangent make with the x axis? (c) Calculate the slope of the curve at the point $x = 2$.

3.23. In a certain physics experiment, the distance s a body moves (from rest) as a function of time is given by

$$s = 2t^3$$

where s is in meters and t is in seconds. (a) Make a graph of s as a function of t for values of t from 0 to 2 seconds at intervals of 0.1 second. (b) Calculate the slope of the curve in (a) at $t = 1$ second. (c) Calculate the velocity v of the body, and make a graph of v as a function of t for the same time interval used in (a). What is the name of this curve? (d) Calculate the slope of the curve in (c) at $t = 1$ second. (e) Calculate the acceleration a of the body, and make a graph of a as a function of t for the same time interval used in (a) and (c). What is the name of this curve? (f) Is the acceleration constant? Give your reasons.

MAXIMA AND MINIMA

We continue our discussion of the applications of derivatives to physics by considering problems involving maxima and minima of functions. We will assume that all of the functions we encounter in elementary physics are well-behaved in that their derivatives exist, are not infinite, etc. Discussion of unusual cases will be found in calculus textbooks.

We review the key results on maxima and minima, which it is assumed you have seen in your calculus course. Given a function $f(x)$, f is said to have a relative *maximum* at the point $x = a$ if

$$f(a) \geq f(a + \epsilon) \qquad (3.194)$$

for all small (i.e., near zero) positive and negative values of ϵ. Equation (3.194) says that the function $f(x)$ has a greater value at the point $x = a$ than it does at the neighboring points $x = a \pm \epsilon$. Similarly, $f(x)$ is said to have a relative *minimum* at the point $x = b$ if

$$f(b) \leq f(b + \epsilon) \qquad (3.195)$$

an equation which says $f(x)$ has a smaller value at the point $x = b$ than it does at the neighboring points $x = b \pm \epsilon$. Figure 3.16 shows a relative maximum at $x = a$, and a relative minimum at $x = b$, for the function

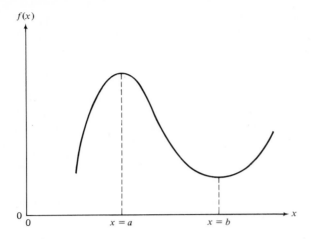

FIGURE 3.16
Graph of the function $f(x)$ showing a relative maximum at $x = a$ and a relative minimum at $x = b$.

$f(x)$. The graph is said to be concave downward around $x = a$ and concave upward around $x = b$.

If the function $f(x)$ has a relative maximum or minimum at the point $x = c$, then it is true that

$$f'(c) = 0 \qquad (3.196)$$

Equation (3.196) says that the derivative $f'(x)$ vanishes at a point $x = c$ at which there is a relative maximum or a relative minimum. A point such as $x = c$ is called a *critical* point. In Fig. 3.16, $x = a$ and $x = b$ are critical points, and it is therefore true that both $f'(a) = 0$ and $f'(b) = 0$. The derivative vanishes at the point $x = a$ where the function has a maximum and at the point $x = b$ where there is a minimum.

The second derivative gives us information on whether we are dealing with a maximum or a minimum. If, at $x = c, f'(c) = 0$ and $f''(c)$ is positive, then the function $f(x)$ has a minimum at $x = c$. If $f'(c) = 0$ and $f''(c)$ is negative, then $f(x)$ has a maximum at $x = c$. [If $f'(c) = 0$ and $f''(c) = 0$, then the test fails and gives no information.] Referring to the curve in Fig. 3.16, $f''(a)$ would be negative since there is a maximum at $x = a$ and $f''(b)$ would be positive since there is a minimum at $x = b$.

As an example, consider the function

$$y = f(x) = 6x - x^2 \qquad (3.197)$$

a downwardly concave parabola whose axis is parallel to the y axis. To find a critical point, we calculate the derivative $f'(x)$ and set it equal to zero, so we have

$$f'(x) = 6 - 2x = 0 \qquad (3.198)$$

We solve Eq. (3.198) and find $x = 3$, so $f'(3) = 0$. Since the derivative equals zero at $x = 3$, there is either a maximum or a minimum at that point. To find out which, we examine the second derivative, which is

$$f''(x) = -2 \qquad (3.199)$$

Since $f''(x)$ at $x = 3$ is negative (it has the value -2 for all values of x), there is a maximum at $x = 3$. Finally, we may calculate the value of the function $f(x)$ at this maximum by finding $f(3)$, the value of the function at the critical point $x = 3$. From Eq. (3.197), $f(3) = 9$, so the function $f(x)$ has the value 9 at this maximum. The graph of the function $f(x) = 6x - x^2$ as shown in Fig. 3.17.

It is often useful in physics to find the maximum or minimum of some function. As an example, let's consider a stone thrown vertically upward with an initial velocity of 9.8 meters per second. By "initial," we mean the velocity at the instant of time $t = 0$ when the upward motion begins. If, as usual, air resistance is neglected, the height y of the stone as a function of time t is found to be

$$y = f(t) = 9.8t - 4.9t^2 \qquad (3.200)$$

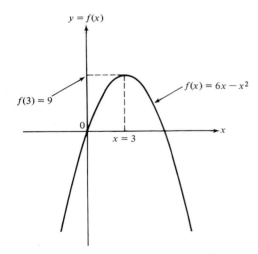

FIGURE 3.17
Graph of the function $y = f(x) = 6x - x^2$, showing the maximum at $x = 3$.

Equation (3.200) gives the vertical height y, measured from zero height ($y = 0$) at the start of the motion when $t = 0$, as a function $f(t)$ of time. We ask two questions. First, how long does it take the stone to reach its maximum height? Second, what is the maximum height?

We answer the first question by calculating the value of the time t at which the height y is a maximum. (We know y will have a maximum, and not a minimum, value based on our physical knowledge of the situation.) To find this value of t, we find the derivative (dy/dt) and set it equal to zero, obtaining

$$\frac{dy}{dt} = f'(t) = 9.8 - 9.8t = 0 \qquad (3.201)$$

We solve this equation for t, obtaining $t = 1$ second as the value of the time at which y is a maximum. Thus it takes the stone 1 second to reach its maximum height. We may check that we are dealing with a maximum in y by noting from Eq. (3.201) that the second derivative $(d^2y/dt^2) = -9.8$ (meters per second per second) and thus is negative.

We answer the second question by finding the maximum value of y, i.e., the value of y when $t = 1$ second. We denote the maximum value of y by the symbol $y_{\max}$, where, from Eq. (3.200),

$$y_{\max} = f(1) = 9.8(1) - 4.9(1)^2 = 4.9 \text{ meters} \qquad (3.202)$$

The maximum height, $y_{\max}$, to which the stone rises is 4.9 meters.

As a final point about this example, we note that the derivative (dy/dt) is the rate of change of vertical height with respect to time. The derivative (dy/dt) is thus the velocity v_y of the stone in the vertical direction, so we have

$$v_y = \frac{dy}{dt} = 9.8 - 9.8t \qquad (3.203)$$

on differentiating Eq. (3.200) with respect to time. Equation (3.203) gives us the vertical velocity v_y at any time t. We note that the requirement $(dy/dt) = 0$ that the height have its maximum value is identical to the statement that the vertical velocity $v_y = 0$. The vertical velocity is zero at the instant at which the height is a maximum, a conclusion that is true in general. In this example, the vertical velocity is zero at the instant ($t = 1$ second) at which the height has its maximum value of 4.9 meters.

EXERCISES

3.24. Given the function $f(x) = \sin x$ and considering only positive values of x, find (a) the value of x at which $f(x)$ has its first maximum; (b) the value of x at which $f(x)$ has its first minimum. (c) Apply the second derivative test to parts (a) and (b).

3.25. You will find in your physics course the following physical problem. Suppose a ball is thrown from the origin $(0, 0)$ with initial velocity v_0 at time $t = 0$. Suppose further that the direction in which it is thrown makes an initial angle θ with the horizontal direction. Then, if the x axis is the horizontal direction and the y axis is the vertical direction, the coordinates (x, y) of the ball are given as functions of time t by the equations

$$x = (v_0 \cos \theta)t$$

$$y = (v_0 \sin \theta)t - 4.9t^2$$

where x and y are in meters, t is in seconds, and v_0 is in meters per second. (a) Calculate the value of the time at which the vertical height is a maximum. (b) Calculate the value of the horizontal distance traveled when the vertical height is a maximum. (Your answers to both parts will be in terms of v_0 and θ.)

SUMMATION NOTATION

We digress briefly at this point to introduce a useful notation for writing sums. Suppose we have a sum of terms, such as

$$a_1 + a_2 + a_3 + a_4 \tag{3.204}$$

where the a's can be anything—numbers, functions, etc. [The terms in Eq. (3.204) are read a sub-one, a sub-two, etc.] The sum of terms in Eq. (3.204) can be written as

$$\sum_{i=1}^{4} a_i \tag{3.205}$$

where the Σ (the Greek letter capital sigma) is called a *summation symbol*. In the expression (3.205), the letter "i" is called the *index* and, by definition, it takes on all of the integral values from the value written under the Σ (in this case, 1) to the value written above the Σ (in this case, 4). Thus, the index i has the values 1, 2, 3, 4, so the expression (3.205) is

$$\sum_{i=1}^{4} a_i = a_1 + a_2 + a_3 + a_4 \tag{3.206}$$

You will frequently see a sum of terms written as

$$\sum_{i=1}^{n} b_i \tag{3.207}$$

The "n" above the Σ means that the index i takes on integral values 1, 2,... up to some value n. The sum in Eq. (3.207) would thus be

$$b_1 + b_2 + \cdots + b_n \tag{3.208}$$

indicating that the last term in the sum is the one for which the index i is equal to n.

Note that the index i is called a *dummy* index because it doesn't matter what symbol is used for the index since

$$\sum_{i=1}^{4} a_i = \sum_{k=1}^{4} a_k = a_1 + a_2 + a_3 + a_4 \tag{3.209}$$

The symbol used for the index in the sum in Eq. (3.209) is immaterial.

A sum which will be useful to us later is

$$\sum_{i=1}^{n} f(x_i) = f(x_1) + f(x_2) + \cdots + f(x_n) \tag{3.210}$$

where $f(x)$ is some function of the variable x. In Eq. (3.210), $f(x_1)$ is the value of the function $f(x)$ at the point $x = x_1$, and so on. The sum Eq. (3.210) is thus a sum of the values of the function $f(x)$ at the points $x = x_1$, $x = x_2$, and so on up to $x = x_n$.

EXERCISES

3.26. Write the following sums using the summation symbol:

(a) $x_1^2 + x_2^2 + x_3^2 + x_4^2$; (b) $1 + y + y^2 + y^3 + y^4 + y^5$;
(c) $1^2 + 2^2 + 3^2$.

POWER SERIES EXPANSIONS OF FUNCTION

An infinite sum of terms, written using the summation notation, is given by the expression

$$\sum_{k=0}^{\infty} a_k x^k = a_0 + a_1 x + a_2 x^2 + \cdots + a_n x^n + \cdots \tag{3.211}$$

The sum (3.211) is called an *infinite power series in the variable x*; in this series, the a_k are constants. We recall that a very important series of this kind is the Taylor series

$$\sum_{k=0}^{\infty} \frac{1}{k!} f^{(k)}(a)(x - a)^k = f(a) + f'(a)(x - a)$$

$$+ \cdots + \frac{1}{n!} f^{(n)}(a)(x - a)^n + \cdots \tag{3.212}$$

where $f^{(n)}(a)$ is the nth derivative of a function $f(x)$, evaluated at the point $x = a$. The series (3.212) is called the *Taylor series expansion of* $f(x)$ *about the point* $x = a$. As an example, if $f(x) = e^x$, then $f^{(n)}(a) = e^a$ for all values of n, and the Taylor series expansion of e^x about the point $x = a$ is

$$e^a + e^a(x - a) + e^a(x - a)^2 + \cdots + e^a(x - a)^n + \cdots \quad (3.213)$$

If $a = 0$ in Eq. (3.212), the series becomes

$$\sum_{k=0}^{\infty} \frac{1}{k!} f^{(k)}(0) x^k = f(0) + f'(0)x + \frac{1}{2!} f''(0)x^2$$

$$+ \cdots + \frac{1}{n!} f^{(n)}(0)x^n + \cdots \quad (3.214)$$

where the series (3.214) is called the *Maclaurin series expansion of* $f(x)$. Thus, if $f(x) = e^x$, $f^{(n)}(0) = 1$ for all values of n, and the Maclaurin series (3.214) for e^x is

$$1 + x + \frac{1}{2!} x^2 + \cdots + \frac{1}{n!} x^n + \cdots \quad (3.215)$$

Note that the Taylor and Maclaurin series (3.211) to (3.215) are all infinite series.

It is clear that the function $f(x)$ must possess derivatives of all orders at $x = a$ for the Taylor series expansion to exist. This is not always true. For example, the function $f(x) = \ln x$ does not possess a Maclaurin series expansion (about $a = 0$) since the function and its derivatives do not have finite values at point $x = 0$. However, as shown in Exercise 3.27, the function $\ln x$ does have a Taylor series expansion about the point $x = 1$.

For applications to physics, one of the most important results concerning Taylor series is the following. Suppose $f(x)$ is a continuous function, whose first $(n + 1)$ derivatives exist and are continuous over an interval of x containing the point $x = a$. Then the value $f(x)$ of the function at the point x is given by

$$f(x) = f(a) + f'(a)(x - a) + \frac{1}{2!} f''(a)(x - a)^2$$

$$+ \cdots + \frac{1}{n!} f^{(n)}(a)(x - a)^n + R_n(x, a) \quad (3.216)$$

or, using the summation notation

$$f(x) = \left\{ \sum_{k=0}^{n} \frac{1}{k!} f^{(k)}(a)(x - a)^k \right\} + R_n(x, a) \quad (3.217)$$

where $R_n(x, a)$ is called the *remainder* of the series. [Equation (3.216) or (3.217) essentially defines the remainder $R_n(x, a)$.] Note that (3.216) and (3.217) say that the function $f(x)$ can be represented by a *finite* number $(n + 1)$ of terms, in powers of $(x - a)$, plus the remainder $R_n(x, a)$. The value of the remainder $R_n(x, a)$ will be a function of the value of the variable x at which $f(x)$ is evaluated, the value of the constant a about which the Taylor series expansion is taken, and the number n, where there are $(n + 1)$ terms in the finite sum representing $f(x)$. We can see from Eq. (3.217), written as

$$R_n(x, a) = f(x) - \sum_{k=0}^{n} \frac{1}{k!} f^{(k)}(a)(x - a)^k \qquad (3.218)$$

that the remainder $R_n(x, a)$ is the difference between the function $f(x)$ and the finite sum of $(n + 1)$ terms on the right-hand side of Eq. (3.218).

As an example, suppose $f(x) = e^x$, and that we wish to represent the function e^x about the point $a = 0$. Then Eq. (3.216) says, since $f(a) = e^0 = 1$ and the derivatives of e^x of all orders are equal to e^x, that

$$e^x = 1 + x + \frac{1}{2!} x^2 + \cdots + \frac{1}{n!} x^n + R_n(x, 0) \qquad (3.219)$$

In (3.219), $R_n(x, 0)$ is the remainder of the series when there are $(n + 1)$ terms in the finite series for e^x and the constant $a = 0$.

In physics, we are very frequently interested in representing a function $f(x)$ by a finite sum of powers of x of the form (3.217). If we do so, then Eq. (3.218) says that the remainder $R_n(x, a)$ is the error made in representing the function $f(x)$ by a power series of $(n + 1)$ terms in which n is the highest power of x. We are thus interested in an expression for $R_n(x, a)$ which will tell us how the value of the remainder depends on the number n and on the value of x at which the function $f(x)$ is evaluated. In calculus books, it is shown that one expression for $R_n(x, a)$ is

$$R_n(x, a) = f^{(n+1)}(c) \frac{(x - a)^{n+1}}{(n + 1)!} \qquad (3.220)$$

In Eq. (3.220), n is the highest power of $(x - a)$ in the finite series expressing $f(x)$ in Eq. (3.217), $f^{(n+1)}(c)$ is the $(n + 1)$th derivative of $f(x)$, evaluated at $x = c$, a is the point about which the expansion is taken, and $R_n(x, a)$ is the remainder or error. The quantity c is some number between a and x, the value of the variable x at which the function $f(x)$ is to be evaluated; c depends on n and x. In using (3.220) to determine the remainder $R_n(x, a)$, we can usually only estimate the value of the derivative $f^{(n+1)}(c)$ because the number c is not itself known exactly. From the point of view of use in physics, the key conclusion drawn from Eq.

(3.220) is the following. The remainder $R_n(x, a)$ is, for given values of n and a, smaller for smaller values of the magnitude of $(x - a)$. This means that, in expressing the function $f(x)$ by the finite series in (3.217), the magnitude of the remainder, or error, $R_n(x, a)$ will be smaller for smaller magnitudes of $(x - a)$ for given values of n and a. A finite series of $(n + 1)$ terms in Eq. (3.217) will, therefore, be a better representation of $f(x)$ for smaller values of the magnitude $(x - a)$.

As an example, let's consider representing e^x by a series of two terms ($n = 1$) using the Maclaurin series (for which $a = 0$) given by (3.219), so we are making the approximation

$$e^x \cong 1 + x \qquad (3.221)$$

If $x = 0.100$, the approximation (3.221) gives $e^{0.100} \cong 1.100$; the exact value is $e^{0.100} = 1.105$, so the error made by using (3.221) is about 0.5 percent. If $x = 0.500$, the approximation (3.221) gives $e^{0.500} \cong 1.500$; the exact value is $e^{0.500} = 1.649$, so the error in this case made by using (3.221) is about 9 percent. We see that the series (3.221) is a better approximation to e^x for smaller values of the magnitude of x. For this reason, one often sees statements in physics books like, "Since $x \ll 1$, we can make the approximation $e^x \cong 1 + x, \ldots$," meaning that the series $(1 + x)$ is an acceptable approximation to e^x for values of the magnitude of x less than one. Of course, the degree of acceptability of the approximation to any particular function depends on how accurate a value one desires. Figure 3.18 shows graphs of e^x and $(1 + x)$ for x between 0 and 1.00 and clearly displays how, as x becomes larger, the series $(1 + x)$ becomes a poorer approximation to the exponential function e^x.

One might well ask why it is useful to approximate functions with power series at all, since exact values of functions such as e^x are so readily available with hand calculators. The answer is that one frequently gains more physical insight from an approximate analytical expression for a quantity than from a table of exact values. For example, consider the function

$$n(x) = \frac{1}{e^x - 1} \qquad (3.222)$$

encountered in statistical physics. In the regime in which x is small and positive, say, $x \ll 1$, we can write, using Eq. (3.221) for e^x, the approximate result

$$n(x) \cong \frac{1}{1 + x - 1} = \frac{1}{x} \qquad (3.223)$$

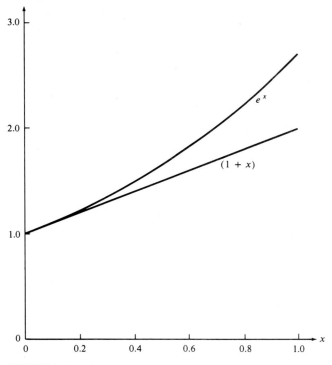

FIGURE 3.18
Graphs of e^x and of $(1 + x)$ as functions of x for $0 \le x \le 1.0$. As x increases, the series $(1 + x)$ becomes a poorer approximation to the exponential function e^x.

Equation (3.223) tells us that, when x is small and positive, the function $n(x)$ defined by (3.222) varies approximately as $(1/x)$, thereby giving us some physical ''feel'' for the behavior of $n(x)$ for small values of x.

As a final point on the use of power series to approximately represent functions in physics, we can see (although we have not proved it) that the remainder or error $R_n(x, a)$ in Eq. (3.217) decreases as the number $(n + 1)$ of terms increases in the finite series. (This statement is not always strictly true, but it usually applies to the elementary functions encountered in introductory physics.) Thus the finite series in Eq. (3.217) becomes a better approximation to the function $f(x)$ as we include more terms in the series. Thus, from Eq. (3.219), the series $[1 + x + (1/2)x^2]$ is a better approximation to the function e^x than is the series $(1 + x)$. The number of terms one uses in a power series to approximate a function will depend on the degree of accuracy required and must be determined for the particular case being studied.

EXERCISES

3.27 Given the function $f(x) = \ln x$, (a) convince yourself that the derivatives of all orders of $\ln x$ are infinite at $x = 0$, and (b) find the Taylor series expansion of $\ln x$ about the point $x = 1$.

3.28 (a) Write down the Maclaurin series expansion for $\sin x$, showing the first four terms. (b) Using your result in (a), calculate the sine of 1.0 radian and compare the value given by the series with the exact value. (c) Repeat (b) for $x = 0.5$ radian.

3.29 Repeat Exercise 3.28 for $f(x) = \cos x$.

CHAPTER
4

SUMS
AND
INTEGRALS

INTRODUCTION

In this chapter, we treat some of the applications of integral calculus to problems in physics. After a review of the integral as an antiderivative and of some techniques for evaluating integrals, the relation between constants of integration and initial conditions in physics problems is discussed. Next, the definition and evaluation of definite integrals are reviewed. The geometric interpretation of the definite integral precedes a discussion of its interpretation as a "sum of infinitesimal elements." Last, some physical applications of the definite integral are presented, using examples from several areas of physics, and emphasizing the use of the integral as a sum.

REVIEW OF INTEGRALS AS ANTIDERIVATIVES

Suppose we have two functions, $F(x)$ and $f(x)$, of the independent variable x, such that the derivative of $F(x)$ is equal to $f(x)$, so

$$\frac{dF(x)}{dx} = f(x) \qquad (4.1)$$

If we multiply both sides of Eq. (4.1) by the differential dx, we obtain

$$dF(x) = f(x)\, dx \qquad (4.2)$$

an equation which says that the differential $dF(x)$, of the function $F(x)$, is equal to the function $f(x)$ times dx.

Suppose further that we know $f(x)$ and want to find $F(x)$. In other words, as seen from Eq. (4.1), we know the *derivative* of $F(x)$ and we want to find the function $F(x)$ itself. We may say the same thing, with reference to Eq. (4.2), by saying that, since we know $f(x)$, we know the *differential* $dF(x)$ and we want to find $F(x)$. The process of finding the function $F(x)$ when we know its derivative $(dF/dx) = f(x)$, and/or its differential $dF = f(x)\, dx$, is called *integration* or finding the *antiderivative*. When we differentiate a function, we go from the function to its derivative and differential. When we integrate, we go from the derivative and differential of the function to the function itself. Integration is thus the *inverse* of differentiation. Thus $f(x)$ is the derivative of $F(x)$ and $F(x)$ is the antiderivative or integral of $f(x)$. We indicate that $F(x)$ is the integral or antiderivative of $f(x)$ by writing

$$F(x) = \int f(x)\, dx \qquad (4.3)$$

where the symbol $\int$ is called the integral sign and the function $f(x)$ under the integral sign is called the *integrand*. Equation (4.3) is read "$F(x)$ is the integral of $f(x)\, dx$" and means that $F(x)$ is the antiderivative of $f(x)$ since $f(x)$ is the derivative of $F(x)$.

Let's consider an example. Suppose the derivative of a function $F(x)$ is $2x$, so

$$\frac{dF(x)}{dx} = 2x \qquad (4.4)$$

and, in terms of differentials,

$$dF(x) = 2x\, dx \qquad (4.5)$$

so the function $f(x)$ is $2x$. We know that x^2 is the function whose derivative is $2x$, so we have

$$F(x) = x^2 \qquad (4.6)$$

We can see that Eqs. (4.4) and (4.6) are consistent because differentiating both sides of (4.6) gives (4.4). We say that we have *integrated* the function $2x$ to obtain its antiderivative x^2. In the notation of Eq. (4.3),

$$x^2 = \int 2x\, dx \qquad (4.7)$$

an equation which says that the antiderivative or integral of $2x$ is x^2. In the notation of Eq. (4.5),

$$d(x^2) = 2x \, dx \qquad (4.8)$$

an equation that says the differential of x^2 is $(2x) \, dx$.

To recapitulate, the process of finding the function $F(x)$ when we know its derivative $f(x)$, or its differential $f(x) \, dx$, is called integration or antidifferentiation. Integration thus constitutes the process that is the inverse of differentiation.

In Eq. (4.6), we found the function $F(x) = x^2$ whose derivative is $f(x) = 2x$, and we saw that the derivative of Eq. (4.6) was Eq. (4.4). Suppose we add a constant C to the right-hand side of Eq. (4.6), which then becomes

$$F(x) = x^2 + C \qquad (4.9)$$

If we differentiate both sides of Eq. (4.9), we obtain

$$\frac{dF(x)}{dx} = 2x \qquad (4.10)$$

because the derivative of any constant is zero. From Eqs. (4.9) and (4.10), we see that not only is the function x^2 the antiderivative of $2x$, but the function $(x^2 + C)$, where C is *any* constant, is also the antiderivative of $2x$. The constant C is called a *constant of integration*. We thus rewrite Eq. (4.3) to read

$$F(x) + C = \int f(x) \, dx \qquad (4.11)$$

which says that the integral (or antiderivative) of $f(x)$ is the function $F(x)$ plus the constant of integration C. The fact that C can be any constant is sometimes stated by saying that C is an arbitrary constant. Integrals containing a constant of integration, like the one in Eq. (4.11), are called *indefinite* integrals; the reason for this name will become clear later.

You will often see Eq. (4.11) written in the form

$$F(x) + C = \int dF(x) \qquad (4.12)$$

where we have used the fact, contained in Eq. (4.2),

$$dF(x) = f(x) \, dx \qquad (4.2)$$

that the differential $dF(x)$ of $F(x)$ is equal to $f(x) \, dx$. The content of Eq. (4.12) may be stated by saying that the integral of the differential $dF(x)$ is the function $F(x)$ plus the constant C. Thus, in Eq. (4.7), x^2 is the integral of the differential $d(x^2) = 2x\,dx$, so we write

$$x^2 + C = \int d(x^2) = \int 2x\,dx \qquad (4.13)$$

Note that Eq. (4.13) is just a combination of Eqs. (4.7) and (4.8). We may combine Eqs. (4.12) and (4.2) to give

$$F(x) + C = \int dF(x) = \int f(x)\,dx \qquad (4.14)$$

In integrals such as those in Eq. (4.14), we call x "the variable of integration" or say we are "integrating over the variable x."

Let's consider another example. Suppose

$$\frac{dF(x)}{dx} = f(x) = e^x \qquad (4.15)$$

where e^x is the exponential function. We know from Eq. (3.37) that e^x is the function whose derivative is e^x. Thus, the antiderivative $F(x) = e^x$, and we have

$$e^x + C = \int e^x\,dx \qquad (4.16)$$

where C is the arbitrary constant of integration. We can test our antiderivative in Eq. (4.16) by noting that the derivative of the left-hand side of Eq. (4.16) does indeed equal e^x, the function whose integral we are seeking.

If $u(x)$ and $v(x)$ are functions of x, and a and n are constants ($n \neq 1$), then the following are some properties of integrals:

$$\int (u + v)\,dx = \int u\,dx + \int v\,dx \qquad (4.17)$$

$$\int au\,dx = a \int u\,dx \qquad (4.18)$$

Thus, as an example,

$$2 \int x\,dx = \int (2x)\,dx = x^2 + C \qquad (4.19)$$

The following are some simple integrals which are frequently encountered in physics.

$$\int dx = x + C \qquad (4.20)$$

$$\int x^n\,dx = \frac{x^{n+1}}{n+1} + C \qquad (n \neq -1) \qquad (4.21)$$

$$\int e^x \, dx = e^x + C \qquad (4.22)$$

$$\int \sin x \, dx = -\cos x + C \qquad (4.23)$$

$$\int \cos x \, dx = \sin x + C \qquad (4.24)$$

As an example of the integration formulas above, consider Eq. (4.21) with $n = 3$. We have

$$\int x^3 \, dx = (x^4/4) + C \qquad (4.25)$$

we can see that Eq. (4.25) is correct because x^3 is, indeed, the derivative of $(x^4/4)$.

How does one find the integral of a function that is more complicated than the simple functions above? There are a variety of techniques of integration which are covered in your calculus book. There are, however, two which are often encountered in physics and which we will discuss here.

The first of these is integration by *substitution*. In this technique, best described by example, a substitution changes a complicated integral into a simpler one which is readily evaluated. As a first example, consider the integral

$$\int e^{ax} \, dx \qquad (4.26)$$

where a is a constant. Suppose we make the substitution

$$ax = u \qquad (4.27)$$

then the differential dx is related to the differential du of the new variable u by

$$a \, dx = du \qquad (4.28)$$

$$dx = (1/a) \, du \qquad (4.29)$$

Substituting Eqs. (4.29) and (4.27) into Eq. (4.26) reduces the integral in Eq. (4.26) to

$$\int e^{ax} \, dx = \int e^u \left(\frac{1}{a}\right) du = \frac{1}{a} \int e^u \, du = \frac{1}{a} e^u + C \qquad (4.30)$$

Then, since $u = ax$, Eq. (4.30) becomes the desired result

$$\int e^{ax} \, dx = \frac{1}{a} e^{ax} + C \qquad (4.31)$$

We can check the correctness of Eq. (4.31) by noting that the derivative of $(1/a)e^{ax}$ is e^{ax}. (Under the heading of notation, it is worth pointing out that the exponential function is often written exp x. Thus

$$\exp x \equiv e^x \tag{4.32}$$

is a form you will encounter frequently.)

As a second example, consider the integral

$$\int x(2x^2 - 1)^{1/2}\, dx \tag{4.33}$$

Let's make the substitution

$$u = 2x^2 - 1 \tag{4.34}$$

$$du = 4x\, dx \tag{4.35}$$

so

$$(1/4)\, du = x\, dx \tag{4.36}$$

Substituting Eqs. (4.36) and (4.34) into the integral in Eq. (4.33) gives

$$\int x(2x^2 - 1)^{1/2}\, dx = \int u^{1/2}\, \frac{du}{4} = \left(\frac{1}{4}\right) \int u^{1/2}\, du$$

$$= \left(\frac{1}{4}\right)\left(\frac{2}{3}\right) u^{3/2} + C \tag{4.37}$$

Since $u = (2x^2 - 1)$, our final result is

$$\int x(2x^2 - 1)^{1/2}\, dx = (1/6)(2x^2 - 1)^{3/2} + C \tag{4.38}$$

Keep in mind that choosing a useful substitution is at least partly based on experience, so practice is very helpful in evaluating integrals.

The second technique of integration we will discuss is called integration *by parts*. This method is based on the differential of the product of two functions $u(x)$ and $v(x)$. Then the differential of the product is, from Eq. (3.164),

$$d(uv) = u\, dv + v\, du \tag{4.39}$$

so

$$u\, dv = d(uv) - v\, du \tag{4.40}$$

If we integrate both sides of Eq. (4.40), we get

$$\int u\, dv = \int d(uv) - \int v\, du \tag{4.41}$$

From Eq. (4.12), the integral of the differential of a function is the function itself, so

$$\int d(uv) = uv \qquad (4.42)$$

Using Eq. (4.42), Eq. (4.41) becomes

$$\int u \, dv = uv - \int v \, du \qquad (4.43)$$

Equation (4.43) expresses the integral $\int u \, dv$ in terms of a second integral $\int v \, du$, and the product uv. Often a wise choice (again usually based on experience) of u and v will make the second integral simpler than the first, so Eq. (4.43) may be used to evaluate $\int u \, dv$.

A standard example illustrating integration by parts is the evaluation of

$$\int \ln x \, dx \qquad (4.44)$$

Choose

$$u = \ln x \qquad (4.45)$$

$$du = \left(\frac{1}{x}\right) dx \qquad (4.46)$$

$$dv = dx \qquad (4.47)$$

so

$$v = \int dv = \int dx = x + C_1 \qquad (4.48)$$

where C_1 is a constant of integration. Then

$$uv = (x + C_1)\ln x = x \ln x + C_1 \ln x \qquad (4.49)$$

and, applying Eq. (4.43), we obtain

$$\int \ln x \, dx = [x \ln x + C_1 \ln x] - \int (x + C_1)\left(\frac{1}{x}\right) dx \qquad (4.50)$$

$$\int \ln x \, dx = [x \ln x + C_1 \ln x] - \int dx - \int \frac{C_1}{x} dx + C_2 \qquad (4.51)$$

where C_2 is another constant of integration. Then, since

$$\int \left(\frac{1}{x}\right) dx = \ln x \qquad (4.52)$$

Eq. (4.51) becomes

$$\int \ln x \, dx = x \ln x + C_1 \ln x - x - C_1 \ln x + C_2 \quad (4.53)$$

so

$$\int \ln x \, dx = x \ln x - x + C_2 = x(\ln x - 1) + C_2 \quad (4.54)$$

gives us the required answer. (Note that the constant C_1 does not appear in the final answer.)

Last, it should be mentioned here that there are a number of collections of tables of integrals available. These contain many integrals; such a table is doubtless included in your calculus text. There are also books which are tables of integrals. A useful one is *Tables of Integrals and Other Mathematical Data* by H. B. Dwight,* which contains several hundred integrals in addition to trigonometric and algebraic material. From now on, it will be assumed that the reader is able to evaluate the integrals we encounter.

EXERCISES

4.1. Evaluate the following integral by substitution: $\int \cos 3x \, dx$.

4.2. Evaluate the following integral by substitution: $\int (x - a)^2 \, dx$, where a is a constant.

4.3. Evaluate the following integral by substitution: $\int x e^{-x^2} \, dx$.

4.4. Evaluate the following integral by parts: $\int x \cos x \, dx$.

4.5. Evaluate the following integral by parts: $\int x e^x \, dx$.

CONSTANTS OF INTEGRATION AND INITIAL CONDITIONS

Let's consider next the application of integration to a physical problem. Suppose a particle moves in one direction along a straight line, and suppose also that its acceleration a has a constant magnitude equal to A. Written as an equation, this statement is

$$a = \frac{dv}{dt} = A \quad (4.55)$$

---

*H. B. Dwight, *Tables of Integrals and Other Mathematical Data*, 4th ed., Macmillan, New York, 1961.

In Eq. (4.55), we also put in the fact that the acceleration a is equal to (dv/dt), the rate of change of velocity v with respect to time. Our aim is to use Eq. (4.55) to find the velocity as a function $v(t)$ of the time t.

Starting with

$$\frac{dv}{dt} = A \qquad (4.56)$$

we multiply both sides of Eq. (4.56) by dt, the differential of the time t, obtaining

$$dv = A\,dt \qquad (4.57)$$

Equation (4.57) gives the differential dv of the velocity v as equal to the constant A times dt, so this equation gives us the differential dv of the function $v(t)$ we are seeking. Since we know dv, we can find $v(t)$ by integrating Eq. (4.57). The result is

$$v(t) = \int dv = \int A\,dt \qquad (4.58)$$

where we write the velocity as $v(t)$ to emphasize that v is a function of the time; the variable of integration in Eq. (4.58) is the time t. Since A is a constant, Eq. (4.58) becomes

$$v(t) + C' = A \int dt \qquad (4.59)$$

where C' is a constant of integration, and so our result is

$$v(t) + C' = At \qquad (4.60)$$

In Eq. (4.60), we put the constant C' on the left-hand side of the equation, thus writing Eq. (4.61) in the same form as that used in Eq. (4.14). Note, however, that we could have equally well put a constant C on the right-hand side of the equation, in which case Eq. (4.60) becomes

$$v(t) = At + C \qquad (4.61)$$

We can see that Eq. (4.61) is just as correct as Eq. (4.60) by differentiating both sides of Eq. (4.61) and Eq. (4.60); both equations then give back Eq. (4.55) stating that (dv/dt) equals A. It is common in physics to use the form Eq. (4.61), in which the constant of integration is on the side of the explicit integral, which, in Eq. (4.61), is At.

Equation (4.61) gives us the result we have been seeking because it gives the velocity as a function $v(t)$ of the time. Equation (4.61) says that the velocity equals the constant magnitude A of the acceleration times the time t, plus the constant of integration C. From what has been said so far, the value of C is undetermined; C can be any constant. If what has been given so far is all the information available, then Eq. (4.61) is as complete a solution as possible of the problem as posed. We are unable to say anything more about the constant C.

However, in many physics problems, we are given additional information which allows us to determine the value of the constant of integration. For example, suppose we are considering the motion of the particle described above and that we are given the value of the particle's velocity at the instant of time $t = 0$. We will use the symbol $v(0)$ for the velocity of the particle at $t = 0$. This symbol is just what we obtain by putting $t = 0$ in the functional notation $v(t)$, so $v(0)$ means the value of $v(t)$ when $t = 0$. Let's consider Eq. (4.61) at the instant of time $t = 0$ by setting $t = 0$ in Eq. (4.61). The result is

$$v(0) = C \qquad (4.62)$$

Equation (4.62) says that the constant of integration C is equal to $v(0)$, the value of the velocity of the particle when $t = 0$. Putting Eq. (4.62) into Eq. (4.61) gives

$$v(t) = v(0) + At \qquad (4.63)$$

Equation (4.63) says that $v(t)$, the particle's velocity at time t, equals the quantity At plus $v(0)$, the particle's velocity at time $t = 0$. We see that the description in Eq. (4.63) of the velocity $v(t)$ as a function of time is more complete than the description in Eq. (4.61) in which the constant C was undetermined. Often in physics problems, some information is known which allows us to determine the value of the constant of integration involved. In the example just discussed, that information was the value of $v(0)$, the velocity at the instant $t = 0$. Since $t = 0$ is the instant at which the motion of the particle begins, knowledge of something (such as the velocity) at $t = 0$ is referred to as an *initial condition* for the problem. Thus a knowledge of the value of the initial velocity $v(0)$ is an initial condition for the problem of the moving particle.

Let's consider a numerical example for concreteness. Suppose a ball is thrown vertically downward with an initial velocity of 10 meters per second. We want to find the ball's velocity as a function of time. We will use the symbol $v_y(t)$ for the velocity of the ball in the vertical (y) direction. We saw in Chap. 3 that the acceleration of the ball (neglecting air resistance) is downward with the magnitude

$$a = 9.8 \text{ meters per second per second} \qquad (4.64)$$

and where we consider the downward vertical direction positive, so a is positive. From the definition of acceleration, we have

$$\frac{dv_y}{dt} = a = 9.8 \qquad (4.65)$$

where we omit explicit mention of the units in Eq. (4.65). Rewriting Eq. (4.65) in terms of differentials gives

$$dv_y = 9.8 \, dt \qquad (4.66)$$

Integrating Eq. (4.66) with respect to time yields

$$v_y(t) = 9.8t + C \qquad (4.67)$$

Setting $t = 0$ in Eq. (4.67) gives us

$$v_y(0) = C \qquad (4.68)$$

Equation (4.68) says that the constant of integration C is equal to $v_y(0)$, the value of the vertical velocity at $t = 0$. In other words, C is equal to the *initial* ($t = 0$) *velocity* of the ball. Since we are given that the initial velocity is 10 meters per second, Eq. (4.68) becomes

$$C = 10 \text{ meters per second} \qquad (4.69)$$

Note in Eq. (4.69) that the initial velocity of 10 meters per second downward has a positive sign because we are considering the downward vertical direction as positive. Substituting Eq. (4.69) into Eq. (4.67) gives

$$v_y(t) = 10 + 9.8t \qquad (4.70)$$

Equation (4.70) gives the downward vertical velocity $v_y(t)$ as a function of time. We can calculate v_y at any instant of time by substituting that value of t into Eq. (4.70). For example, when $t = 2$ seconds, the velocity of the ball is given by

$$v_y(2) = 10 + 9.8(2) = 29.6 \text{ meters per second} \qquad (4.71)$$

We note also that Eq. (4.70) is, of course, of just the same form as the general result in Eq. (4.63). If we substitute $A = 9.8$ meters per second per second and $v(0) = v_y(0) = 10$ meters per second into the general result in Eq. (4.63), we obtain Eq. (4.70) describing our numerical example.

To recapitulate, we have seen that a knowledge of an initial condition enables us to determine the constant of integration in the kinematics problem we have been discussing. This is generally true in problems in which time is the independent variable, as it so frequently is in physics. One initial condition (like the value of the velocity) known at the initial instant $t = 0$ of the motion allows us to determine one constant of integration. Some problems involve two integrations and hence involve two constants of integration. In such a case, it is necessary to know two initial conditions in order to determine the two constants of integration.

It is useful at this point to make a graph of Eq. (4.63) giving the velocity $v(t)$ as a function of time t; this graph is shown in Fig. 4.1. If we examine Eq. (4.63), repeated below for convenience,

$$v(t) = v(0) + At \qquad (4.63)$$

we see that it is of the form

$$y = b + mx \qquad (2.39)$$

the equation of a straight line, seen earlier in Eq. (2.39), of slope m and intercept b. Comparing Eq. (2.39) and Eq. (4.63), we see that a graph of $v(t)$ as a function of time t is a straight line of slope A and of intercept $v(0)$ on the v axis. These features are shown in Fig. 4.1. Since the derivative gives the slope of the curve, we calculate

$$\frac{dv}{dt} = A \qquad (4.72)$$

from Eq. (4.63), showing that the straight line in Fig. 4.1 has a slope equal to A. Since we were given that A is a constant, the slope is constant, as it should be for a straight line. The intercept on the vertical velocity axis is $v(0)$, the value of the velocity when the time $t = 0$. The intercept

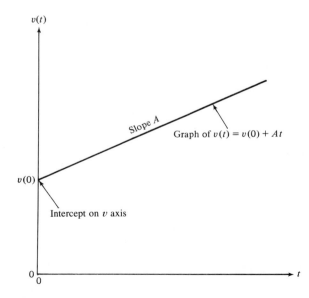

FIGURE 4.1
Graph of the straight line $v(t) = v(0) + At$, of slope A and intercept $v(0)$ on the v axis, plotted as a function of t.

on the v axis in Fig. 4.1 is thus the initial velocity, that is, the velocity at $t = 0$.

In our discussion so far of constants of integration, we considered a problem in which the independent variable was the time. While this is a very important type of problem in physics, we will sometimes integrate over a variable other than the time. Consider the following example. Suppose we know that the derivative (dy/dx) of a function $y(x)$ is equal to $(x/2)$, so

$$\frac{dy}{dx} = \frac{x}{2} \qquad (4.73)$$

and, in addition, we know that the function $y(x)$ has the value 1 when $x = 0$, so

$$y(0) = 1 \qquad (4.74)$$

We wish to find the function $y(x)$. From Eq. (4.73), we have the differential dy as

$$dy = \tfrac{1}{2}x \, dx \qquad (4.75)$$

Integrating Eq. (4.75) gives us

$$y = \int dy = \int \tfrac{1}{2}x \, dx = \tfrac{1}{4}x^2 \qquad (4.76)$$

so, adding a constant of integration, we have

$$y(x) = \tfrac{1}{4}x^2 + C \qquad (4.77)$$

We can use the information contained in the condition in Eq. (4.74) to determine the constant of integration C. To find $y(0)$, the value of y when $x = 0$, we substitute $x = 0$ into Eq. (4.77), obtaining

$$y(0) = C \qquad (4.78)$$

Equations (4.78) and (4.74) together tell us that

$$C = 1 \qquad (4.79)$$

so the condition that $y = 1$ when $x = 0$ determines the value of the constant C as equal to 1. Then, from Eq. (4.77),

$$y(x) = \tfrac{1}{4}x^2 + 1 \qquad (4.80)$$

is the complete form of the function $y(x)$. This function is a parabola passing through the point (0, 1) and is shown in Fig. 3.12 of Chap. 3.

In both of the examples in this section, we were given the derivative of a function and found the function by integration. In both cases, we were also given an additional condition or piece of information that enabled us to determine the value of the constant of integration in the problem. In the example in which time was the independent variable, we were told the value of the desired function (the velocity) at the initial instant ($t = 0$) of the problem; this is called an initial condition. In the second example, we were again given the value of the function $y(x)$ at some value of the independent variable x and this condition allowed us to determine the constant of integration.

EXERCISES

4.6. A particle moves with constant velocity in a straight line in one direction. The value of its constant velocity is V meters per second and the distance s it has moved is 100 meters at the initial instant of time $t = 0$. Find the equation giving s as a function of time.

4.7. The derivative of a certain function $y(x)$ is given by

$$\frac{dy}{dx} = 6 - 2x$$

and it is known that $y = 9$ when $x = 3$. Find the function $y(x)$.

4.8. A certain particle is moving with a constant acceleration equal to zero, and its initial velocity at $t = 0$ has the value 100 meters per second. Find the equation for the particle's velocity as a function of time.

REVIEW OF THE DEFINITION OF THE DEFINITE INTEGRAL

We now *review* the definition of the definite integral on the assumption that you will refresh your memory, on any points about which you may be rusty, by using your calculus book. The definite integral is extremely important in physics and is the second major concern (with the derivative) of this book. The definition will aim to be simple rather than the most general and rigorous possible.

Consider a function $f(x)$ in the interval $a \leq x \leq b$ shown in Fig. 4.2. Suppose we subdivide the interval between $x = a$ and $x = b$ into n subintervals of equal length. (It is convenient, but not necessary, that the subintervals be of equal length.) The subdivision is accomplished by inserting the $(n - 1)$ intermediate points $x_1, x_2, \ldots, x_{n-1}$ shown in Fig. 4.2. We will give the point $x = a$ the label x_0 and give the point $x = b$ the label x_n. Thus there are $(n + 1)$ points x_k indicated, where $k = 0, 1, 2, \ldots, n$.

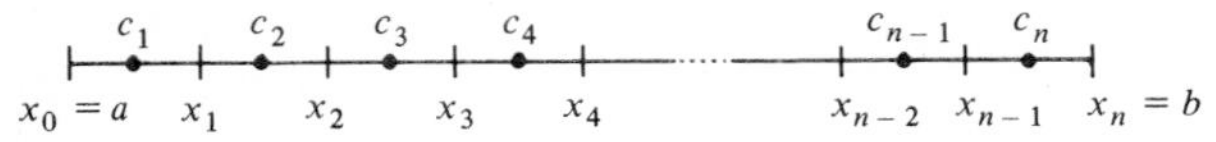

FIGURE 4.2

Subdivision of the interval $a \leq x \leq b$ into n subintervals by the $(n - 1)$ points x_1, x_2, . . . , x_{n-1}. In each subinterval, of length $\Delta x_k = x_k - x_{k-1}$, a point c_k is chosen as shown. For example, in the second subinterval, between x_2 and x_1, the point chosen is $x = c_2$.

Next, we choose a point in each subinterval. While this point may be chosen in any way we like, in the interests of simplicity of visualization, we choose this point to be in the center of such subinterval. We give the chosen point in the subinterval between x_0 and x_1 the label c_1; we give the chosen point in the subinterval between x_1 and x_2 the label c_2, and so on. Thus c_k is the chosen point in the center of the subinterval between x_{k-1} and x_k. The length of the subinterval between x_{k-1} and x_k will be denoted by Δx_k, where

$$\Delta x_k = x_k - x_{k-1} \tag{4.81}$$

Next, we find the value of the function $f(x)$ at each of the n chosen points within the n subintervals: $f(c_1)$ is the value of the function f at the point $x = c_1$, $f(c_2)$ is the value of f at the point $x = c_2$, and so on through $f(c_n)$, the value of f at the point $x = c_n$. Then we construct the *sum*

$$f(c_1)\,\Delta x_1 + f(c_2)\,\Delta x_2 + \cdots + f(c_{n-1})\,\Delta x_{n-1} + f(c_n)\,\Delta x_n \tag{4.82}$$

which may be written using the summation notation as

$$\sum_{k=1}^{n} f(c_k)\,\Delta x_k \tag{4.83}$$

The sum in Eq. (4.83) thus has n terms, one for each of the n subintervals between $x = a$ and $x = b$.

Consider a sequence of sums of the form in Eq. (4.83). These sums are constructed by dividing the interval $a \leq x \leq b$ into a larger and larger number of subintervals of decreasing length. Thus, we are considering a sequence of sums like those in Eq. (4.83) as the number n of subintervals gets very large and the length Δx_k of each subinterval gets very small. We are therefore taking the *limit* of the sum in Eq. (4.83) as the length Δx_k of the subintervals gets very small, a process we indicate by writing $\Delta x_k \to 0$. (In this book we assume that this limit will always exist in the cases in which we are interested.) The limit approached by the sum in Eq. (4.83) is a *number* which we denote by A, so we have

$$\lim_{\Delta x_k \to 0} \sum_{k=1}^{n} f(c_k)\,\Delta x_k = A \tag{4.84}$$

By definition, the number A is called the *definite integral* of the function $f(x)$ from $x = a$ to $x = b$. The definite integral A is denoted by

$$A \equiv \int_a^b f(x)\, dx \qquad (4.85)$$

In expression (4.85), the number a is the *lower limit* of integration, the number b is the *upper limit* of integration, and the symbol x is called the *variable* of integration.

The preceding is the formal definition of the definite integral as the limit of a sum. The definition will become clearer and more readily visualized when we discuss the geometric interpretation and applications of the definite integral. First, however, we must discuss the evaluation of definite integrals.

EVALUATION OF DEFINITE INTEGRALS

Given the definition (4.84) of the definite integral of the function $f(x)$ from a to b, how do we evaluate it? The answer is supplied by the fundamental theorem of integral calculus, which, in simplified form, is as follows. Suppose $f(x)$ is a continuous function in interval $a \le x \le b$, and is the derivative of another function $F(x)$, so

$$\frac{dF(x)}{dx} = f(x) \qquad (4.86)$$

Then it follows that

$$dF(x) = f(x)\, dx \qquad (4.87)$$

and

$$F(x) = \int f(x)\, dx \qquad (4.88)$$

meaning that $F(x)$ is an indefinite integral of $f(x)$. The fundamental theorem then asserts that the definite integral of $f(x)$ from $x = a$ to $x = b$ is given by

$$\int_a^b f(x)\, dx = F(b) - F(a) \qquad (4.89)$$

Equation (4.89) says that, to obtain the definite integral of $f(x)$, we find the indefinite integral $F(x)$ from Eq. (4.88) and then evaluate $F(x)$ at $x = b$ and at $x = a$. As a notational point, one often sees the definite integral (4.89) written as

$$\int_a^b dx\, f(x) \tag{4.90}$$

The meaning of (4.90) is the same as that of (4.89); the form (4.90) merely has dx, indicating the variable of integration, written before the function $f(x)$ rather than after it.

Consider an example; let's calculate

$$\int_1^2 x\, dx \tag{4.91}$$

so the function $f(x) = x$, $b = 2$, and $a = 1$. We find $F(x)$ as the indefinite integral

$$F(x) = \int x\, dx = \frac{x^2}{2} \tag{4.92}$$

so

$$F(2) = \frac{2^2}{2} = 2 \qquad F(1) = \frac{1^2}{2} = \frac{1}{2} \tag{4.93}$$

and the desired definite integral is

$$\int_1^2 x\, dx = F(2) - F(1) = 2 - \frac{1}{2} = \frac{3}{2} \tag{4.94}$$

Note that it is not necessary to consider a constant of integration in the indefinite integral in Eq. (4.92).

A common notation for the quantity $F(b) - F(a)$ is the following:

$$[F(x)]_a^b \equiv F(b) - F(a) \tag{4.95}$$

so Eq. (4.89) can also be written as

$$\int_a^b f(x)\, dx = [F(x)]_a^b \tag{4.96}$$

where, again, the relation between $F(x)$ and $f(x)$ is given by Eq. (4.86), that is, $f(x) = dF(x)/dx$.

Consider another example. We will evaluate

$$\int_0^{\pi/2} \cos x\, dx \tag{4.97}$$

From our results above,

$$\int_0^{\pi/2} \cos x\, dx = [\sin x]_0^{\pi/2} = \sin \frac{\pi}{2} - \sin 0 = 1 \tag{4.98}$$

Note that the variable of integration in a definite integral is a *dummy* variable in the mathematical sense. This means that the *value* of the definite integral (which is just a number) does not depend on the variable of integration. For example,

$$\int_0^{\pi/2} \cos x \, dx = 1 \qquad \int_0^{\pi/2} \cos \theta \, d\theta = 1 \qquad \int_0^{\pi/2} \cos z \, dz = 1$$

$$(4.99)$$

All three definite integrals in Eq. (4.99) have the same value, namely, unity.

We close this section with two important and useful properties of definite integrals. First, it is true that

$$\int_b^a f(x) \, dx = -\int_a^b f(x) \, dx \qquad (4.100)$$

Equation (4.100) tells us that interchanging the limits of integration in a definite integral multiplies the integral by (-1). Second,

$$\int_a^b f(x) \, dx = \int_a^c f(x) \, dx + \int_c^b f(x) \, dx \qquad (4.101)$$

In Eq. (4.101), it is not necessary that the point c be between the points a and b.

Finally, one sometimes sees the form

$$\int_a^x f(x) \, dx = F(x) - F(a) \qquad (4.102)$$

where, as before, $f(x) = dF(x)/dx$. The form (4.102) is used to indicate a definite integral whose upper limit is an arbitrary value of the variable of integration x. Thus, if $f(x) = x$, we have

$$\int_a^x x \, dx = \frac{x^2}{2} - \frac{a^2}{2} = \frac{1}{2}(x^2 - a^2)$$

where a is the constant lower limit of the integral.

EXERCISES

4.9. Evaluate $\int_0^{\pi} \sin x \, dx$.

4.10. Evaluate $\int_0^2 x^2 \, dx$.

4.11. Evaluate $\displaystyle\int_0^\infty e^{-x}\,dx$.

4.12. Evaluate $\displaystyle\int_0^a (x - a)^2\,dx$, where a is a constant.

4.13. Evaluate $\displaystyle\int_\infty^b x^{-2}\,dx$, where b is a constant.

4.14. Evaluate $\displaystyle\int_0^a \frac{x\,dx}{(d^2 + x^2)^{1/2}}$ where d and a are constants.

GEOMETRIC INTERPRETATION OF THE DEFINITE INTEGRAL

We now consider the *geometric* meaning of the definite integral. This interpretation will provide a concrete and visual meaning for the integral which will pave the way for the physical applications in which we are primarily interested.

We return to the sum in Eq. (4.83)

$$\sum_{k=1}^n f(c_k)\,\Delta x_k \tag{4.83}$$

on which the definition (4.84) of the definite integral is based, and look into its geometric interpretation in a specific case. Consider the graph of the function $f(x)$, as a function of x, shown in Fig. 4.3, between $x = a$ and $x = b$. We divide the interval $a \le x \le b$ on the x axis into four subintervals of equal length by inserting three points x_1, x_2, x_3 between the points $x_0 = a$ and $x_4 = b$. The lengths of the four subintervals are equal, so

$$\Delta x_1 = (x_1 - x_0) = \Delta x_2 = (x_2 - x_1) = \cdots = \Delta x_4 = (x_4 - x_3)$$

We will denote the length of each subinterval by Δx, so

$$\Delta x \equiv \Delta x_1 = \Delta x_2 = \Delta x_3 = \Delta x_4 \tag{4.103}$$

We choose a point in the center of each subinterval: these are the points $x = c_1$; $x = c_2$; $x = c_3$; $x = c_4$ shown in Fig. 4.3.

Next, we construct the sum

$$\sum_{k=1}^4 f(c_k)\,\Delta x_k = f(c_1)\,\Delta x_1 + f(c_2)\,\Delta x_2 + f(c_3)\,\Delta x_3 + f(c_4)\,\Delta x_4$$

$$\tag{4.104}$$

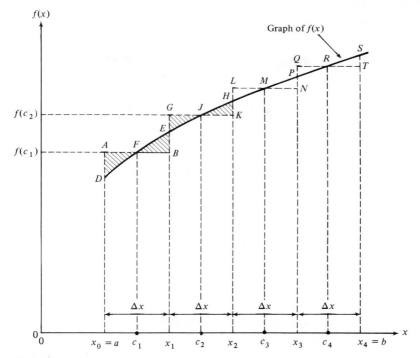

FIGURE 4.3
The area between the graph of the function $f(x)$ and the x axis, between $x = a$ and $x = b$, divided into four rectangles, each of width Δx.

Since all of the Δx_k's are, from Eq. (4.103), equal to Δx, the sum in Eq. (4.104) becomes

$$\sum_{k=1}^{4} f(c_k)\, \Delta x = f(c_1)\, \Delta x + f(c_2)\, \Delta x + f(c_3)\, \Delta x + f(c_4)\, \Delta x$$

$$(4.105)$$

We now want to give a geometric interpretation to each of the four terms of the form $[f(c_k)\, \Delta x]$ in the sum in Eq. (4.105).

As seen in Fig. 4.3, the quantity $[f(c_1)\, \Delta x]$ is the area of the rectangle $(aABx_1)$. The quantity $[f(c_2)\, \Delta x]$ is the area of the rectangle (x_1GKx_2), and so on for the other two rectangles (x_2LNx_3) and (x_3QTx_4) in the figure. The sum in Eq. (4.105) thus is the sum of the areas of the four vertical rectangles, centered at c_1, c_2, c_3, c_4, in Fig. 4.3. Consider the rectangle $(aABx_1)$ centered at $x = c_1$. We assert that the area $(aABx_1)$ is approximately equal to the irregularly shaped area $(aDFEx_1)$. In other words, we say

$$\text{Area of } (aABx_1) \cong \text{area of } (aDFEx_1) \qquad (4.106)$$

by assuming that the shaded area DAF is approximately equal to the shaded area FEB and that these two shaded areas "cancel each other out," thereby making the statement in Eq. (4.106) correct. The rectangle $(aABx_1)$ has an area $[f(c_1)\,\Delta x]$ where $f(c_1)$ is the height of the rectangle and Δx is its width. From Eq. (4.106), we conclude

$$f(c_1)\,\Delta x \cong \text{area of } (aDFEx_1) \qquad (4.107)$$

meaning that the irregular area $(aDFEx_1)$ is approximately equal to the area $f(c_1)\,\Delta x$ of the rectangle of $aABx_1$. For convenience of notation, we denote the area of $(aDFEx_1)$ by A_1, so we have, from Eq. (4.107),

$$A_1 \cong f(c_1)\,\Delta x \qquad (4.108)$$

for the area A_1 of the irregular shape $(aDFEx_1)$. Similarly, the area A_2 of the irregular shape (x_1EJHx_2) is approximately equal to the area $[f(c_2)\,\Delta x]$ of the rectangle (x_1GKx_2), so we have

$$A_2 \cong f(c_2)\,\Delta x \qquad (4.109)$$

In the same way we have, for the areas A_3 and A_4 of the shapes (x_2HMPx_3) and (x_3PRSb), that

$$A_3 \cong f(c_3)\,\Delta x \qquad (4.110)$$

$$A_4 \cong f(c_4)\,\Delta x \qquad (4.111)$$

The sum of A_1 to A_4 is the area $(aDSb)$ contained between the curve of $f(x)$ and the x axis from $x = a$ to $x = b$. Denoting this area $(aDSb)$ by A, we have

$$A = A_1 + A_2 + A_3 + A_4 \qquad (4.112)$$

or

$$A \cong f(c_1)\,\Delta x + f(c_2)\,\Delta x + f(c_3)\,\Delta x + f(c_4)\,\Delta x \qquad (4.113)$$

which is just the sum in Eq. (4.105). We conclude that the area A contained between the curve $f(x)$ and the x axis between $x = a$ and $x = b$ is given approximately by the sum in Eq. (4.105), so

$$A \cong \sum_{k=1}^{4} f(c_k)\,\Delta x \qquad (4.114)$$

The content of Eq. (4.114), relating the area A between the curve $f(x)$ and the x axis to the sum in Eq. (4.105), is the basis for the geometric interpretation of the definite integral. This area is often referred to as the "area under the curve of the function $f(x)$."

It is intuitively clear from Fig. 4.3 that the approximation expressed by Eq. (4.114) becomes better as the number of rectangles is increased. In other words, a better approximation to the area under the curve in Fig. 4.3 is obtained by using a larger number of narrower rectangles. Using narrower rectangles is achieved by letting the width Δx of each rectangle become smaller. In the limit as Δx becomes very small, the number n of terms of the form $f(c_k) \Delta x$ in the sum in Eq. (4.114) increases, so we are taking the *limit* of the sum in Eq. (4.83),

$$A = \lim_{\Delta x \to 0} \sum_{k=1}^{n} f(c_k) \Delta x \qquad (4.115)$$

as $\Delta x \to 0$ and as $n \to \infty$. In the limit as $\Delta x \to 0$ in Eq. (4.115), the area A becomes *exactly* the area under the curve. Thus the limit of the sum in Eq. (4.115) is exactly the area between the curve of $f(x)$ and the x axis between $x = a$ and $x = b$. But from Eqs. (4.84) and (4.85), the limit of the sum in Eq. (4.115) is just the definite integral of $f(x)$ from $x = a$ to $x = b$. We therefore conclude that the definite integral

$$\int_a^b f(x) \, dx \qquad (4.116)$$

is exactly equal to the area A between the graph of the function $f(x)$ and the x axis between $x = a$ and $x = b$.

Let's illustrate this result with the concrete example in Fig. 4.4, which shows the graph of the function

$$f(x) = x^2 + 1 \qquad (4.117)$$

in the interval $0 \le x \le 4$. We will calculate the area A, shown shaded in the figure, between the curve of $f(x)$ and the x axis from $x = 1$ to $x = 3$. From the discussion above, the area A is

$$A = \int_1^3 f(x) \, dx = \int_1^3 (x^2 + 1) \, dx \qquad (4.118)$$

We evaluate the definite integral in Eq. (4.118) as

$$\int_1^3 (x^2 + 1) \, dx = \left[\frac{x^3}{3} + x \right]_1^3$$

$$= \left[\frac{3^3}{3} + 3 - \frac{1^3}{3} - 1 \right] = 10\frac{2}{3} \qquad (4.119)$$

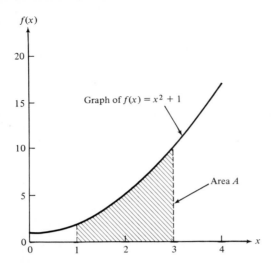

FIGURE 4.4
Area A between the graph of the function $f(x) = x^2 + 1$ and the x axis between $x = 1$ and $x = 3$. The area A is shaded.

The shaded area is thus $10\frac{2}{3}$ units of area. (If length on the graph in Fig. 4.4 is in meters, the area will be in square meters, etc. Since usually no unit of length is specified in drawings like Fig. 4.4, we just say that the area is so many units of area.)

EXERCISES

4.15. Calculate the area between the graph of $y = f(x) = 2x + 1$ and the x axis between $x = 1$ and $x = 2$.

4.16. Express in your own words the interpretation of Eq. (4.101) in terms of areas for the case in which $a < c < b$.

4.17. Consider a function $p(V)$ of an independent variable V, where

$$p(V) = \frac{C}{V}$$

and C is a positive constant. Calculate the area under the curve of $p(V)$ between the point $V = V_1$ and $V = V_2$, where $V_2 > V_1$.

INTERPRETATION OF THE DEFINITE INTEGRAL AS A "SUM OF INFINITESIMAL ELEMENTS"

We now reconsider the definite integral as the area A under a curve in a somewhat different way. We have just seen that the area A is the limit of the sum in Eq. (4.84) as $\Delta x_k \to 0$ and this limit is defined as the definite integral in Eq. (4.85). Thus we have

$$A = \lim_{\Delta x_k \to 0} \sum_{k=1}^{n} f(c_k)\, \Delta x_k = \int_{a}^{b} f(x)\, dx \qquad (4.120)$$

where $a \le x \le b$. We will now construct the definite integral giving the area A under the curve $f(x)$ in a different manner. This approach omits the sum and limit in Eq. (4.120) and constructs the integral for the area directly. While this approach is mathematically rather casual, it is very useful and is used constantly in physics.

Consider the graph of the function $f(x)$ for $a \le x \le b$ shown in Fig. 4.5, and consider the shaded area in the figure. This shaded area is a vertical strip of width dx, where dx is the differential of x, the independent variable. The geometric interpretation of dx in Fig. 4.5 is that dx is a very small ("infinitesimal") length along the x axis. The shaded strip is located at some point $x = x'$ on the x axis, and we denote the area of the strip by dA. The geometric interpretation of the differential dA is that dA is the very small ("infinitesimal") area of the shaded strip. We will call dA an *infinitesimal element of area* under the curve of $f(x)$. Similarly, we call dx an *infinitesimal element of length* along the x axis.

The area of the element is dA. The area dA is equal to the area of a rectangle of width dx and height $f(x')$, where $f(x')$ is the value of the function $f(x)$ at the point $x = x'$ at which the element is located. We

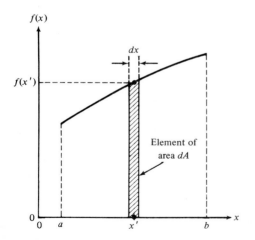

FIGURE 4.5
Graph of the function $f(x)$ for $a \le x \le b$, showing the infinitesimal element of area dA as the shaded strip. The element of area is located at the point $x = x'$.

have

$$dA = f(x') \, dx \tag{4.121}$$

Since x' can be *any* point x between $x = a$ and $x = b$, we can drop the prime on x', and write Eq. (4.121) as

$$dA = f(x) \, dx \tag{4.122}$$

where dA is the area of the infinitesimal element of area located at the point x. We note from Eq. (4.122) that the area dA of the element *depends on x*. To emphasize that fact, we write Eq. (4.122) as

$$dA(x) = f(x) \, dx \tag{4.123}$$

an equation that says that the area $dA(x)$ of an element of area depends on the point x at which it is located. This is seen in Fig. 4.6, which shows two elements, both of the same width dx, but with different areas, located at two different points on the x axis. The reason that the area of the element of area $dA(x)$ depends on x is because the function $f(x)$ in Eq. (4.123) has different values at different points x on the x axis.

Now that we have the element of area $dA(x)$ we may calculate the *total* area A under the curve by *adding up* the areas of all of the elements between $x = a$ and $x = b$ in Fig. 4.6. We "add up" the areas of all the elements by *integrating dA(x)*, which depends on x, between $x = a$ and $x = b$. Thus we have

$$A = \int_a^b dA(x) \tag{4.124}$$

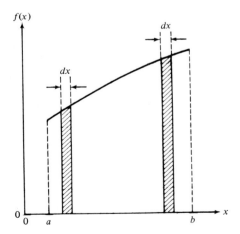

FIGURE 4.6
Graph of the function $f(x)$ showing elements of area $dA(x) = f(x) \, dx$ at two different points on the x axis.

where in Eq. (4.124) the variable of integration is x because the area $dA(x)$ of each element is a function of x.

Keep in mind that, in our calculation of the area A under the curve in the preceding section, we took the limit of the sum in Eq. (4.84) as $\Delta x_k \to 0$ and arrived at the definite integral (4.85). Here we have "replaced the sum by an integral," as in Eq. (4.124). You will see that phrase often in physics. We now substitute Eq. (4.123) for $dA(x)$ into Eq. (4.124), obtaining

$$A = \int_a^b f(x)\,dx \qquad (4.125)$$

for the area A under the curve of $f(x)$ for $a \le x \le b$. Equation (4.125) for the area A as the definite integral is just the result we obtained by the more precise process of taking the limit of the sum.

The procedure, described above, of adding up infinitesimal elements of some quantity by integrating, is much used in physics. In the discussion above, we added up elements of area to get the total area under a curve, but the infinitesimal elements can be elements of many quantities of physical interest. The next section of this chapter will describe several examples of this procedure.

Let's redo the example in the preceding section by the procedure of adding up or integrating elements of area. We found earlier the area between the graph of

$$f(x) = x^2 + 1 \qquad (4.126)$$

and the x axis between $x = 1$ and $x = 3$. The curve in Fig. 4.7 shows the graph of the function and an element of area dA, where

$$dA(x) = f(x)\,dx = (x^2 + 1)\,dx \qquad (4.127)$$

so the element of area $dA(x)$ depends on x. We find the total area A by integrating $dA(x)$, so

$$A = \int dA(x) = \int_1^3 (x^2 + 1)\,dx \qquad (4.128)$$

In Eq. (4.128), the variable of integration is x, and we want the area between $x = 1$ and $x = 3$, so those are the limits of integration. In this way, by adding up elements of area, we arrive at the same definite integral for the area under the curve that we found earlier in Eq. (4.118).

Let's conclude this section with another geometric example of a calculation in which we add up infinitesimal elements by integrating. We will calculate the circumference C of a circle of radius r. We recall from Chap. 2 that the arc length s, subtending an angle θ (in radians) in a circle

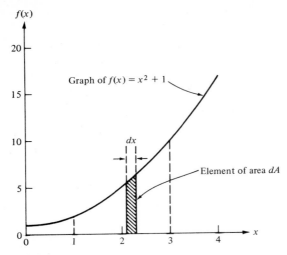

FIGURE 4.7
Graph of the function $f(x) = x^2 + 1$ showing an element of area dA.

of radius r, is, from Eq. (2.47), given by

$$s = r\theta \tag{4.129}$$

We take differentials of both sides of (4.129), obtaining

$$ds = r\,d\theta \tag{4.130}$$

because the radius r of a circle is a constant. The geometric significance of ds in Eq. (4.130) is that ds is a small length of arc along the circumference, as shown in Fig. 4.8. We call ds an *infinitesimal element of arc length along the circumference*. The element of arc length ds subtends an infinitesimal angle $d\theta$, also shown in Fig. 4.8. Note that the infinitesimal element ds is located at some value of the angle θ, which is measured so that $\theta = 0$ at the horizontal axis. (This is exactly analogous to the element of area dA being located at some point on the x axis in Fig. 4.5.) Note that, in Eq. (4.130), the element ds does *not* depend on θ because r is a constant and not a function of θ. Hence the element ds in this example is constant in magnitude [unlike the element of area $dA(x) = f(x)\,dx$ we discussed previously].

The value of the circumference C is the total arc length, all around the circumference of the circle, so we add up all the elements of arc length ds by integrating. We get

$$C = \int ds \tag{4.131}$$

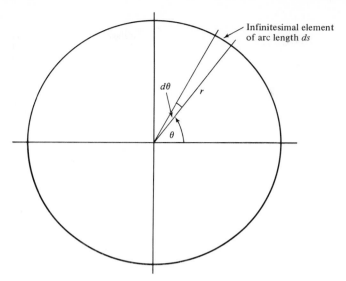

FIGURE 4.8
An element of arc length ds subtending an infinitesimal angle $d\theta$ in a circle of radius r. The angle θ, measured from the horizontal, locates the position of $d\theta$ and, hence, of ds.

Using Eq. (4.130), this becomes

$$C = \int r\, d\theta = r \int d\theta \qquad (4.132)$$

an integral in which the variable of integration is the angle θ shown in Fig. 4.8. To evaluate the integral in Eq. (4.132), we need to know the limits of the definite integral, that is, the range of values over which the variable of integration θ varies in the problem. We can see from Fig. 4.8 that, in order to trace out the entire circumference of the circle, θ must vary from 0 radians to 2π radians, so

$$0 \le \theta \le 2\pi \qquad (4.133)$$

is the range of values of θ. The lower limit of the integral is 0 and the upper limit is 2π. The complete integral for the circumference C is thus

$$C = r \int_0^{2\pi} d\theta \qquad (4.134)$$

Evaluating the integral in Eq. (4.134) gives

$$\int_0^{2\pi} d\theta = [\theta]_0^{2\pi} = [2\pi - 0] = 2\pi \qquad (4.135)$$

so we obtain

$$C = 2\pi r \tag{4.136}$$

the familiar relation between the circumference C and the radius r of a circle.

The important point of this calculation of the circumference of a circle is the procedure by which it was done. In Eq. (4.131), we said that the length C of the circumference is obtained by integrating ("adding up") all of the infinitesimal elements of arc length ds. Once we had Eq. (4.131), we expressed the element of arc length ds as $r\,d\theta$ by using Eq. (4.129). This expressed ds in terms of the variable θ whose range of values we found in Eq. (4.133). Again, the essential thing we did was to "add up" or integrate the infinitesimal elements in the problem. This procedure is widely used in physics and is the subject of the next section of this chapter.

It is worth pointing out the mathematical similarity between the calculation of the area under the curve of $f(x) = x^2 + 1$ and the calculation of the circumference of the circle. In the former, when we said that the area A was the sum (integral) of the elements of area $dA(x)$, we wrote

$$A = \int dA(x) \tag{4.137}$$

Then our next step was finding the element of area $dA(x)$ in terms of a variable of integration, which in that case was x, the distance along the x axis. This we did by calculating

$$dA(x) = f(x)\,dx = (x^2 + 1)\,dx \tag{4.127}$$

in Eq. (4.127). The combination of Eqs. (4.127) and (4.137) allowed us to calculate A, the area we sought. In the calculation of the circumference C, we said C was the sum (integral) of the elements of arc length ds and wrote

$$C = \int ds \tag{4.131}$$

Again, our next step was finding the element of arc length ds in terms of a variable of integration, which in this case was the angle θ in Fig. 4.8. This we did by calculating

$$ds = r\,d\theta \tag{4.130}$$

Combining Eqs. (4.130) and (4.131) allowed us to calculate C in Eq. (4.134). Note that, in both cases, once we had set up the integral of the elements of the quantity of interest (area or arc length), the next step was to express that element in terms of a variable of integration. Sometimes that step is very simple (as in the case of calculating the area) or is more complicated (as in the case of the arc length). We will see a number of examples of varying degrees of complexity in the next section on physical applications of integration.

EXERCISES

4.18. Use the procedure of adding up infinitesimal elements of length by integration to calculate the length (distance) along the x axis from $x = a$ to $x = b$, where $b > a$.

4.19. Consider the straight line $f(x) = x$. Calculate, by integrating elements of area, the total area A between the graph of $f(x) = x$ and the x axis from $x = 0$ to $x = a$, where a is a constant.

PHYSICAL APPLICATIONS OF THE DEFINITE INTEGRAL

In this section, we will discuss a number of examples of the application of the definite integral to physics. The approach will be the same in each one—the addition of infinitesimal elements of some quantity by integration. The physics will be kept as simple as possible in order to emphasize the mathematical techniques, which, in this book, are the primary interest.

As our first example, we will discuss the work done by a force. We recall that, if a constant force F acts on a body and moves it a distance d, where the directions of the force and the distance are the same, then the work W done by the force is

$$W = Fd \qquad (4.138)$$

Equation (4.138) assumes that the magnitude of the force F is constant. We now want to calculate the work done by a force whose magnitude is *variable* but whose direction is constant.

Consider, as shown in Fig. 4.9, a body being pulled along the x axis by a force F, where the directions of F and of the motion of the body are both along the x axis. Suppose, however, that the magnitude of F

FIGURE 4.9
A force of magnitude F, in a direction parallel to the x axis, moving a body along the x axis.

varies with position on the x axis, so the magnitude F of the force depends on the x coordinate of the body on which the force is exerted. We write this fact as

$$F = F(x) \tag{4.139}$$

an equation which says that the magnitude F of the force is a function $F(x)$ of the x coordinate of the body. For example, when the body is at the point $x = x'$, then the magnitude of the force at that point is $F(x')$, and so on. Suppose the body is pulled along the x axis, starting at the point $x = x_s$ and finishing at the point $x = x_f$. How can we calculate the *total* amount of work W done by the force in moving the body from $x = x_s$ to $x = x_f$?

Since the magnitude of the force is *not* constant, we cannot just multiply force times the total distance moved as was done in Eq. (4.138). What we do to handle this situation of a variable force is the following. Consider Fig. 4.10, showing the x axis in the problem, and consider an infinitesimal element of length dx located at some point x on the x axis between x_s and x_f. Let us calculate the work done by the force in moving the body the infinitesimal distance dx located at point x. We denote this infinitesimal amount of work by dW. We next make the reasonable assumption that the magnitude of the force F is essentially constant over the very small distance dx, even though, strictly speaking, F varies with position on the x axis. At the point x where dx is located, the force F has the magnitude

$$F = F(x) \tag{4.140}$$

Since we're assuming that the magnitude of the force has the essentially constant value $F(x)$ over the infinitesimal length dx we're considering, we can calculate the infinitesimal amount of work dW by multiplying the magnitude of the force and the distance moved. The result is

$$dW = F(x)\,dx \tag{4.141}$$

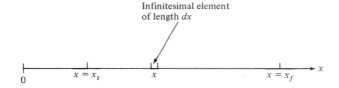

FIGURE 4.10
The x axis, showing an infinitesimal element of length dx located at the point x. The points $x = x_s$ and $x = x_f$ are, respectively, the starting and finishing points of the motion of the body.

where, to repeat, dW is the amount of work done by the force in moving the body the distance dx located at the point x. Note that, because $F(x)$ depends on x, dW depends on x. To emphasize that fact we rewrite Eq. (4.141) as

$$dW(x) = F(x)\, dx \qquad (4.142)$$

To find the *total* work W done by the force in moving the body from x_s to x_f, we *add up* all of the infinitesimal elements (amounts) of work $dW(x)$, so we have

$$W = \int dW(x) \qquad (4.143)$$

where, in Eq. (4.143), the variable of integration is x because $dW(x)$ depends on x. Equation (4.143) says that the total work W is the sum of all of the infinitesimal amounts of work $dW(x)$ done by the force in moving the body the infinitesimal distances dx located at different points x on the x axis.

Then, from Eq. (4.142), we have the expression for $dW(x)$ in terms of $F(x)$ and dx, so Eq. (4.143) becomes

$$W = \int F(x)\, dx \qquad (4.144)$$

where the variable of integration remains distance x because the integrand $F(x)$ depends on x. To find the limits of integration in Eq. (4.144), we know the body moves from its starting point $x = x_s$ to its final point $x = x_f$, so these values are the endpoints of the range of the variable of integration x. The value x_s is the lower limit and x_f is the upper limit in Eq. (4.144), which becomes

$$W = \int_{x_s}^{x_f} F(x)\, dx \qquad (4.145)$$

Equation (4.145) gives the total work W done by the force $F(x)$, of variable magnitude, in moving the body from $x = x_s$ to $x = x_f$, assuming the directions of the force and the motion of the body are the same.

Equation (4.145) is a general expression for any functional form $F(x)$ of the dependence of the force F on position x. In order to calculate the total work W using Eq. (4.145), one must know the particular function $F(x)$. As a specific example, let's consider that the force applied to the body is given by

$$F = F(x) = kx \qquad (4.146)$$

where k is a constant of proportionality. Equation (4.146) says that the magnitude of the force F is proportional to the first power of the position coordinate x, so F varies linearly with x. Let's calculate the work W done by the force F given by Eq. (4.146) in moving the body from the point $x = 1$ to $x = 2$. Using Eq. (4.145), the starting point is $x = 1$ and the finishing point is $x = 2$, so W is given by

$$W = \int_1^2 kx \, dx \qquad (4.147)$$

We can evaluate the integral in Eq. (4.147). Our answer will be expressed in terms of the constant k, and Eq. (4.147) becomes

$$W = k \int_1^2 x \, dx = k \left[\frac{x^2}{2} \right]_1^2 = k \left[2 - \frac{1}{2} \right] = \frac{3k}{2} \qquad (4.148)$$

so the total work $W = (3k/2)$ units of work. (One would need to know the numerical value of k to obtain a numerical value of W.)

As a last point about this example, note that, in dealing with a physical problem, we assigned a physical interpretation (distance) to the mathematical variable of integration x in the problem. It is always useful to keep in mind the physical meaning of the mathematical symbols being used. Thus, in this example, when we integrate over the variable x, we would say we were "integrating over distance" because distance is the physical meaning of the variable x.

Our second example of the application of the definite integral comes from the field of heat and thermodynamics. The specific heat c of a substance may be defined by the equation

$$Q = mc(T_2 - T_1) \qquad (4.149)$$

where Q is the amount of heat necessary to raise a mass m of the substance from temperature $T = T_1$ to temperature $T = T_2$. In the elementary definition of the specific heat in Eq. (4.149), c is regarded as a constant which is independent of temperature. This is not really true; c does in general depend on temperature, so

$$c = c(T) \qquad (4.150)$$

In Exercise 3.21, it was found that the infinitesimal amount of heat dQ necessary to raise a mass m of a substance of specific heat $c(T)$ by an infinitesimal temperature dT was

$$dQ = mc(T) \, dT \qquad (4.151)$$

Since the specific heat $c(T)$ depends on the temperature T, the infinitesimal amount of heat dQ depends on the temperature, and we write

$$dQ(T) = mc(T) \, dT \qquad (4.152)$$

Equation (4.152) says that the amount of heat $dQ(T)$ necessary to increase the temperature of a mass m by an amount dT is different at different temperatures.

Suppose the specific heat of a substance varies with temperature, as in Eq. (4.150). What is the *total* amount of heat Q necessary to increase the temperature of a mass m of the substance from T_1 to T_2? Suppose we construct a temperature axis, as shown in Fig. 4.11, and consider an infinitesimal temperature interval, of magnitude dT, located at temperature T. The infinitesimal amount of heat $dQ(T)$ necessary to increase the temperature of the substance by the infinitesimal amount dT is, from Eq. (4.152),

$$dQ(T) = mc(T)\, dT \qquad (4.152)$$

Then the *total* amount of heat Q necessary to raise the temperature from T_1 to T_2 is obtained by adding up or integrating all of the infinitesimal amounts of heat $dQ(T)$. We have

$$Q = \int dQ(T) \qquad (4.153)$$

where the variable of integration in Eq. (4.153) is the temperature T because $dQ(T)$ depends on T. Since $dQ(T)$ is given by Eq. (4.152), the expression for Q becomes

$$Q = \int mc(T)\, dT \qquad (4.154)$$

where, in Eq. (4.154), the variable of integration is still the temperature T because the specific heat $c(T)$ depends on T. Since the initial temperature of the substance is $T = T_1$ and the final temperature is $T = T_2$, these temperatures are the limits of integration in Eq. (4.154), which becomes

$$Q = m \int_{T_1}^{T_2} c(T)\, dT \qquad (4.155)$$

where the mass m is a constant independent of temperature and can be taken outside the integral. Equation (4.155) gives the total amount of heat

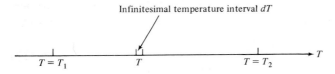

FIGURE 4.11
Temperature axis, showing an infinitesimal temperature interval of magnitude dT located at a temperature T between the initial temperature T_1 and the final temperature T_2.

Q required to increase the temperature of a mass m of a substance, of temperature-dependent specific heat $c(T)$, from T_1 to T_2. To evaluate the definite integral in Eq. (4.155), one would have to know how the specific heat depends on the temperature, that is, to know the particular functional form of $c(T)$.

As a concrete calculation involving a temperature-dependent specific heat, we consider solid argon at very low temperatures. It is known that, below about 2 kelvins, the specific heat of solid argon is proportional to T^3. Thus we have

$$c = c(T) = BT^3$$

where the constant B has the experimentally determined value $B = 6.26 \times 10^{-2}$ joule (kilogram)$^{-1}$ (kelvin)$^{-4}$. Let's calculate the amount of heat Q required to increase the temperature of one kilogram of solid argon from 1 kelvin to 2 kelvins. From Eq. (4.155), the necessary amount of heat is

$$Q = m \int_{T_1}^{T_2} c(T)\, dT = m \int_1^2 BT^3\, dT = (6.26 \times 10^{-2}) \int_1^2 T^3\, dT$$

on setting $m = 1$ kilogram and using $T_2 = 2$ kelvins and $T_1 = 1$ kelvin for the final and initial temperatures. Evaluating the integral yields

$$Q = (6.26 \times 10^{-2}) \left[\frac{T^4}{4} \right]_1^2 = (6.26 \times 10^{-2}) \left[\frac{16}{4} - \frac{1}{4} \right] \text{joule}$$

so our answer is $Q = 0.235$ joule for the amount of heat required to raise the temperature from 1 kelvin to 2 kelvins.

Note again how we have added up the infinitesimal amounts of heat $dQ(T)$ in Eq. (4.153) to find the total amount of heat Q. The process of adding up infinitesimal elements of some quantity by integrating is just what we did in the previous example of the work done by a variable force. The idea of using the definite integral as a sum of infinitesimal quantities (or differentials) was the same in both examples.

Our next example is from mechanics, and concerns the moment of inertia. The moment of inertia I of a *point* mass m located a distance r from an axis of rotation is

$$I = mr^2 \qquad (4.156)$$

Figure 4.12 shows the mass m relative to an axis of rotation perpendicular to the plane of the paper and passing through the point 0. The moment of inertia I is the moment of inertia about this axis of rotation. If we have several point masses m_1, m_2, m_3 located at distances r_1, r_2, r_3 from the axis of rotation, we have the situation shown in Fig. 4.13. The moment

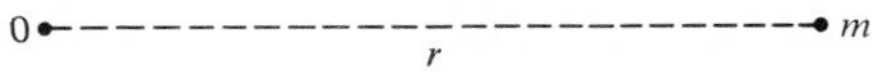

0 •– – – – – – – – – – – – – – – – – – – –• m

r

FIGURE 4.12
A point mass m located at a perpendicular distance r from an axis of rotation normal to the plane of the paper and passing through the point 0. The moment of inertia of the mass with respect to the axis of rotation is $I = mr^2$.

of inertia I of this system of point masses, relative to an axis of rotation normal to the plane of the paper and passing through the point 0, is given by

$$I = m_1 r_1^2 + m_2 r_2^2 + m_3 r_3^2 \qquad (4.157)$$

Equation (4.157) is an extension of the definition (4.156) to a number of point masses. We note that I is a *sum* of terms of the form mr^2.

Given this definition of the moment of inertia, we would like to be able to calculate the moment of inertia of an *extended body*, rather than of a system of point masses. Examples of an extended body are a solid cylinder and a long thin rod. How do we calculate the moment of inertia of an extended body? Consider the homogeneous extended body of mass M and constant mass density ρ shown schematically in Fig. 4.14. We divide the body into infinitesimal elements of mass; the mass of each element is dm. We denote by r the perpendicular distance of an element dm from the axis shown. Each of the elements dm constituting the body is at a different distance r from the axis. Next, we construct products of the form

$$r^2 \, dm \qquad (4.158)$$

for each element of mass dm. Noting that the expression (4.158) is the same as that in Eq. (4.156) for the moment of inertia I, we write

$$dI(r) = r^2 \, dm \qquad (4.159)$$

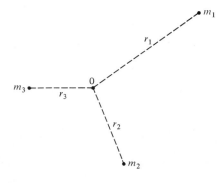

FIGURE 4.13
Three point masses m_1, m_2, m_3 at perpendicular distances r_1, r_2, r_3 from an axis of rotation normal to the plane of the paper and passing through the point 0. The moment of inertia with respect to the axis of rotation is $I = m_1 r_1^2 + m_2 r_2^2 + m_3 r_3^2$ and is a sum of terms of the form mr^2.

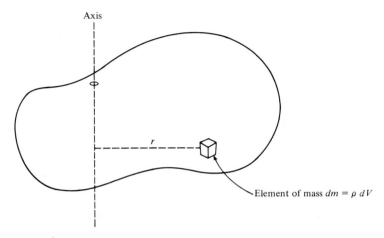

Axis

r

Element of mass $dm = \rho\, dV$

FIGURE 4.14
An extended body and its axis of rotation. The mass of the body is considered to be made up of infinitesimal elements of mass $dm = \rho\, dV$, where ρ is the constant mass density of the homogeneous body and dV is an infinitesimal element of volume. The element of mass dm is located at a perpendicular distance r from the axis.

where $dI(r)$ is the infinitesimal moment of inertia of the element of mass dm located at a distance r from the axis. We write $dI(r)$ to emphasize that the infinitesimal moment of inertia dI depends on the distance r. To calculate the moment of inertia I of the entire extended body, we add up all the infinitesimal moments of inertia $dI(r)$ by integration, and get

$$I = \int dI(r) = \int r^2\, dm \qquad (4.160)$$

The variable of integration in Eq. (4.160) is r, the distance of an element of mass dm from the axis, because dm depends on r.

Next we must express the element of mass dm in terms of r, the variable of integration. We consider the volume V of the extended body in Fig. 4.14 to be divided up into infinitesimal elements of volume dV. The *shape* of the element of volume dV will be determined by what is convenient for the shape of the body. For a volume element dV of any shape, we have

$$dm = \rho\, dV \qquad (4.161)$$

because the body is homogeneous with a constant mass density ρ. In Eq. (4.161), the element of volume dV will depend in some way on the coordinate r and the dependence on r will be different for volume elements of different shapes. We emphasize the dependence of dV on r by rewriting

Eq. (4.161) as

$$dm = \rho \, dV(r) \tag{4.162}$$

Substituting Eq. (4.162) into Eq. (4.160) gives us

$$I = \int \rho \, r^2 \, dV(r) \tag{4.163}$$

for the moment of inertia I and where the variable of integration in Eq. (4.163) is the coordinate r described above. The calculation of the moment of inertia using Eq. (4.163) becomes a question of using a convenient volume element dV for the shape of the body being considered. Keep in mind that, in calculating I using Eq. (4.160) or Eq. (4.163), we are again adding up, via integration, all of the infinitesimal elements dI to obtain the total moment of inertia.

Let's now use these results to calculate the moment of inertia I of a particular body. We will calculate I for a homogeneous solid right circular cylinder of height h, radius a, density ρ, and mass M, with respect to an axis passing through the center of the cylinder, as shown in Fig. 4.15. Our element of volume is a thin cylindrical shell (a hollow pipe) of height h and thickness dr located a distance r from the axis of the cylinder. The volume V of a right circular cylinder of radius r and height h is

$$V = \pi r^2 h \tag{4.164}$$

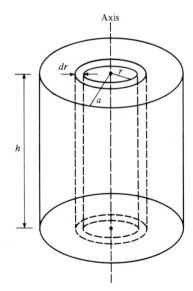

FIGURE 4.15
A solid right circular cylinder of height h and radius a, showing a volume element which is a thin cylindrical shell or pipe. The volume element, of height h and thickness dr, is located at a distance r from the axis of the cylinder. The element of mass $dm = \rho \, dV = 2\pi\rho hr \, dr$, where ρ is the constant mass density of the homogeneous cylinder.

The volume dV of the thin cylindrical shell is obtained by taking the differential of V given by Eq. (4.164) with respect to r. Thus

$$dV(r) = 2\pi hr \, dr \qquad (4.165)$$

is the volume of the thin shell, which is also shown in Fig. 4.15. Then, from Eq. (4.162), the element of mass dm is

$$dm = 2\pi\rho hr \, dr \qquad (4.166)$$

and the integral in Eq. (4.160) for the moment of inertia I is

$$I = \int r^2 \, dm \qquad (4.167)$$

$$I = 2\pi\rho h \int r^3 \, dr \qquad (4.168)$$

The variable of integration in Eq. (4.168) is r, the distance from the cylinder axis to the cylindrical shell. The integral in Eq. (4.168) is essentially the "adding up" of all of the terms ($r^2 \, dm$) for all of the shells comprising the cylinder. The distance r varies from $r = 0$ at the axis of the cylinder to $r = a$ at the surface of the cylinder. The limits in the integral in Eq. (4.168) are thus $r = 0$ and $r = a$, so Eq. (4.168) becomes

$$I = 2\pi\rho h \int_0^a r^3 \, dr \qquad (4.169)$$

We evaluate the integral in Eq. (4.169) as

$$\int_0^a r^3 \, dr = \left[\frac{r^4}{4} \right]_0^a = \frac{a^4}{4} \qquad (4.170)$$

so the moment of inertia becomes

$$I = (\pi\rho h a^4/2) = (\pi h a^2 \rho)\left(\frac{a^2}{2}\right) \qquad (4.171)$$

We note that $\pi h a^2$ is the volume of the cylinder of height h and radius a so $\pi h a^2 \rho$ is the mass M of the cylinder. Substituting this result into Eq. (4.171) gives

$$I = \frac{1}{2} M a^2 \qquad (4.172)$$

for the moment of inertia of the solid cylinder with respect to the axis shown in Fig. 4.15.

Note that once again we have used, in the integrals in Eqs. (4.160) and (4.163), the procedure of treating the integral as a sum of infinitesimal elements of the quantity of interest. (It should be pointed out, however, that certain subtle points apply to the calculation of the moments of inertia of some bodies of high symmetry, such as a sphere. A discussion of the physics involved is beyond the scope of this book. The interested reader is referred to, for example, *Berkeley Physics Course*, vol. 1: *Mechanics.**)

Our last example of the use of the definite integral as a sum of infinitesimal elements is from electricity, and concerns electrostatic potential. Consider a *point* electric charge of ($+q$) coulombs (for convenience, we consider a positive charge) located at a point 0 as shown in Fig. 4.16. Consider also another point P located a distance r from the charge q. Then it may be shown that the electrostatic potential V at the point P due to the charge q is

$$V = \frac{1}{4\pi\epsilon_0}\frac{q}{r} \qquad (4.173)$$

In Eq. (4.173), the quantity ϵ_0 is a universal constant (called the permittivity of free space) and where we have *defined* the electrostatic potential V at point P as equal to zero when P is infinitely far from the charge. To emphasize the fact that the electrostatic potential V at the point P depends on the distance r from P to the point charge q, we write

$$V(r) = \frac{1}{4\pi\epsilon_0}\frac{q}{r} \qquad (4.174)$$

The requirement that $V = 0$ when r is very large ($r \to \infty$) is fulfilled by the electrostatic-potential function $V(r)$ in Eq. (4.174). If we have several point charges (also positive for convenience) q_1, q_2, q_3, located at different distances r_1, r_2, r_3 from a point P, then the electrostatic potential V at the point P is

$$V = \frac{1}{4\pi\epsilon_0}\left[\frac{q_1}{r_1} + \frac{q_2}{r_2} + \frac{q_3}{r_3}\right] \qquad (4.175)$$

where, again, the electrostatic potential is defined to be zero at a point P very distant from the charges.

The problem we want to address is the calculation of the electro-

---

*C. Kittel, W. D. Knight, and M. A. Ruderman, *Berkeley Physics Course*, vol. 1: *Mechanics*, 1st ed., McGraw-Hill, New York, 1962, p. 243.

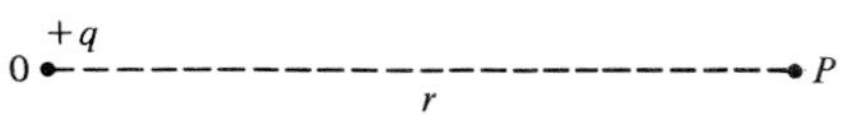

FIGURE 4.16
A point charge $+q$ located a distance r from a point P.

static potential, at a point, due to a *continuous* distribution of electric charge, rather than a system of point charges. Examples of a continuous distribution of charge are a wire with a linear density of electric charge (in coulombs per meter) and a flat plate with a surface density of electric charge (in coulombs per square meter). Given some continuous distribution of electric charge, how do we calculate the electrostatic potential (at some point) due to that continuous charge distribution?

Our approach is to treat the continuous distribution of charge as an assembly of infinitesimal elements of charge, each of magnitude dq. Then we treat each infinitesimal element of charge dq as if it were a point charge. Suppose we have an infinitesimal element of charge dq located at a point 0, as shown in Fig. 4.17, and consider a point P a distance r from the element of charge. Then the electrostatic potential dV at point P due to the element of charge dq is

$$dV = \frac{1}{4\pi\epsilon_0} \frac{dq}{r} \qquad (4.176)$$

Note, in Eq. (4.176), the analogy to Eq. (4.173) for the electrostatic potential due to a point charge. In Eq. (4.176), we are treating the element of charge dq as if it were a point charge. We see from Eq. (4.176) that the infinitesimal element of electrostatic potential dV depends on the distance r; to emphasize this, we write

$$dV(r) = \frac{1}{4\pi\epsilon_0} \frac{dq}{r} \qquad (4.177)$$

(Incidentally, it is assumed that the universal use of the symbol V for both electrostatic potential and volume will not cause difficulty.)

Equation (4.177) gives the element of electrostatic potential $dV(r)$ at a distance r from an element of charge dq. Suppose we have a continuous distribution of charge, like that indicated schematically in Fig. 4.18, and we want to calculate the electrostatic potential V at some point P. We treat the continuous distribution of charge as an assembly of infinitesimal elements of charge dq, each at a different distance r from the point P. Then the element of electrostatic potential at point P, due to the element of charge dq, is $dV(r)$ given by Eq. (4.177). The *total* electrostatic poten-

FIGURE 4.17
An infinitesimal element of charge dq at a distance r from a point P. The electrostatic potential dV at point P due to the element of charge dq is $dV = (1/4\pi\epsilon_0)(dq/r)$.

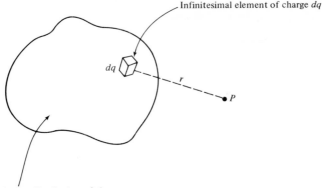

Infinitesimal element of charge dq

dq

r

P

Continuous distribution of charge

FIGURE 4.18
A continuous distribution of charge treated as an assembly of infinitesimal elements of charge dq. Each element dq is at a different distance r from the point P. The electrostatic potential $dV(r)$ at point P, due to the charge element dq, is $dV(r) = (1/4\pi\epsilon_0)(dq/r)$.

tial V at point P is obtained by adding up all of the elements $dV(r)$ by integration, so we have

$$V = \int dV(r) \tag{4.178}$$

and

$$V = \frac{1}{4\pi\epsilon_0} \int \frac{dq}{r} \tag{4.179}$$

for the electrostatic potential V at point P. In the integrals in Eqs. (4.178) and (4.179), the variable of integration is r, the distance from the charge element dq to the point P.

Let's illustrate the calculation of the electrostatic potential due to a continuous distribution of charge. Figure 4.19 shows a circular loop of wire, of radius a, on which is a linear distribution of charge of constant density λ coulombs per meter. We want to calculate the electrostatic potential V at the point P at the center of the circle. We let ds denote the element of arc length along the circumference of the circle, so the infinitesimal element of charge dq on the wire is

$$dq = \lambda \, ds \tag{4.180}$$

where, dimensionally, we see that dq is in coulombs, λ is coulombs per meter, and ds is in meters. To find the electrostatic potential V at the

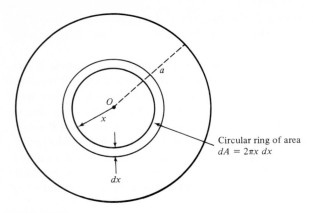

FIGURE 4.21
The flat circular disk with a surface charge density σ on it. The element of charge dq is the amount of charge on a circular ring of area $dA = 2\pi x\, dx$, so $dq = \sigma\, dA = 2\pi\sigma x\, dx$. (The drawing shows a top view of the disk.)

Next, we have to find the distance r from each circular ring to the point P. Returning to Fig. 4.20, we see that all points on a circular ring of radius x are at the same distance r from point P, where

$$r^2 = d^2 + x^2 \tag{4.188}$$

by the pythagorean theorem. Thus the distance r is given by

$$r = (d^2 + x^2)^{1/2} \tag{4.189}$$

an equation giving the distance r in terms of the constant distance d and the radius x of the circular ring. Note from Eq. (4.189) that circular rings near the edge of the disk (those with larger values of x) are farther from point P than are rings near the center of the disk.

Since we now know dq from Eq. (4.187) and r from Eq. (4.189), we know the element dV of electrostatic potential at point P. Using Eq. (4.177), we have

$$dV(x) = \frac{1}{4\pi\epsilon_0} \frac{2\pi\sigma x\, dx}{(d^2 + x^2)^{1/2}} \tag{4.190}$$

where we write $dV(x)$ to emphasize that the magnitude of the element dV of electrostatic potential at P depends on the radius x of the circular ring producing that element of potential. Simplifying Eq. (4.190), we have

$$dV(x) = \frac{\sigma}{2\epsilon_0} \frac{x\, dx}{(d^2 + x^2)^{1/2}} \tag{4.191}$$

Adding up all of the elements $dV(x)$ given by Eq. (4.191) by integrating, we get

$$V = \int dV(x) = \frac{\sigma}{2\epsilon_0} \int \frac{x \, dx}{\left(d^2 + x^2\right)^{1/2}} \qquad (4.192)$$

for the total electrostatic potential V at point P due to all of the charge on the disk. The variable of integration x in Eq. (4.192) is the radius of the circular rings, so x varies from $x = 0$ (at the center of the disk) to $x = a$ at the rim of the disk of radius a. The limits of integration are thus $x = 0$ and $x = a$, and Eq. (4.192) becomes

$$V = \frac{\sigma}{2\epsilon_0} \int_0^a \frac{x \, dx}{\left(d^2 + x^2\right)^{1/2}} \qquad (4.193)$$

To complete the problem, we evaluate the integral in Eq. (4.193) using the result found in Exercise 4.14 that

$$\int_0^a \frac{x \, dx}{\left(d^2 + x^2\right)^{1/2}} = \left[\left(d^2 + x^2\right)^{1/2}\right]_0^a = \left(d^2 + a^2\right)^{1/2} - \left(d^2\right)^{1/2}$$

$$(4.194)$$

Substituting Eq. (4.194) into Eq. (4.193) gives the final result

$$V = \frac{\sigma}{2\epsilon_0} \left[\left(d^2 + a^2\right)^{1/2} - d\right] \qquad (4.195)$$

for the electrostatic potential V at a distance d from the center of a circular disk, of radius a, bearing a surface charge density of σ coulombs per square meter. We note that, reasonably, V depends on d, a, and σ.

At the risk of verbal overkill, let me reiterate that, once again, all of the problems in this section were done in the same basic way. We found the infinitesimal element of the quantity of interest, whether it was work, heat, moment of inertia, or electrostatic potential. Then we added up all of the infinitesimal elements to get the total amount of the quantity of interest. This method is constantly used in physics and is also applied to vector quantities as well as the scalar quantities we have used in our examples.

EXERCISES

4.20. Calculate the moment of inertia of a hollow circular cylindrical "pipe" of outer radius R_2, inner radius R_1, length L, and mass M, and whose solid portion has a constant mass density ρ. The axis is through the center of the cylinder, parallel to its length.

4.21. Given a circular loop of wire of radius a bearing a linear charge density of λ coulombs per meter. Consider a point P that is a perpendicular distance d from the plane of the loop and on a line passing through the center of the loop. Calculate the electrostatic potential at point P due to the charge on the wire loop.

AVERAGE VALUE OF A FUNCTION

As our last topic in the application of the definite integral to physics, we consider the *average value* of a function. If we have a continuous function $f(x)$ over the interval $a \le x \le b$, then the average value of f, denoted by $\bar{f}$, with respect to x, is defined as

$$\bar{f} = \frac{1}{b-a} \int_a^b f(x)\,dx \qquad (4.196)$$

That the definition in Eq. (4.196) of the average value $\bar{f}$ is plausible may be seen in a casual way as follows. We divide the x axis between $x = a$ and $x = b$ into n intervals of infinitesimal (very small) length dx, where

$$n = \frac{b-a}{dx} \qquad (4.197)$$

Then the average value f may be thought of, roughly, as the sum of the n values of the function $f(x)$ in each of n intervals dx, divided by n. If we "sum" the function $f(x)$ by integration and divide by n as given by Eq. (4.197), we obtain the expression for $\bar{f}$ in the definition given in Eq. (4.196).

It is important in calculating the average value of a function to keep in mind the interval of the independent variable being considered. For example, consider the function

$$f(t) = \sin^2 \omega t \qquad (4.198)$$

where t is the time and ω is a constant. Let us calculate $\bar{f}$ over the time interval from $t = 0$ to $t = (2\pi/\omega)$ seconds. We note that the period of the sine function is 2π radians, so the function $\sin \omega t$ has a period or "repeat time" of $(2\pi/\omega)$ seconds. We are thus finding the average value of $\sin^2 \omega t$ over a time interval of one period. We have from Eq. (4.196) that

$$\overline{\sin^2 \omega t} = \frac{1}{(2\pi/\omega)} \int_0^{2\pi/\omega} \sin^2 \omega t\,dt = \frac{1}{2} \qquad (4.199)$$

where the bar over $\sin^2 \omega t$ indicates its average value. Our result is thus that the average value of $\sin^2 \omega t$ over the interval $0 \leq t \leq (2\pi/\omega)$ is $(1/2)$.

EXERCISES

4.22. Calculate the average value of $\cos^2 \omega t$ over the interval $0 \leq t \leq (2\pi/\omega)$.

CHAPTER
5

VECTORS

INTRODUCTION

This chapter is an introduction to vectors and their uses in introductory physics. However, this material is not considered a review and is presented from the beginning with all the steps put in for the student. This is because it has been my experience that most beginning students of physics have had little exposure to vectors and, especially, to vector calculus. The chapter covers the basic operations and definitions, scalar and vector products, and unit vectors in both rectangular and plane-polar coordinates. It concludes with an introduction to some topics in vector calculus, the vector derivative and the line integral, which are usually used in treating mechanics early in an introductory course. Examples have been chosen from the same field.

DEFINITIONS AND BASIC OPERATIONS

A *vector* is a quantity which has both a magnitude and a direction. An example is the vector quantity called *displacement*, which is the distance moved in a particular direction. The displacement thus has a magnitude (the distance moved) and a direction (the direction in which the motion takes place). For example, a particle might move 1 meter in the ($+x$) direction, so the (vector) displacement of the particle would be 1 meter in the ($+x$) direction. Another particle might move 1 meter in the ($+y$)

138

direction, so its (vector) displacement would be 1 meter in the (+y) direction. The two particles move the same distance, but in different directions, so their (vector) displacements are in different directions even though the magnitudes (the distance moved) are the same.

A quantity that has only a magnitude, but no direction associated with it, is called a *scalar*. Examples of scalars are time and temperature, two quantities which clearly have no direction assigned to them. The magnitude of any vector is a positive scalar quantity. For example, the magnitude of a displacement vector is the distance moved. In the example given above, the magnitude of both displacement vectors is 1 meter, even though the two displacement vectors are in different directions.

Another example of a vector quantity is velocity, which is the rate of change (with time) of the vector quantity displacement. Since velocity is a vector, a velocity of 10 meters per second north is not the same as a velocity of 10 meters per second east. Both of these vector velocities have the same magnitude (called the *speed*) of 10 meters per second, but their directions are different, so these two velocities are not the same.

In printed matter, vectors are usually denoted by boldface letters. Thus **r** would be a displacement vector and **v** a velocity vector. In handwriting and in typed matter, one often underlines a vector (as in r and v) or puts an arrow over it (as in $\vec{r}$ and $\vec{v}$). In this book, vectors will be denoted by boldface letters. If **A** is a particular vector, then A (the same symbol in nonboldface type) stands for the scalar magnitude of the vector **A**; we will use this notation for scalars. In handwriting, the scalar magnitude of a vector **A** is usually denoted by A or $|\underline{A}|$.

It is useful to have a geometric method of representing vectors pictorially. A way of doing this is to represent a vector by an arrow whose point is in the direction of the vector and whose length is proportional to the magnitude of the vector. Suppose we want to represent a vector displacement of 20 meters in a straight line in the direction to the right. We choose a scale such that 1 centimeter of arrow length corresponds to a displacement of 10 meters, and draw an arrow 2 centimeters long with its point to the right. This arrow, shown in Fig. 5.1, represents a vector displacement of 20 meters in a straight line to the right. In representing

FIGURE 5.1
Representation of a vector displacement of 20 meters to the right by an arrow 2 centimeters long pointing in the direction to the right. The scale of 1 centimeter of arrow length indicates a displacement of 10 meters.

vectors in this way, it is important to state the scale being used, so that the magnitude of the vector is evident.

We can now consider the geometric addition of two vectors to form their sum. Suppose that the vector quantity we are considering is displacement, and consider two successive displacements, say, by a particle. In the first displacement, the particle moves 2 meters in the ($+x$) direction; in the second displacement, the particle moves 1 meter in the ($+y$) direction. Figure 5.2 shows these two displacement vectors, using a scale in which 1 centimeter equals 1 meter. The first displacement, from point A to point B, is represented by an arrow 2 centimeters long in the ($+x$) direction, which is taken to be to the right. The second displacement, from point B to point C, is represented by an arrow 1 centimeter long in the ($+y$) direction, which is taken as upward in the drawing. We denote the first displacement by $\mathbf{r}_1$ and the second by $\mathbf{r}_2$. The overall result of displacement $\mathbf{r}_1$ followed by displacement $\mathbf{r}_2$ is that the particle undergoes a vector displacement, which we call $\mathbf{r}$, from point A to point C. The vector displacement $\mathbf{r}$ is just the same as the vector displacement $\mathbf{r}_1$ plus the vector displacement $\mathbf{r}_2$. As an equation, this last statement is written

$$\mathbf{r} = \mathbf{r}_1 + \mathbf{r}_2 \tag{5.1}$$

Equation (5.1) says that the vector (displacement) $\mathbf{r}$ is equal to the sum of the vector (displacement) $\mathbf{r}_1$ plus the vector (displacement) $\mathbf{r}_2$. One also refers to the vector $\mathbf{r}$ as the resultant of the vectors $\mathbf{r}_1$ and $\mathbf{r}_2$. Physically, the displacement vector $\mathbf{r}$ is the resultant (or sum) of the successive displacements $\mathbf{r}_1$ and $\mathbf{r}_2$.

Since we know the scale in Fig. 5.2 (1 centimeter equals 1 meter of displacement) we can find the magnitude r of the vector $\mathbf{r}$ by measuring the length of the vector from A to C in the drawing. We find the length of $\mathbf{r}$ equal to 2.24 centimeters, so the displacement $\mathbf{r}$ has a magnitude r equal to 2.24 meters. Since ABC is a right triangle, the length of $\mathbf{r}$, which is the length of the hypotenuse AC, is equal to $(2^2 + 1^2)^{1/2}$, so $r = \sqrt{5} = 2.24$ centimeters, as above.

We can always find the sum of two vectors graphically, as was done

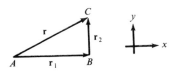

FIGURE 5.2
Geometric addition of displacement vectors $\mathbf{r}_1$ and $\mathbf{r}_2$ to give the sum $\mathbf{r}$. The scale in the drawing of 1 centimeter is equal to 1 meter of displacement.

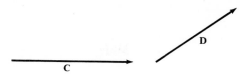

FIGURE 5.3
Two vectors, **C** and **D**, whose sum **E** = **C** + **D** we wish to find graphically.

in Fig. 5.2. Suppose, as shown in Fig. 5.3, we have two vectors (of unspecified meaning) **C** and **D**. We can find the sum **E** of the vectors **C** and **D**, given by

$$\mathbf{E} = \mathbf{C} + \mathbf{D} \tag{5.2}$$

as follows. As shown in Fig. 5.4, place the "tail" of the arrow representing D at the "tip" of the arrow representing **C**, and draw the sum vector **E** as shown. If the meaning and lengths of vectors **C** and **D** are known, we can measure the length of **E** to find its magnitude.

It should be emphasized that the sum of two vectors is itself also a vector. Thus the quantities above whose symbols were ($\mathbf{r}_1 + \mathbf{r}_2$) and (**C** + **D**), where the parentheses are used for emphasis, are themselves both vectors, to which we gave the symbols, respectively, **r** and **E**.

Next, we consider two vectors which are parallel, as shown in Fig. 5.5, in which the vector $\mathbf{v}_1$ has twice the magnitude (length) of vector $\mathbf{v}_2$. Two vectors, such as $\mathbf{v}_1$ and $\mathbf{v}_2$, which are parallel, are considered to be in the same direction. We can see geometrically from Fig. 5.5 that $\mathbf{v}_1$ is in the same direction as $\mathbf{v}_2$ and has twice the magnitude, so we write

$$\mathbf{v}_1 = 2\mathbf{v}_2 \tag{5.3}$$

Equation (5.3) says that the vector $\mathbf{v}_1$ is two times the vector $\mathbf{v}_2$, meaning that $\mathbf{v}_1$ and $\mathbf{v}_2$ are parallel and their magnitudes v_1 and v_2 are related by

$$v_1 = 2v_2 \tag{5.4}$$

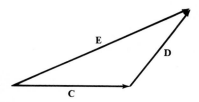

FIGURE 5.4
The vector **E** is the sum of the vectors **C** and **D**, which were shown in Fig. 5.3.

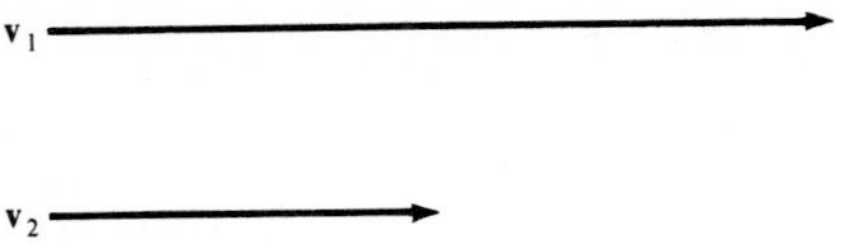

$\mathbf{v}_1$

$\mathbf{v}_2$ ————————▶

FIGURE 5.5
The vectors $\mathbf{v}_1$ and $\mathbf{v}_2$ are parallel and hence in the same direction. The magnitude v_1 of vector $\mathbf{v}_1$ is twice the magnitude v_2 of vector $\mathbf{v}_2$.

Our conclusion from Eq. (5.3) is that multiplying a vector (such as $\mathbf{v}_2$) by a positive constant (such as 2) produces a new vector (such as $\mathbf{v}_1$) in the same direction as (parallel to) the original vector.

In general, then, if vectors $\mathbf{A}$ and $\mathbf{B}$ are related by

$$\mathbf{B} = k\mathbf{A} \qquad (5.5)$$

where k is a positive constant (a scalar), then $\mathbf{B}$ and $\mathbf{A}$ are in the same direction (parallel) and their magnitudes are related by

$$B = kA \qquad (5.6)$$

so the magnitude B of $\mathbf{B}$ is k times the magnitude A of $\mathbf{A}$.

An interesting special case occurs when the constant $k = 1$. Then Eqs. (5.5) and (5.6) become

$$\mathbf{B} = \mathbf{A} \qquad (5.7)$$

and

$$B = A \qquad (5.8)$$

Equations (5.7) and (5.8) tell us that two parallel vectors of the same magnitude are identical or, in other words, are the same vector.

Another important special case occurs if the constant k in Eq. (5.5) is equal to (-1). Then Eq. (5.5) becomes

$$\mathbf{B} = -\mathbf{A} \qquad (5.9)$$

Equation (5.9) says that the vector $\mathbf{B}$ is the negative of the vector $\mathbf{A}$, which means that $\mathbf{B}$ has the same magnitude as $\mathbf{A}$ but is in the opposite direction. Figure 5.6 illustrates this. One also says that two vectors in opposite directions are antiparallel to each other.

We can use the concept of the negative of a vector to define the difference $(\mathbf{A} - \mathbf{B})$ of two vectors by the equation

$$(\mathbf{A} - \mathbf{B}) \equiv \mathbf{A} + (-\mathbf{B}) \qquad (5.10)$$

Equation (5.10) says that the vector $(\mathbf{A} - \mathbf{B})$ is equal to the sum of the vector $\mathbf{A}$ and the vector $(-\mathbf{B})$. As an example, consider the vectors $\mathbf{A}$

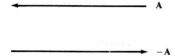

FIGURE 5.6
The vectors **A** and (−**A**) have the same magnitude but are in opposite or antiparallel directions.

and **B** shown in Fig. 5.7*a*, which also shows the vector (−**B**). To find the vector (**A** − **B**), as shown in Fig. 5.7*b*, we graphically add the vectors **A** and (−**B**). If a vector **C** is equal to the difference of two vectors **A** and **B**, we express this by the equation

$$\mathbf{C} = \mathbf{A} - \mathbf{B} \qquad (5.11)$$

an equation which also emphasizes the fact that the difference (**A** − **B**) of two vectors is itself also a vector.

Next, we define the components of a vector. We will consider vectors in a plane in which we will use the familiar *x* and *y* cartesian coordinate axes. (Plane-polar coordinates will be discussed later.) If a vector **C** can be expressed as the sum of two other vectors **A** and **B**, so that

$$\mathbf{C} = \mathbf{A} + \mathbf{B} \qquad (5.12)$$

then the vectors **A** and **B** are called the *components* of the vector **C**. It is often very useful to express a vector in terms of components which are perpendicular to each other. Figure 5.8 shows the cartesian coordinate axes and two vectors **A** and **B**. The vector **A** is in the (+*x*) direction and

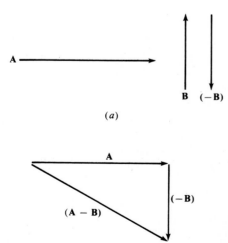

(*a*)

(*b*)

FIGURE 5.7
(*a*) The vectors **A**, **B**, and (−**B**). (*b*) To find the vector (**A** − **B**), add **A** and (−**B**) as shown.

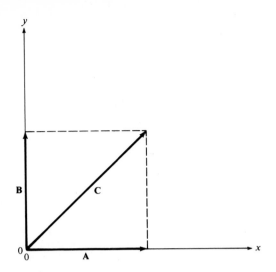

FIGURE 5.8
The vector $\mathbf{C} = (\mathbf{A} + \mathbf{B})$, where $\mathbf{A}$ is in the ($+x$) direction and $\mathbf{B}$ is in the ($+y$) direction. The vector $\mathbf{A}$ is the x component of $\mathbf{C}$, and the vector $\mathbf{B}$ is the y component of $\mathbf{C}$.

the vector $\mathbf{B}$ is in the ($+y$) direction, and the sum vector $\mathbf{C} = (\mathbf{A} + \mathbf{B})$ is also shown. We refer to the vector $\mathbf{A}$ as the x component of the vector $\mathbf{C}$ and the vector $\mathbf{B}$ as the y component of the vector $\mathbf{C}$. Components $\mathbf{A}$ and $\mathbf{B}$ such as these are often referred to as the *rectangular* or *cartesian* coordinates of the vector $\mathbf{C}$.

   In physics, one is often interested in the x and y components of some velocity vector $\mathbf{v}$. Then we would have

$$\mathbf{v} = \mathbf{v}_x + \mathbf{v}_y \qquad (5.13)$$

where $\mathbf{v}_x$ is the x component of the velocity vector $\mathbf{v}$ and $\mathbf{v}_y$ is the y component of the velocity vector $\mathbf{v}$. The geometric picture of Eq. (5.13) is shown in Fig. 5.9, which shows these vectors in the usual xy plane. Since $\mathbf{v}_x$ and $\mathbf{v}_y$ are perpendicular to each other, the vectors $\mathbf{v}$, $\mathbf{v}_x$, and $\mathbf{v}_y$ form a right triangle of which $\mathbf{v}$ is the hypotenuse. This means that the magnitudes v, v, and v_y are related, through the pythagorean theorem, by

$$v^2 = v_x^2 + v_y^2 \qquad (5.14)$$

or, equivalently, the magnitude v is given by

$$v = (v_x^2 + v_y^2)^{1/2} \qquad (5.15)$$

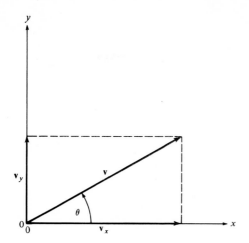

FIGURE 5.9
The velocity vector **v** is the sum of the x component $\mathbf{v}_x$ and the y component $\mathbf{v}_y$. Since $\mathbf{v}_y$ and $\mathbf{v}_x$ are perpendicular to each other, the magnitudes v, v_x, v_y of the three vectors are related by $v^2 = v_x^2 + v_y^2$, or, equivalently, $v = (v_x^2 + v_y^2)^{1/2}$. If θ is the angle between the vectors **v** and $\mathbf{v}_x$, then the magnitudes of the components are given by $v_x = v \cos \theta$ and $v_y = v \sin \theta$.

If θ is the angle between the vectors **v** and $\mathbf{v}_x$, as shown in Fig. 5.9, then elementary trigonometry tells us that

$$\frac{v_x}{v} = \cos \theta \qquad (5.16)$$

$$\frac{v_y}{v} = \sin \theta \qquad (5.17)$$

$$\frac{v_y}{v_x} = \tan \theta \qquad (5.18)$$

The first two of these useful relations are often seen written as

$$v_x = v \cos \theta \qquad (5.19)$$

$$v_y = v \sin \theta \qquad (5.20)$$

Equations (5.19) and (5.20) allow us to calculate the magnitudes v_x and v_y of the components $\mathbf{v}_x$ and $\mathbf{v}_y$ of the velocity vector **v** if we know the angle θ and the magnitude v of **v**.

Since acceleration is so important in mechanics, we often deal with the acceleration vector $\mathbf{a}$ and its x and y components $\mathbf{a}_x$ and $\mathbf{a}_y$, where

$$\mathbf{a} = \mathbf{a}_x + \mathbf{a}_y \tag{5.21}$$

Again, since $\mathbf{a}_x$ and $\mathbf{a}_y$ are perpendicular to each other, the relations derived for perpendicular velocity components hold for these acceleration components. For the magnitudes a, a_x, and a_y, one finds that

$$a^2 = a_x^2 + a_y^2 \tag{5.22}$$

$$a = (a_x^2 + a_y^2)^{1/2} \tag{5.23}$$

$$a_x = a \cos \theta \tag{5.24}$$

$$a_y = a \sin \theta \tag{5.25}$$

$$\frac{a_y}{a_x} = \tan \theta \tag{5.26}$$

where θ is the angle between the vectors $\mathbf{a}$ and $\mathbf{a}_x$. Equations (5.22) to (5.26) are the analogs for the acceleration vector of Eqs. (5.14), (5.15), (5.19), (5.20), and (5.18) for the velocity vector.

A useful theorem concerning the rectangular components of a vector is the following. Suppose two vectors $\mathbf{A}$ and $\mathbf{B}$ have rectangular components $\mathbf{A}_x$ and $\mathbf{A}_y$, and $\mathbf{B}_x$ and $\mathbf{B}_y$, so

$$\mathbf{A} = \mathbf{A}_x + \mathbf{A}_y \qquad \mathbf{B} = \mathbf{B}_x + \mathbf{B}_y \tag{5.27}$$

Then, if the vectors $\mathbf{A}$ and $\mathbf{B}$ are equal, so

$$\mathbf{A}_x + \mathbf{A}_y = \mathbf{B}_x + \mathbf{B}_y \tag{5.28}$$

then the respective components are equal, and

$$\mathbf{A}_x = \mathbf{B}_x \qquad \mathbf{A}_y = \mathbf{B}_y \tag{5.29}$$

This theorem may also be stated as follows. Two equal vectors have the same rectangular components.

EXERCISES

5.1. (a) Give an example of a vector quantity (in addition to displacement and velocity). Give the name of the scalar magnitude of this vector. Write symbols for this vector and for its scalar magnitude. (b) Give an example of a scalar quantity (in addition to time and temperature) that is not the magnitude of some vector.

5.2. Represent a vector velocity of 10 meters per second in the $(+y)$ direction by an arrow, analogous to Fig. 5.1. Define carefully your $(+y)$ direction in your drawing and give the scale used for speed.

5.3. Given two velocity vectors. The velocity v_1 has a magnitude of 4 meters per second and is in the ($+x$) direction. The velocity v_2 has a magnitude of 3 meters per second and is in the ($+y$) direction. (a) Using a graphical method, determine the magnitude v of the sum vector v, where $v = v_1 + v_2$. (b) From the drawing you made to answer part (a), measure (with a protractor) the angle made by the vector v with the ($+x$) axis. This angle specifies the direction of the vector v. Since both the magnitude and the direction of vector v are known, the vector v is now completely specified.

5.4. If A is a linear displacement of 5 meters in the positive y direction and B is a linear displacement of 2 meters in the negative x direction, determine graphically: (a) the vector $(A + B)$; (b) the vector $(A - B)$. Measure the lengths of the vectors to obtain magnitudes and measure the angles made with the positive x axis to obtain directions.

UNIT VECTORS IN RECTANGULAR COORDINATES

While the graphical construction of a sum of vectors is useful, it is not really practical for more than two or three vectors. An analytical method of representing and operating on vectors is necessary and useful. To do this, we introduce the idea of a unit vector. A unit vector is a vector of unit magnitude (length) in some direction. We will consider first unit vectors in rectangular (cartesian) coordinates and treat unit vectors in plane-polar coordinates later.

Consider the x and y axes shown in Fig. 5.10, where 0 is the origin. Also shown is a vector $\hat{x}$ (read "x caret" or "x hat") of unit magnitude and directed in the ($+x$) direction. The term "unit magnitude" means that the magnitude or length of the vector $\hat{x}$ is one unit along the direction in question, which, in Fig. 5.10, is the positive x axis. From Eq. (5.5), we know that multiplying a vector A by a positive scalar constant k yields a vector (kA) in the same direction as the vector A and with a magnitude k times the magnitude A of A. Using this idea, we see that multiplying the unit vector $\hat{x}$ by a positive scalar constant a gives a vector ($a\hat{x}$) parallel to $\hat{x}$ and with a magnitude a times as large as the magnitude of $\hat{x}$. Since the unit vector $\hat{x}$ has a magnitude of one unit, the vector ($a\hat{x}$) has a magnitude of a units and is in the same direction as $\hat{x}$, that is, along the ($+x$) axis, as also shown in Fig. 5.10. From these results, we can see that any vector A in the positive x direction can be represented as a multiple of the unit vector $\hat{x}$, so

$$A = A\hat{x} \tag{5.30}$$

where the vector A has a magnitude of A units. As an example, suppose a particle moves with a velocity v of magnitude 10 meters per second in

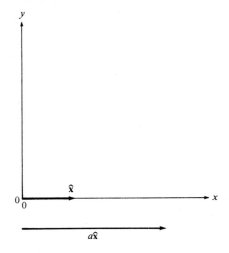

FIGURE 5.10
Rectangular x and y axes showing $\hat{\mathbf{x}}$, a vector of unit magnitude in the $(+x)$ direction. Also shown is a vector $(a\hat{\mathbf{x}})$, where a is a positive scalar constant, so the vector $(a\hat{\mathbf{x}})$ is also in the $(+x)$ direction.

the positive x direction. We represent $\mathbf{v}$ as 10 times the unit vector $\hat{\mathbf{x}}$, so

$$\mathbf{v} = 10\hat{\mathbf{x}} \tag{5.31}$$

The vector $\mathbf{v}$ in Eq. (5.31) has a magnitude of 10 meters per second (because $\mathbf{v}$ is a velocity) and the direction of $\mathbf{v}$ is in the $(+x)$ direction because the unit vector $\hat{\mathbf{x}}$ is in the $(+x)$ direction.

On multiplying the unit vector $\hat{\mathbf{x}}$ by (-1), we get a unit vector $(-\hat{\mathbf{x}})$ in the $(-x)$ direction. Thus a vector $\mathbf{B}$ of magnitude B in the $(-x)$ direction would be written

$$\mathbf{B} = B(-\hat{\mathbf{x}}) \tag{5.32}$$

or, equivalently,

$$\mathbf{B} = -B\hat{\mathbf{x}} \tag{5.33}$$

Both of the forms (5.32) and (5.33) for $\mathbf{B}$ mean the same thing: a vector of magnitude B (the magnitude of a vector is a positive quantity) in the $(-x)$ direction.

We can also define the unit vector $\hat{\mathbf{y}}$ in the positive y direction and $(-\hat{\mathbf{y}})$ in the negative y direction. These unit vectors can be used to express vectors along the positive or negative y axes. Thus the vector

$$\mathbf{C} = -C\hat{\mathbf{y}} \tag{5.34}$$

is a vector of magnitude C in the negative y direction. Thus a particle undergoing a displacement of 5 meters in the negative y direction would have a displacement vector

$$\mathbf{r} = -5\hat{\mathbf{y}} \tag{5.35}$$

The magnitude r of the displacement **r** is 5 meters, and the direction of **r** is in the $(-y)$ direction.

We can use the unit vectors $\hat{x}$ and $\hat{y}$ to express any vector in the xy plane. Suppose a vector **A** has an x component $\mathbf{A}_x$ and a y component $\mathbf{A}_y$, so

$$\mathbf{A} = \mathbf{A}_x + \mathbf{A}_y \tag{5.36}$$

Since the component vector $\mathbf{A}_x$ is along the x axis, we can write $\mathbf{A}_x$ as a multiple of the unit vector $\hat{x}$, as

$$\mathbf{A}_x = A_x\hat{x} \tag{5.37}$$

where A_x is the magnitude (a scalar) of the component vector $\mathbf{A}_x$. Similarly, the y component $\mathbf{A}_y$ can be written as

$$\mathbf{A}_y = A_y\hat{y} \tag{5.38}$$

where A_y is the (scalar) magnitude of the component vector $\mathbf{A}_y$. Using Eqs. (5.37) and (5.38), we can write **A** as

$$\mathbf{A} = A_x\hat{x} + A_y\hat{y} \tag{5.39}$$

thereby expressing the vector **A** in terms of the scalars A_x and A_y and the unit vectors $\hat{x}$ and $\hat{y}$. In Eq. (5.39), one refers to the vectors $(A_x\hat{x})$ and $(A_y\hat{y})$ as the components of the vector **A**. Unfortunately, one also refers to the scalars A_x and A_y as the components of the vector **A**. While not strictly correct, calling the scalars A_x and A_y the components of **A** is so common that one rarely hears objections. We will probably employ both usages so that the reader will become familiar with both.

Figure 5.11 shows the vector **A** and its vector components $(A_x\hat{x})$ and $(A_y\hat{y})$. Again, since the vector $(A_x\hat{x})$ is perpendicular to the vector $(A_y\hat{y})$, the magnitudes A, A_x, and A_y are related by the pythagorean theorem as

$$A^2 = A_x^2 + A_y^2 \tag{5.40}$$

Further, if θ is the angle between vector **A** and the positive x axis, trigonometry gives the results

$$\cos\theta = \frac{|A_x\hat{x}|}{|\mathbf{A}|} = \frac{A_x}{A} \tag{5.41}$$

where $|\mathbf{A}|$ is the magnitude A of **A**, and so on. Then from Eq. (5.41),

$$A_x = A\cos\theta \tag{5.42}$$

In the same way, one can show

$$A_y = A\sin\theta \tag{5.43}$$

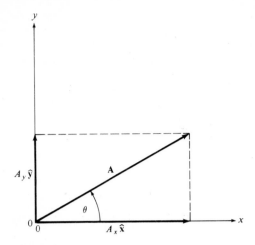

FIGURE 5.11
The vector $\mathbf{A} = A_x\hat{\mathbf{x}} + A_y\hat{\mathbf{y}}$ and its rectangular vector components $(A_x\hat{\mathbf{x}})$ and $(A_y\hat{\mathbf{y}})$. The magnitude of the vector $(A_x\hat{\mathbf{x}})$ is the scalar A_x and the magnitude of the vector $(A_y\hat{\mathbf{y}})$ is the scalar A_y. The angle θ is between $\mathbf{A}$ and the positive x axis (or, equivalently, between $\mathbf{A}$ and the unit vector $\hat{\mathbf{x}}$).

so Eqs. (5.42) and (5.43) allow calculation of the (scalar) components A_x and A_y from A and θ. Also,

$$\frac{A_y}{A_x} = \tan\theta \qquad (5.44)$$

obtained by dividing Eq. (5.43) by Eq. (5.42). Equation (5.44) allows us to calculate the angle θ between $\mathbf{A}$ and the positive x axis if we know A_x and A_y.

As a specific example, suppose that the x component of a certain velocity vector $\mathbf{v}$ is 4 meters per second and the y component is 3 meters per second. We can write $\mathbf{v}$ as

$$\mathbf{v} = v_x\hat{\mathbf{x}} + v_y\hat{\mathbf{y}} \qquad (5.45)$$

where, in this example, $v_x = 4$ meters per second and $v_y = 3$ meters per second. The vector $\mathbf{v}$ is thus

$$\mathbf{v} = 4\hat{\mathbf{x}} + 3\hat{\mathbf{y}} \qquad (5.46)$$

Using Eq. (5.44), we can calculate the angle θ between the vector $\mathbf{v}$ and the positive x axis as

$$\theta = \tan^{-1}\left(\frac{v_y}{v_x}\right) = \tan^{-1}(0.75) \cong 37°$$

so the vector **v** makes an angle of about $37°$ with the x axis and an angle of about $53°$ with the positive y axis.

In order to handle vectors in three dimensions, we need a third unit vector $\hat{\mathbf{z}}$, along the positive z direction. Then a general vector **A** in three dimensions is

$$\mathbf{A} = A_x\hat{\mathbf{x}} + A_y\hat{\mathbf{y}} + A_z\hat{\mathbf{z}} \tag{5.47}$$

where A_x, A_y, and A_z are, respectively, the (scalar) x, y, and z components of **A**.

Addition of vectors is easy to do when the vectors are expressed using unit vectors. Limiting ourselves to two dimensions (the xy plane) for the moment, suppose we have the vectors

$$\mathbf{A} = A_x\hat{\mathbf{x}} + A_y\hat{\mathbf{y}} \tag{5.48}$$

$$\mathbf{B} = B_x\hat{\mathbf{x}} + B_y\hat{\mathbf{y}} \tag{5.49}$$

where A_x, A_y, B_x, and B_y are the scalar components of **A** and **B**. Then the sum of **A** and **B** is

$$(\mathbf{A} + \mathbf{B}) = A_x\hat{\mathbf{x}} + A_y\hat{\mathbf{y}} + B_x\hat{\mathbf{x}} + B_y\hat{\mathbf{y}}$$

$$(\mathbf{A} + \mathbf{B}) = (A_x + B_x)\,\hat{\mathbf{x}} + (A_y + B_y)\,\hat{\mathbf{y}} \tag{5.50}$$

Equation (5.50) says that the sum vector $(\mathbf{A} + \mathbf{B})$ has a scalar x component equal to $(A_x + B_x)$ and a scalar y component equal to $(A_y + B_y)$. As a specific example, consider the vectors

$$\mathbf{A} = 3\hat{\mathbf{x}} - 4\hat{\mathbf{y}} \qquad \mathbf{B} = -4\hat{\mathbf{x}} + 2\hat{\mathbf{y}} \tag{5.51}$$

so the scalar components of **A** and **B** are $A_x = 3$, $A_y = (-4)$, $B_x = (-4)$, and $B_y = 2$. From Eq. (5.50), the sum

$$(\mathbf{A} + \mathbf{B}) = (3 - 4)\hat{\mathbf{x}} + (-4 + 2)\hat{\mathbf{y}} = -\hat{\mathbf{x}} - 2\hat{\mathbf{y}} \tag{5.52}$$

Equation (5.52) says that the sum vector $(\mathbf{A} + \mathbf{B})$ is a vector whose scalar x component is (-1) and whose scalar y component is (-2). Figure 5.12 shows the vectors **A**, **B**, and $(\mathbf{A} + \mathbf{B})$. If we denote the vector sum of **A** and **B** by **C**, so

$$\mathbf{C} = \mathbf{A} + \mathbf{B} \tag{5.53}$$

and write **C** in terms of its components as

$$\mathbf{C} = C_x\hat{\mathbf{x}} + C_y\hat{\mathbf{y}} \tag{5.54}$$

then, comparing Eq. (5.54) with Eq. (5.52) tells us that the scalar components of **C** are $C_x = (-1)$ and $C_y = (-2)$. This agrees with the values above for the scalar components of the vector $(\mathbf{A} + \mathbf{B})$, which, of course, is equal to the vector **C**.

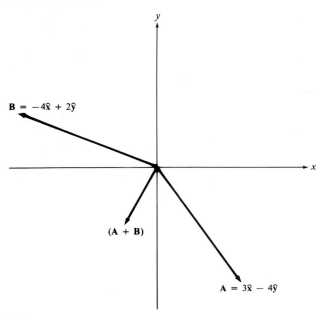

FIGURE 5.12
Vector $(\mathbf{A} + \mathbf{B}) = -\hat{x} - 2\hat{y}$ is the sum of vectors $\mathbf{A} = 3\hat{x} - 4\hat{y}$ and $\mathbf{B} = -4\hat{x} + 2\hat{y}$.

In physics books, one often sees the velocity vector $\mathbf{v}$ and the acceleration vector $\mathbf{a}$ written using unit vectors. From Eq. (5.45), we have

$$\mathbf{v} = v_x\hat{x} + v_y\hat{y} \tag{5.45}$$

and we may write the acceleration vector $\mathbf{a}$ given by Eq. (5.21) as

$$\mathbf{a} = a_x\hat{x} + a_y\hat{y} \tag{5.55}$$

From Eqs. (5.19) and (5.20), we have the scalar components v_x and v_y given by

$$v_x = v\cos\theta; \qquad v_y = v\sin\theta \tag{5.56}$$

where, as before, θ is the angle between the vector $\mathbf{v}$ and the positive x axis. Then Eq. (5.45) for $\mathbf{v}$ becomes

$$\mathbf{v} = (v\cos\theta)\hat{x} + (v\sin\theta)\hat{y} \tag{5.57}$$

Similarly, using Eqs. (5.24) and (5.25), respectively, for the scalar components a_x and a_y of the acceleration vector $\mathbf{a}$ gives, from Eq. (5.55), the expression

$$\mathbf{a} = (a\cos\theta)\hat{x} + (a\sin\theta)\hat{y} \tag{5.58}$$

where a is the magnitude of **a** and θ is the angle between the vector **a** and the positive x axis.

As an example, suppose a certain acceleration vector **a** has a magnitude of 10 meters per second per second and makes an angle of 30° with the positive x axis. We want to find the vector **a** in terms of unit vectors. Since the magnitude a = 10 meters per second per second, we have

$$a \cos \theta = (10)(\cos 30°) = 8.66 \text{ meters per second per second}$$

$$a \sin \theta = (10)(\sin 30°) = 5.00 \text{ meters per second per second}$$

From Eq. (5.58), then, the vector **a** is

$$\mathbf{a} = (8.66)\hat{\mathbf{x}} + (5.00)\hat{\mathbf{y}}$$

which is shown in Fig. 5.13, as are the vector components $\mathbf{a}_x = (8.66)\hat{\mathbf{x}}$ and $\mathbf{a}_y = (5.00)\hat{\mathbf{y}}$ and the angle $\theta = 30°$ between **a** and the positive x axis.

Now that we have unit vectors at our command, we can introduce the important position vector in cartesian coordinates. Consider, as shown in Fig. 5.14, the point P of coordinates (x, y) in the xy plane. The vector

$$\mathbf{r} \equiv x\hat{\mathbf{x}} + y\hat{\mathbf{y}} \tag{5.59}$$

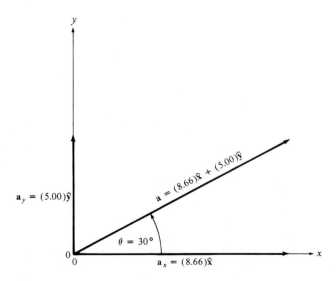

FIGURE 5.13
The acceleration vector $\mathbf{a} = (8.66)\hat{\mathbf{x}} + (5.00)\hat{\mathbf{y}}$. The vector components $\mathbf{a}_x = (8.66)\hat{\mathbf{x}}$ and $\mathbf{a}_y = (5.00)\hat{\mathbf{y}}$ are also shown, as is the angle $\theta = 30°$ between the vector **a** and the positive x axis.

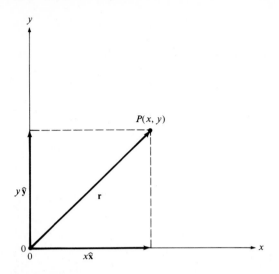

FIGURE 5.14
The position vector $\mathbf{r} \equiv x\hat{\mathbf{x}} + y\hat{\mathbf{y}}$ from the origin $(0, 0)$ to the point P of rectangular coordinates (x, y). The vector components of $\mathbf{r}$ are $x\hat{\mathbf{x}}$ and $y\hat{\mathbf{y}}$.

has (vector) components $x\hat{\mathbf{x}}$ and $y\hat{\mathbf{y}}$, where x and y are the coordinates of point P. As seen from Fig. 5.14, $\mathbf{r}$ is the vector from the origin $(0, 0)$ to the point (x, y) and is called the *position vector of point P*. In three dimensions, the position vector

$$\mathbf{r} \equiv x\hat{\mathbf{x}} + y\hat{\mathbf{y}} + z\hat{\mathbf{z}} \qquad (5.60)$$

is the vector from the origin $(0, 0, 0)$ to the point of coordinates (x, y, z). As an example, let us find the position vector $\mathbf{r}$ of the point whose coordinates in the xy plane are $(1, 1)$. Using Eq. (5.59), we have

$$\mathbf{r} = \hat{\mathbf{x}} + \hat{\mathbf{y}} \qquad (5.61)$$

as the position vector from the origin to the point $(1, 1)$.

EXERCISES

5.5. A vector $\mathbf{C}$ has a magnitude of 100 units and makes an angle of $(\pi/6)$ radian with the positive x axis. (a) Calculate the magnitudes C_x and C_y of its components along x and y axes. (b) Write the vector $\mathbf{C}$ in terms of rectangular coordinate unit vectors.

5.6. A certain velocity vector $\mathbf{v}$ makes an angle of $(\pi/4)$ radian with the positive x axis, and its magnitude (speed) v is 100 meters per second. (a) Calculate the magnitudes v_x and v_y of the rectangular components of $\mathbf{v}$. (b) Write the vector **v** in terms of the unit vectors $\hat{x}$ and $\hat{y}$. (c) As a check, show explicitly that $(v_x^2 + v_y^2)$ equals v^2.

5.7. Given the vectors $\mathbf{A} = 5\hat{x} + 3\hat{y}$ and $\mathbf{B} = -\hat{x} - 2\hat{y}$. Calculate (a) the vector $(\mathbf{A} + \mathbf{B})$; (b) the vector $(\mathbf{A} - \mathbf{B})$; (c) the sum of $(\mathbf{A} + \mathbf{B})$ and $(\mathbf{A} - \mathbf{B})$. (d) Draw the vectors $(\mathbf{A} + \mathbf{B})$ and $(\mathbf{A} - \mathbf{B})$.

5.8. Calculate the position vector **r** from the origin $(0, 0)$ to the point $(5, 4)$ in terms of the unit vectors $\hat{x}$ and $\hat{y}$.

SCALAR (DOT) PRODUCT OF TWO VECTORS

We now introduce the first of two different products of vectors. Given two vectors **A** and **B**, the *scalar product* of **A** and **B**, written $(\mathbf{A} \cdot \mathbf{B})$, is defined to be a scalar given by

$$\mathbf{A} \cdot \mathbf{B} = AB \cos \theta \qquad (5.62)$$

where A is the magnitude of **A**, B is the magnitude of **B**, and θ is the angle between the vectors **A** and **B**. Since A, B, and $\cos \theta$ are all scalars, the scalar product $(\mathbf{A} \cdot \mathbf{B})$ is also, from the definition (5.62), a scalar. [The name "dot product" for $(\mathbf{A} \cdot \mathbf{B})$ comes from the notation used.] Figure 5.15 illustrates the definition (5.62). If we consider the scalar

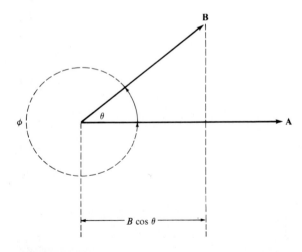

FIGURE 5.15
Diagram illustrating the definition of the scalar product $(\mathbf{A} \cdot \mathbf{B}) = AB \cos \theta$, where θ is the angle between **A** and **B**. The angle ϕ is the angle between **B** and **A**, and $(\theta + \phi) = 2\pi$ radians. The quantity $(B \cos \theta)$ is the scalar component of **B** in the direction of **A**; $(B \cos \theta)$ is also called the *projection of* **B** *on* **A**.

product ($\mathbf{B} \cdot \mathbf{A}$), the definition (5.62) gives

$$\mathbf{B} \cdot \mathbf{A} = BA \cos \phi \qquad (5.63)$$

where ϕ, shown in Fig. 5.15, is the angle between vector $\mathbf{B}$ and vector $\mathbf{A}$. From the figure, we can see that $(\theta + \phi) = 2\pi$ radians, so Eq. (5.63) becomes

$$\mathbf{B} \cdot \mathbf{A} = BA \cos (2\pi - \theta) = BA \cos \theta \qquad (5.64)$$

where we have used the fact [see Eq. (1.44)] that $\cos (2\pi - \theta) = \cos \theta$. Comparison of Eq. (5.64) with Eq. (5.62) shows that

$$\mathbf{A} \cdot \mathbf{B} = \mathbf{B} \cdot \mathbf{A} \qquad (5.65)$$

an equation which says that the scalar product is commutative.

An important use of the scalar product in physics is calculating the work W done by a force $\mathbf{F}$ in moving a body through a displacement $\mathbf{r}$. The work W is given by

$$W = \mathbf{F} \cdot \mathbf{r} = Fr \cos \theta \qquad (5.66)$$

where θ is the angle between the vectors $\mathbf{F}$ and $\mathbf{r}$. For example, if $\mathbf{F} = 10$ newtons, $\mathbf{r} = 5$ meters, and $\theta = 60°$, the work W done by the force $\mathbf{F}$ is given by

$$W = (10)(5)(\cos 60°) \text{ newton-meters} = 25 \text{ joules}$$

since 1 newton-meter equals 1 joule of work.

Returning to Fig. 5.15 showing the vectors $\mathbf{A}$ and $\mathbf{B}$, we see that the scalar component of vector $\mathbf{B}$ in the direction of vector $\mathbf{A}$ is equal to ($B \cos \theta$). [The quantity ($B \cos \theta$) is also called the *projection of* $\mathbf{B}$ *on* $\mathbf{A}$.] Using the definition (5.62) of the scalar product, we see that ($\mathbf{A} \cdot \mathbf{B}$) is equal to the magnitude A of $\mathbf{A}$ times the component ($B \cos \theta$) of vector $\mathbf{B}$ in the direction of vector $\mathbf{A}$. Applying this interpretation to the definition (5.66) of work, we see that the work W done by the force $\mathbf{F}$ is equal to the magnitude r of the displacement $\mathbf{r}$ times the component ($F \cos \theta$) of the force $\mathbf{F}$ in the direction of the displacement $\mathbf{r}$. This is another statement of the definition of the work W done by a force $\mathbf{F}$ in moving a body through a displacement $\mathbf{r}$.

From the definition (5.62), we see that if the vector $\mathbf{A}$ is normal (perpendicular) to the vector $\mathbf{B}$, then $\theta = 90°$, $\cos \theta = 0$, and the scalar product ($\mathbf{A} \cdot \mathbf{B}$) is equal to zero. Conversely, if the scalar product of two vectors vanishes, the two vectors are perpendicular to each other. We can use this result to find the scalar products of the various rectangular coordinate unit vectors with each other. Consider first the scalar product ($\hat{\mathbf{x}} \cdot \hat{\mathbf{x}}$), where

$$\hat{\mathbf{x}} \cdot \hat{\mathbf{x}} = |\hat{\mathbf{x}}||\hat{\mathbf{x}}| \cos 0 = 1 \qquad (5.67)$$

since the magnitude $|\hat{\mathbf{x}}|$ of $\hat{\mathbf{x}}$ is unity (1) and $\cos 0 = 1$. We conclude that the scalar product of any of the rectangular coordinate unit vectors with itself is unity, so we have

$$\hat{\mathbf{x}} \cdot \hat{\mathbf{x}} = \hat{\mathbf{y}} \cdot \hat{\mathbf{y}} = \hat{\mathbf{z}} \cdot \hat{\mathbf{z}} = 1 \qquad (5.68)$$

Considering scalar products such as $(\hat{\mathbf{x}} \cdot \hat{\mathbf{y}})$, we have

$$\hat{\mathbf{x}} \cdot \hat{\mathbf{y}} = |\hat{\mathbf{x}}||\hat{\mathbf{y}}| \cos 90° = 0 \qquad (5.69)$$

since the magnitudes $|\hat{\mathbf{x}}|$ of $\hat{\mathbf{x}}$ and $|\hat{\mathbf{y}}|$ of $\hat{\mathbf{y}}$ both equal unity, the angle θ between $\hat{\mathbf{x}}$ and $\hat{\mathbf{y}}$ is $90°$, and $\cos 90° = 0$. We conclude, recalling also that the scalar product is commutative, that

$$\begin{aligned} \hat{\mathbf{x}} \cdot \hat{\mathbf{y}} = 0 \qquad \hat{\mathbf{y}} \cdot \hat{\mathbf{z}} = 0 \qquad \hat{\mathbf{z}} \cdot \hat{\mathbf{x}} = 0 \\ \hat{\mathbf{y}} \cdot \hat{\mathbf{x}} = 0 \qquad \hat{\mathbf{z}} \cdot \hat{\mathbf{y}} = 0 \qquad \hat{\mathbf{x}} \cdot \hat{\mathbf{z}} = 0 \end{aligned} \qquad (5.70)$$

Thus the scalar product of any two different cartesian unit vectors vanishes because $\hat{\mathbf{x}}$, $\hat{\mathbf{y}}$, and $\hat{\mathbf{z}}$ are all mutually perpendicular.

We can use the results on the scalar products of unit vectors to obtain an additional expression for the scalar product. If

$$\mathbf{A} = A_x\hat{\mathbf{x}} + A_y\hat{\mathbf{y}} + A_z\hat{\mathbf{z}} \qquad \mathbf{B} = B_x\hat{\mathbf{x}} + B_y\hat{\mathbf{y}} + B_z\hat{\mathbf{z}} \qquad (5.71)$$

are two vectors, then

$$\mathbf{A} \cdot \mathbf{B} = (A_x\hat{\mathbf{x}} + A_y\hat{\mathbf{y}} + A_z\hat{\mathbf{z}}) \cdot (B_x\hat{\mathbf{x}} + B_y\hat{\mathbf{y}} + B_z\hat{\mathbf{z}}) \qquad (5.72)$$

Taking the various scalar products between terms in Eq. (5.72) gives

$$\begin{aligned} \mathbf{A} \cdot \mathbf{B} = {}&A_xB_x(\hat{\mathbf{x}} \cdot \hat{\mathbf{x}}) + A_xB_y(\hat{\mathbf{x}} \cdot \hat{\mathbf{y}}) + A_xB_z(\hat{\mathbf{x}} \cdot \hat{\mathbf{z}}) \\ &+ A_yB_x(\hat{\mathbf{y}} \cdot \hat{\mathbf{x}}) + A_yB_y(\hat{\mathbf{y}} \cdot \hat{\mathbf{y}}) + A_yB_z(\hat{\mathbf{y}} \cdot \hat{\mathbf{z}}) \\ &+ A_zB_x(\hat{\mathbf{z}} \cdot \hat{\mathbf{x}}) + A_zB_y(\hat{\mathbf{z}} \cdot \hat{\mathbf{y}}) + A_zB_z(\hat{\mathbf{z}} \cdot \hat{\mathbf{z}}) \end{aligned} \qquad (5.73)$$

Using the results (5.68) and (5.70), Eq. (5.73) becomes

$$\mathbf{A} \cdot \mathbf{B} = A_xB_x + A_yB_y + A_zB_z \qquad (5.74)$$

giving the scalar product $(\mathbf{A} \cdot \mathbf{B})$ in terms of the (scalar) components of $\mathbf{A}$ and $\mathbf{B}$.

As an example, suppose the vectors $\mathbf{A}$ and $\mathbf{B}$ are

$$\mathbf{A} = 5\hat{\mathbf{x}} + 4\hat{\mathbf{y}} \qquad \mathbf{B} = -\hat{\mathbf{x}} + 2\hat{\mathbf{y}}$$

so the components of $\mathbf{A}$ and $\mathbf{B}$ are $A_x = 5$, $A_y = 4$, $B_x = -1$, $B_y = 2$. Then, from Eq. (5.74),

$$\mathbf{A} \cdot \mathbf{B} = (5)(-1) + (4)(2) = 3$$

so the value of the scalar product of $\mathbf{A}$ and $\mathbf{B}$ is 3. Another example is

$\mathbf{A} = 6\hat{x}$ and $\mathbf{B} = 5\hat{y}$, so the components of $\mathbf{A}$ and $\mathbf{B}$ are $A_x = 6$, $A_y = 0$, $B_x = 0$, $B_y = 5$. Then from Eq. (5.74),

$$\mathbf{A} \cdot \mathbf{B} = (6)(0) + (0)(5) = 0$$

so $\mathbf{A}$ is perpendicular to $\mathbf{B}$ because their scalar product is zero.

As another example, let's redo the calculation of work done earlier. Suppose the displacement $\mathbf{r}$ of 10 meters is along the x axis. (Since this example specifies only the *relative* orientation of the vectors $\mathbf{F}$ and $\mathbf{r}$, we can place *one* of the vectors in any convenient direction and we choose $\mathbf{r}$ along the x axis.) Then the displacement vector

$$\mathbf{r} = 5\hat{x} \tag{5.75}$$

since $\mathbf{r}$ has a magnitude r of 5 (meters) and is in the positive x direction. We must now express $\mathbf{F}$ in terms of unit vectors; we assume that $\mathbf{F}$ lies in the xy plane, has a magnitude F of 10 (newtons), and makes an angle of $(\pi/3)$ radians $(60°)$ with the vector $\mathbf{r}$ and, hence, with the positive x axis. As shown in Fig. 5.16, the components of $\mathbf{F}$ along the x and y axes are

$$F_x = F \cos 60° = (10)(0.5) = 5.00 \tag{5.76}$$

$$F_y = F \sin 60° = (10)(0.866) = 8.66 \tag{5.77}$$

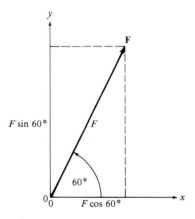

FIGURE 5.16
Components of the force vector $\mathbf{F}$, of magnitude $F = 10$ newtons, which makes an angle of 60° with the positive x axis. The component F_x along the x axis is $(F \cos 60°)$ and the component F_y along the y axis is $(F \sin 60°)$. Since $F = 10$ newtons, $F_x = 5$ newtons and $F_y = 8.66$ newtons, giving the expression (5.78) for the force vector $\mathbf{F}$.

so the vector **F** is given by

$$\mathbf{F} = (5.00)\hat{\mathbf{x}} + (8.66)\hat{\mathbf{y}} \tag{5.78}$$

Then, from the definition (5.66) of the work W done by the force **F**, we have

$$W = (\mathbf{F} \cdot \mathbf{r}) = \left[(5.00)\hat{\mathbf{x}} + (8.66)\hat{\mathbf{y}} \right] \cdot \left[5\hat{\mathbf{x}} \right] \tag{5.79}$$

$$W = (\mathbf{F} \cdot \mathbf{r}) = (5.00)(5)(\hat{\mathbf{x}} \cdot \hat{\mathbf{x}}) + (8.66)(5)(\hat{\mathbf{y}} \cdot \hat{\mathbf{x}}) \tag{5.80}$$

$$W = 25 \text{ joules}$$

since $(\hat{\mathbf{x}} \cdot \hat{\mathbf{x}}) = 1$ and $(\hat{\mathbf{y}} \cdot \hat{\mathbf{x}}) = 0$ in Eq. (5.80). We find that this solution, in terms of unit vectors, gives us the same answer for the work that was obtained earlier.

We can obtain a useful result by considering scalar product $(\mathbf{A} \cdot \mathbf{A})$ of any vector **A** with itself. For simplicity, we will consider first a vector **A** in the xy plane (two dimensions) and then generalize the result to three dimensions. If

$$\mathbf{A} = A_x\hat{\mathbf{x}} + A_y\hat{\mathbf{y}} \tag{5.81}$$

then

$$\mathbf{A} \cdot \mathbf{A} = (A_x\hat{\mathbf{x}} + A_y\hat{\mathbf{y}}) \cdot (A_x\hat{\mathbf{x}} + A_y\hat{\mathbf{y}}) \tag{5.82}$$

so

$$\mathbf{A} \cdot \mathbf{A} = A_x^2 + A_y^2 \tag{5.83}$$

on using the properties (5.68) and (5.70) of the cartesian unit vectors. We can see the significance of the quantity $(A_x^2 + A_y^2)$ by considering Fig. 5.17, which shows the vector **A** and its vector components $\mathbf{A}_x$ (of length A_x) and $\mathbf{A}_y$ (of length A_y) in the xy plane. From the pythagorean theorem, the magnitude A of vector **A** is given by

$$A^2 = A_x^2 + A_y^2 \tag{5.84}$$

by the pythagorean theorem. We see then that $(A_x^2 + A_y^2)$ equals A^2, the square of the magnitude A of the vector **A**. Combining Eqs. (5.84) and (5.83), we obtain

$$\mathbf{A} \cdot \mathbf{A} = A^2 \tag{5.85}$$

an equation which says that the scalar product of any vector with itself equals the square of the magnitude of the vector. Equivalently, the magnitude A is

$$A = (\mathbf{A} \cdot \mathbf{A})^{1/2} \tag{5.86}$$

The results (5.85) and (5.86) hold also in three dimensions.

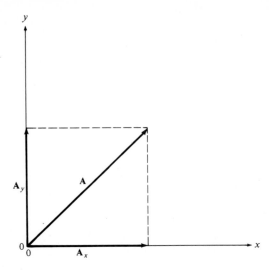

FIGURE 5.17
The vector $\mathbf{A} = \mathbf{A}_x + \mathbf{A}_y$ in the xy plane. The magnitudes A, A_x, and A_y are related by $A^2 = A_x^2 + A_y^2$ by the pythagorean theorem.

We can use these results to construct a unit vector in any direction we wish. Suppose

$$\mathbf{A} = A_x\hat{\mathbf{x}} + A_y\hat{\mathbf{y}} + A_z\hat{\mathbf{z}} \tag{5.87}$$

is a vector of magnitude A, where, from Eq. (5.85),

$$A^2 = (\mathbf{A} \cdot \mathbf{A}) = (A_x^2 + A_y^2 + A_z^2) \tag{5.88}$$

We will denote by $\hat{\mathbf{A}}$ a unit vector in the direction of $\mathbf{A}$, where

$$\hat{\mathbf{A}} \equiv \left(\frac{1}{A}\right)\mathbf{A} \tag{5.89}$$

We can see from Eq. (5.89) that $\hat{\mathbf{A}}$ is a vector which is the positive scalar constant $(1/A)$ times the vector $\mathbf{A}$, so $\hat{\mathbf{A}}$ is a vector parallel to $\mathbf{A}$. The magnitude $|\hat{\mathbf{A}}|$ of $\hat{\mathbf{A}}$ is given by Eqs. (5.85) and (5.89) as

$$|\hat{\mathbf{A}}|^2 = \hat{\mathbf{A}} \cdot \hat{\mathbf{A}} = \frac{1}{A^2}(\mathbf{A} \cdot \mathbf{A}) = \frac{A^2}{A^2} = 1 \tag{5.90}$$

so $\hat{\mathbf{A}}$ is a vector of unit magnitude. We conclude that $\hat{\mathbf{A}}$ given by Eq. (5.89) is a unit vector parallel to the vector $\mathbf{A}$.

As an example, consider the vector

$$\mathbf{r} = \hat{\mathbf{x}} + \hat{\mathbf{y}} \tag{5.61}$$

given by Eq. (5.61) as the position vector from the origin to the point (1, 1). We want to find the unit vector $\hat{\mathbf{r}}$ parallel to $\mathbf{r}$. From Eq. (5.89),

$$\hat{\mathbf{r}} = \frac{1}{r}\,\mathbf{r} \tag{5.91}$$

where the magnitude r of $\mathbf{r}$ is given by Eq. (5.86) as

$$r = (\mathbf{r} \cdot \mathbf{r})^{1/2} = (1^2 + 1^2)^{1/2} = \sqrt{2} \tag{5.92}$$

Therefore, the unit vector $\hat{\mathbf{r}}$ we desire is, from Eq. (5.91),

$$\hat{\mathbf{r}} = \left(\frac{1}{\sqrt{2}}\right)(\hat{\mathbf{x}} + \hat{\mathbf{y}}) \tag{5.93}$$

We can see that the magnitude $|\hat{\mathbf{r}}|$ of $\hat{\mathbf{r}}$ is unity since

$$|\hat{\mathbf{r}}|^2 = \hat{\mathbf{r}} \cdot \hat{\mathbf{r}} = \tfrac{1}{2}(\hat{\mathbf{x}} + \hat{\mathbf{y}}) \cdot (\hat{\mathbf{x}} + \hat{\mathbf{y}}) = \tfrac{1}{2}(1 + 1) = 1$$

so $|\hat{\mathbf{r}}| = 1$, and $\hat{\mathbf{r}}$ is of unit length. We can also check to be sure $\hat{\mathbf{r}}$ is parallel to $\mathbf{r}$ by calculating the angle θ between $\hat{\mathbf{r}}$ and $\mathbf{r}$. If $\hat{\mathbf{r}}$ and $\mathbf{r}$ are parallel, the angle θ will be zero. From the definition (5.62) of the scalar product,

$$\hat{\mathbf{r}} \cdot \mathbf{r} = |\hat{\mathbf{r}}|\, r \cos\theta \tag{5.94}$$

so we can find θ by evaluating the scalar product $(\hat{\mathbf{r}} \cdot \mathbf{r})$. Using Eqs. (5.61) and (5.93), we have

$$\hat{\mathbf{r}} \cdot \mathbf{r} = \left(\frac{1}{\sqrt{2}}\right)(\hat{\mathbf{x}} + \hat{\mathbf{y}}) \cdot (\hat{\mathbf{x}} + \hat{\mathbf{y}}) = \left(\frac{1}{\sqrt{2}}\right)(1 + 1) = \sqrt{2}$$

and also, from Eq. (5.92), $r = \sqrt{2}$, so Eq. (5.94) gives us, with $|\hat{\mathbf{r}}| = 1$,

$$\sqrt{2} = (1)(\sqrt{2})\cos\theta$$

so $\cos\theta = 1$ and $\theta = 0$. We conclude that the vectors $\hat{\mathbf{r}}$ and $\mathbf{r}$ are, indeed, parallel.

EXERCISES

5.9. Given the vectors $\mathbf{A} = \hat{\mathbf{x}} + \hat{\mathbf{y}}$ and $\mathbf{B} = \hat{\mathbf{x}} - \hat{\mathbf{y}}$. (a) Calculate $(\mathbf{A} \cdot \mathbf{B})$. (b) Use your answer to (a) to find the angle ϕ between the vectors $\mathbf{A}$ and $\mathbf{B}$. (c) Draw the vectors $\mathbf{A}$ and $\mathbf{B}$ and verify that your answer to part (b) is correct.

5.10. A force $\mathbf{F} = 10\hat{\mathbf{x}} + 5\hat{\mathbf{y}}$ moves a particle from the origin $(0, 0)$ to the point $(10, 0)$ along the x axis. (All distances are in meters, and forces are in newtons.) Calculate the work done by this force on the particle.

5.11. Calculate the magnitude a of the three-dimensional acceleration vector $\mathbf{a} = 3\hat{\mathbf{x}} + 2\hat{\mathbf{y}} + \hat{\mathbf{z}}$.

5.12. Given the vector $\mathbf{A} = \hat{\mathbf{x}} + \hat{\mathbf{y}}$, (a) find a unit vector $\hat{\mathbf{A}}$ in the direction of $\mathbf{A}$. (b) Make a drawing showing $\mathbf{A}$ and $\hat{\mathbf{A}}$. (c) Show explicitly that $\mathbf{A} \cdot \hat{\mathbf{A}} = A$.

5.13. Consider a plane in space and let point O be an origin not lying in the plane. Let $\mathbf{N}$ be the normal to the plane drawn from point O and $\mathbf{R}$ be the vector from O to any point on the plane. Show that the equation of the plane is $(\mathbf{R} \cdot \mathbf{N}) = N^2$.

UNIT VECTORS IN PLANE-POLAR COORDINATES

So far we have been discussing vectors only in rectangular or cartesian coordinates. Plane-polar coordinates (r, θ), discussed in Chap. 2, are very useful in physics, particularly for discussing the motion of a particle in a circular orbit in a plane. We want to be able to use vectors in plane-polar coordinates, so we need an appropriate set of unit vectors.

We recall the relations between rectangular coordinates (x, y) in two dimensions and plane-polar coordinates (r, θ) as

$$x = r \cos \theta \tag{5.95}$$

$$y = r \sin \theta \tag{5.96}$$

Then the two-dimensional position vector $\mathbf{r}$ from the origin to a point (x, y), given by Eq. (5.59) as

$$\mathbf{r} = x\hat{\mathbf{x}} + y\hat{\mathbf{y}} \tag{5.59}$$

can be written as

$$\mathbf{r} = (r \cos \theta)\hat{\mathbf{x}} + (r \sin \theta)\hat{\mathbf{y}} \tag{5.97}$$

$$\mathbf{r} = r[(\cos \theta)\hat{\mathbf{x}} + (\sin \theta)\hat{\mathbf{y}}] \tag{5.98}$$

The vector $\mathbf{r}$, given by either Eq. (5.97) or Eq. (5.98), is the position vector of the point whose rectangular coordinates are (x, y) and whose plane-polar coordinates are (r, θ), where from Eqs. (5.95) and (5.96), r and θ are related to x and y by

$$r = (x^2 + y^2)^{1/2} \tag{5.99}$$

$$\theta = \tan^{-1}\left(\frac{y}{x}\right) \tag{5.100}$$

Equations (5.99) and (5.100) give (r, θ) in terms of (x, y), so we can calculate the plane-polar coordinates (r, θ) of a point if we know its cartesian coordinates (x, y).

Using Eq. (5.89), we can find a unit vector $\hat{\mathbf{u}}_r$ in the direction of the position vector $\mathbf{r}$ as

$$\hat{\mathbf{u}}_r = \frac{1}{r}\mathbf{r} = (\cos\theta)\hat{\mathbf{x}} + (\sin\theta)\hat{\mathbf{y}} \qquad (5.101)$$

on using the expression (5.98) for the vector $\mathbf{r}$. Equation (5.101) is the unit vector $\hat{\mathbf{u}}_r$ in the direction of $\mathbf{r}$, so the vector $\hat{\mathbf{u}}_r$ varies with the angle θ made by the vector $\mathbf{r}$ with the positive x axis. Figure 5.18 shows $\mathbf{r}$, θ, and $\hat{\mathbf{u}}_r$ for one particular value of θ. The vector $\hat{\mathbf{u}}_r$ is called the *unit vector in the direction of increasing r*, as also seen in Fig. 5.18.

We can prove, using the scalar product, that $\hat{\mathbf{u}}_r$ is parallel to $\mathbf{r}$ and that the magnitude $|\hat{\mathbf{u}}_r| = 1$. First, we have

$$\left|\hat{\mathbf{u}}_r\right|^2 = \hat{\mathbf{u}}_r \cdot \hat{\mathbf{u}}_r = [\cos^2\theta](\hat{\mathbf{x}}\cdot\hat{\mathbf{x}}) + [\sin^2\theta](\hat{\mathbf{y}}\cdot\hat{\mathbf{y}}) = 1 \qquad (5.102)$$

so, since $[\sin^2\theta + \cos^2\theta] = 1$, $|\hat{\mathbf{u}}_r| = 1$. Second,

$$\hat{\mathbf{u}}_r \cdot \mathbf{r} = \left|\hat{\mathbf{u}}_r\right| r \cos\phi = r\cos\phi \qquad (5.103)$$

where ϕ is the angle between $\hat{\mathbf{u}}_r$ and $\mathbf{r}$. Then, from Eqs. (5.101) and (5.98), we have

$$\hat{\mathbf{u}}_r \cdot \mathbf{r} = \left[(\cos\theta)\hat{\mathbf{x}} + (\sin\theta)\hat{\mathbf{y}}\right]\cdot r\left[(\cos\theta)\hat{\mathbf{x}} + (\sin\theta)\hat{\mathbf{y}}\right]$$

$$\hat{\mathbf{u}}_r \cdot \mathbf{r} = r(\cos^2\theta + \sin^2\theta) = r \qquad (5.104)$$

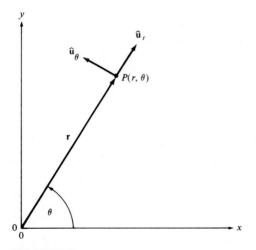

FIGURE 5.18
Position vector $\mathbf{r}$ of point P whose plane-polar coordinates are (r, θ). The unit vector $\hat{\mathbf{u}}_r = (\cos\theta)\hat{\mathbf{x}} + (\sin\theta)\hat{\mathbf{y}}$. The unit vector $\hat{\mathbf{u}}_\theta = (-\sin\theta)\hat{\mathbf{x}} + (\cos\theta)\hat{\mathbf{y}}$ is normal to $\hat{\mathbf{u}}_r$. The magnitudes $|\hat{\mathbf{u}}_r|$ and $|\hat{\mathbf{u}}_\theta|$ are constant with the value unity as the angle θ changes, but the directions of $\hat{\mathbf{u}}_r$ and $\hat{\mathbf{u}}_\theta$ change as θ varies.

Comparing (5.104) and (5.103) gives

$$\cos \phi = 1$$

so $\phi = 0$, meaning $\hat{\mathbf{u}}_r$ and $\mathbf{r}$ are parallel.

Next, we need a second unit vector. Although it is not an immediately obvious choice, we will choose the vector $\hat{\mathbf{u}}_\theta$ defined by the equation

$$\hat{\mathbf{u}}_\theta \equiv (-\sin \theta)\hat{\mathbf{x}} + (\cos \theta)\hat{\mathbf{y}} \qquad (5.105)$$

We will now investigate the properties of $\hat{\mathbf{u}}_\theta$ and will find that it is a vector of unit magnitude which is normal to the unit vector $\hat{\mathbf{u}}_r$. To find the magnitude $|\hat{\mathbf{u}}_\theta|$, we calculate

$$|\hat{\mathbf{u}}_\theta|^2 = \hat{\mathbf{u}}_\theta \cdot \hat{\mathbf{u}}_\theta = \sin^2 \theta + \cos^2 \theta = 1$$

so we have $|\hat{\mathbf{u}}_\theta| = 1$, and $\hat{\mathbf{u}}_\theta$ is a unit vector. Next we examine the scalar product

$$\hat{\mathbf{u}}_r \cdot \hat{\mathbf{u}}_\theta = \left[(\cos \theta)\hat{\mathbf{x}} + (\sin \theta)\hat{\mathbf{y}}\right] \cdot \left[(-\sin \theta)\hat{\mathbf{x}} + (\cos \theta)\hat{\mathbf{y}}\right]$$

$$\hat{\mathbf{u}}_r \cdot \hat{\mathbf{u}}_\theta = (-\cos \theta \sin \theta + \sin \theta \cos \theta) = 0 \qquad (5.106)$$

Equation (5.106) says that the scalar product of $\hat{\mathbf{u}}_\theta$ and $\hat{\mathbf{u}}_r$ vanishes, so $\hat{\mathbf{u}}_\theta$ is perpendicular to $\hat{\mathbf{u}}_r$, directed as shown in Fig. 5.18. We say that $\hat{\mathbf{u}}_\theta$ is the *unit vector in the direction of increasing angle θ*.

From the defining Eqs. (5.101) and (5.105), we see that $\hat{\mathbf{u}}_r$ and $\hat{\mathbf{u}}_\theta$ are functions of θ, which we emphasize by rewriting those equations as

$$\hat{\mathbf{u}}_r(\theta) = (\cos \theta)\hat{\mathbf{x}} + (\sin \theta)\hat{\mathbf{y}} \qquad (5.107)$$

$$\hat{\mathbf{u}}_\theta(\theta) = (-\sin \theta)\hat{\mathbf{x}} + (\cos \theta)\hat{\mathbf{y}} \qquad (5.108)$$

The last two equations emphasize the fact that $\hat{\mathbf{u}}_r(\theta)$ and $\hat{\mathbf{u}}_\theta(\theta)$ vary as θ changes. This means that the directions of the vectors $\hat{\mathbf{u}}_r$ and $\hat{\mathbf{u}}_\theta$ change with θ even though the magnitudes $|\hat{\mathbf{u}}_r|$ and $|\hat{\mathbf{u}}_\theta|$ are constant and equal to unity.

As an example, let's calculate $\hat{\mathbf{u}}_r(\theta)$ and $\hat{\mathbf{u}}_\theta(\theta)$ for some values of θ. First, let $\theta = 0$, so Eqs. (5.107) and (5.108) give

$$\hat{\mathbf{u}}_r(0) = (\cos 0)\hat{\mathbf{x}} + (\sin 0)\hat{\mathbf{y}} = \hat{\mathbf{x}} \qquad (5.109)$$

$$\hat{\mathbf{u}}_\theta(0) = (-\sin 0)\hat{\mathbf{x}} + (\cos 0)\hat{\mathbf{y}} = \hat{\mathbf{y}} \qquad (5.110)$$

Equations (5.109) and (5.110) say that, when $\theta = 0$, $\hat{\mathbf{u}}_r = \hat{\mathbf{x}}$ and $\hat{\mathbf{u}}_\theta = \hat{\mathbf{y}}$. Thus, when $\theta = 0$, the unit vector $\hat{\mathbf{u}}_r$ in the direction of increasing r is a unit vector in the positive x direction, and the unit vector $\hat{\mathbf{u}}_\theta$ in the direction of increasing θ is a unit vector in the positive y direction. Figure 5.19 shows $\hat{\mathbf{u}}_r(0) = \hat{\mathbf{x}}$ and $\hat{\mathbf{u}}_\theta(0) = \hat{\mathbf{y}}$. (Note that this example shows

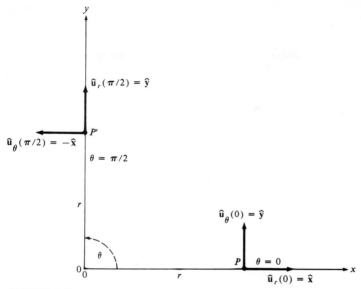

FIGURE 5.19

The unit vectors $\hat{\mathbf{u}}_r(0) = \hat{\mathbf{x}}$ and $\hat{\mathbf{u}}_\theta(0) = \hat{\mathbf{y}}$, when $\theta = 0$. These unit vectors are shown at a point P a distance r from the origin, at cartesian coordinates $(r, 0)$ and plane-polar coordinates $(r, 0)$. Also shown are $\hat{\mathbf{u}}_r(\pi/2) = \hat{\mathbf{y}}$ and $\hat{\mathbf{u}}_\theta(\pi/2) = (-\hat{\mathbf{x}})$, when $\theta = \pi/2$, at the point P' of cartesian coordinates $(0, r)$ and plane-polar coordinates $(r, \pi/2)$.

that the relative orientation of $\hat{\mathbf{u}}_\theta$ and $\hat{\mathbf{u}}_r$ is as shown in Fig. 5.18, and not the other possibility, in which $\hat{\mathbf{u}}_\theta$ would have the opposite direction but would still be normal to $\hat{\mathbf{u}}_r$.)

Continuing this example, we will calculate $\hat{\mathbf{u}}_r(\theta)$ and $\hat{\mathbf{u}}_\theta(\theta)$ when $\theta = (\pi/2)$ radians $= 90°$. From Eqs. (5.107) and (5.108), we have

$$\hat{\mathbf{u}}_r\left(\frac{\pi}{2}\right) = \left[\cos\left(\frac{\pi}{2}\right)\right]\hat{\mathbf{x}} + \left[\sin\left(\frac{\pi}{2}\right)\right]\hat{\mathbf{y}} = \hat{\mathbf{y}} \qquad (5.111)$$

$$\hat{\mathbf{u}}_\theta\left(\frac{\pi}{2}\right) = \left[-\sin\left(\frac{\pi}{2}\right)\right]\hat{\mathbf{x}} + \left[\cos\left(\frac{\pi}{2}\right)\right]\hat{\mathbf{y}} = -\hat{\mathbf{x}} \qquad (5.112)$$

Equations (5.111) and (5.112) say that when $\theta = \pi/2$ radians, $\hat{\mathbf{u}}_r = \hat{\mathbf{y}}$ and $\hat{\mathbf{u}}_\theta = -\hat{\mathbf{x}}$. Thus, when $\theta = \pi/2$, the unit vector $\hat{\mathbf{u}}_r$ in the direction of increasing r is a unit vector in the positive y direction, and the unit vector $\hat{\mathbf{u}}_\theta$ in the direction of increasing θ is a unit vector in the negative x direction. Figure 5.19 also shows $\hat{\mathbf{u}}_r(\pi/2) = \hat{\mathbf{y}}$ and $\hat{\mathbf{u}}_\theta(\pi/2) = -\hat{\mathbf{x}}$.

From this example we see that the unit vectors $\hat{\mathbf{u}}_r$ and $\hat{\mathbf{u}}_\theta$ in plane-polar coordinates vary as the angle θ changes. The magnitudes $|\hat{\mathbf{u}}_r|$ and $|\hat{\mathbf{u}}_\theta|$ remain constant at the value unity for all values of θ.

An important use of these unit vectors in physics is in the description of plane circular motion of a particle. However, we can also use the unit vector $\hat{\mathbf{u}}_r$ to write the two-dimensional position vector

$$\mathbf{r} = x\hat{\mathbf{x}} + y\hat{\mathbf{y}} \tag{5.113}$$

in terms of $\hat{\mathbf{u}}_r$. From Eqs. (5.95) and (5.96), we have

$$\mathbf{r} = (r\cos\theta)\hat{\mathbf{x}} + (r\sin\theta)\hat{\mathbf{y}} = r\left[(\cos\theta)\hat{\mathbf{x}} + (\sin\theta)\hat{\mathbf{y}}\right] \tag{5.114}$$

so

$$\mathbf{r} = r\hat{\mathbf{u}}_r \tag{5.115}$$

Equation (5.115) says that $\mathbf{r}$ is a vector of length r in the direction of the unit vector $\hat{\mathbf{u}}_r$, that is, in the direction of increasing r.

EXERCISES

5.14. A certain particle, of mass m, is moving in a plane circular orbit of radius R. The centripetal force exerted on the particle is $\mathbf{F}$ and its centripetal acceleration is of magnitude a. (a) Write down an expression for $\mathbf{F}$ in terms of m, a, and the unit vector $\hat{\mathbf{u}}_r$. (b) Write $\mathbf{F}$ in terms of the cartesian unit vectors $\hat{\mathbf{x}}$ and $\hat{\mathbf{y}}$ and the angle θ of plane-polar coordinates. (c) Write the position vector $\mathbf{r}$ of the particle relative to the center of the circular orbit.

5.15. In Exercise 5.14, assume that the particle moves so that its tangential velocity $\mathbf{v}$ has a constant magnitude v. The vector $\mathbf{v}$ is always tangent to the circular orbit of the particle. (a) Draw a sketch showing the orbit and the vector $\mathbf{v}$. (b) Write down an expression for $\mathbf{v}$ in terms of the unit vector $\mathbf{u}_\theta$. (c) Write an expression for $\mathbf{v}$ in terms of $\hat{\mathbf{x}}$, $\hat{\mathbf{y}}$, and the angle θ of plane-polar coordinates. (d) Write down a unit vector $\hat{\mathbf{v}}$ in the direction of the tangential velocity $\mathbf{v}$.

VECTOR (CROSS) PRODUCT OF TWO VECTORS

In Eq. (5.62), the scalar product of two vectors $(\mathbf{A} \cdot \mathbf{B})$ of vectors $\mathbf{A}$ and $\mathbf{B}$ was defined; the result of the product was a scalar. A second type of product of two vectors $\mathbf{A}$ and $\mathbf{B}$ is called the *vector product* or the *cross product*, written $(\mathbf{A} \times \mathbf{B})$ and defined as follows. The product $(\mathbf{A} \times \mathbf{B})$ is a vector and has a magnitude

$$\left|\mathbf{A} \times \mathbf{B}\right| \equiv AB\sin\theta \tag{5.116}$$

where θ is the angle (not larger than $180°$) between $\mathbf{A}$ and $\mathbf{B}$. Thus the magnitude of the vector $(\mathbf{A} \times \mathbf{B})$ is equal to the magnitude A of $\mathbf{A}$ times the magnitude B of $\mathbf{B}$ times the sine of the angle between them. The direction of the vector $(\mathbf{A} \times \mathbf{B})$ is perpendicular to both $\mathbf{A}$ and $\mathbf{B}$ and is oriented so that $(\mathbf{A} \times \mathbf{B})$ is in the direction in which a right-handed screw advances when vector $\mathbf{A}$ is rotated into $\mathbf{B}$, as shown in Fig. 5.20.

Unlike the scalar product, the vector product of $\mathbf{A}$ and $\mathbf{B}$ does not commute, so $(\mathbf{A} \times \mathbf{B})$ is not equal to $(\mathbf{B} \times \mathbf{A})$. It can be proved from the definition (5.116), on interchanging $\mathbf{B}$ and $\mathbf{A}$, that

$$(\mathbf{B} \times \mathbf{A}) = -(\mathbf{A} \times \mathbf{B}) \qquad (5.117)$$

Equation (5.117) says that the vector $(\mathbf{B} \times \mathbf{A})$ is the negative of the vector $(\mathbf{A} \times \mathbf{B})$, so $(\mathbf{B} \times \mathbf{A})$ has the same magnitude as $(\mathbf{A} \times \mathbf{B})$ but is opposite (antiparallel) in direction. The vector $(\mathbf{B} \times \mathbf{A})$ is also shown in Fig. 5.20.

Next we consider the cross products of the cartesian unit vectors with each other; the results will be used to evaluate the cross product of two vectors expressed in terms of the unit vectors. From the definition (5.116), we can see that

$$\hat{\mathbf{x}} \times \hat{\mathbf{x}} = |\hat{\mathbf{x}}||\hat{\mathbf{x}}| \sin 0 = 0 \qquad (5.118)$$

and the same is true for $\hat{\mathbf{y}}$ and $\hat{\mathbf{z}}$. Thus we conclude

$$(\hat{\mathbf{x}} \times \hat{\mathbf{x}}) = \mathbf{0} \qquad (\hat{\mathbf{y}} \times \hat{\mathbf{y}}) = \mathbf{0} \qquad (\hat{\mathbf{z}} \times \hat{\mathbf{z}}) = \mathbf{0} \qquad (5.119)$$

where $\mathbf{0}$ is the zero vector, all of whose components are zero. [We will usually simply write $(\hat{\mathbf{z}} \times \hat{\mathbf{z}}) = 0$, and so on.] Considering next $(\hat{\mathbf{x}} \times \hat{\mathbf{y}})$ and applying the definition (5.116), we have

$$|\hat{\mathbf{x}} \times \hat{\mathbf{y}}| = |\hat{\mathbf{x}}||\hat{\mathbf{y}}| \sin 90° = 1 \qquad (5.120)$$

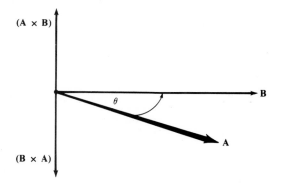

FIGURE 5.20
The vector $(\mathbf{A} \times \mathbf{B})$ is directed in the direction in which a right-handed screw would advance when $\mathbf{A}$ is rotated into $\mathbf{B}$ as shown. The angle θ is not larger than $180°$, the magnitude $|\mathbf{A} \times \mathbf{B}| = AB \sin \theta$, and the vector $(\mathbf{A} \times \mathbf{B})$ is perpendicular to both vectors $\mathbf{A}$ and $\mathbf{B}$. The vector $(\mathbf{B} \times \mathbf{A})$, which equals $-(\mathbf{A} \times \mathbf{B})$, is also shown.

so ($\hat{\mathbf{x}} \times \hat{\mathbf{y}}$) is a unit vector, of magnitude unity. To find the direction of the vector ($\hat{\mathbf{x}} \times \hat{\mathbf{y}}$), we see that it is perpendicular to both $\hat{\mathbf{x}}$ and $\hat{\mathbf{y}}$, so ($\hat{\mathbf{x}} \times \hat{\mathbf{y}}$) must be directed along either the positive or negative z axis. Using the right-handed coordinate system in Fig. 5.21 (which is common in physics) showing the positive x, y, and z axes, we compare Fig. 5.21 with Fig. 5.20, and conclude that the vector ($\hat{\mathbf{x}} \times \hat{\mathbf{y}}$) is along the positive z axis. Since ($\hat{\mathbf{x}} \times \hat{\mathbf{y}}$) is a unit vector in the positive z direction, we conclude that

$$(\hat{\mathbf{x}} \times \hat{\mathbf{y}}) = \hat{\mathbf{z}} \qquad (5.121)$$

and also

$$(\hat{\mathbf{y}} \times \hat{\mathbf{x}}) = -\hat{\mathbf{z}} \qquad (5.122)$$

In a similar way, one can show that

$$(\hat{\mathbf{y}} \times \hat{\mathbf{z}}) = \hat{\mathbf{x}} \qquad (\hat{\mathbf{z}} \times \hat{\mathbf{y}}) = -\hat{\mathbf{x}} \qquad (5.123)$$

$$(\hat{\mathbf{z}} \times \hat{\mathbf{x}}) = \hat{\mathbf{y}} \qquad (\hat{\mathbf{x}} \times \hat{\mathbf{z}}) = -\hat{\mathbf{y}} \qquad (5.124)$$

completing the relations between cross products of the cartesian unit vectors.

The results (5.120) to (5.123) can be employed to find the cross

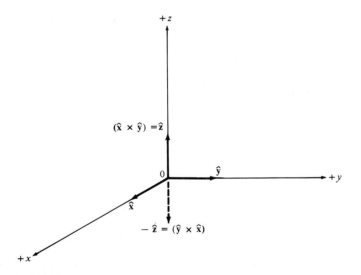

FIGURE 5.21
Right-handed cartesian coordinate system showing unit vectors $\hat{\mathbf{x}}$, $\hat{\mathbf{y}}$, and ($\hat{\mathbf{x}} \times \hat{\mathbf{y}}$) = $\hat{\mathbf{z}}$. Also shown (dashed line) is the unit vector ($-\hat{\mathbf{z}}$) = ($\hat{\mathbf{y}} \times \hat{\mathbf{x}}$).

product ($\mathbf{A} \times \mathbf{B}$) of two vectors

$$\mathbf{A} = A_x\hat{\mathbf{x}} + A_y\hat{\mathbf{y}} + A_z\hat{\mathbf{z}} \qquad (5.125)$$

$$\mathbf{B} = B_x\hat{\mathbf{x}} + B_y\hat{\mathbf{y}} + B_z\hat{\mathbf{z}} \qquad (5.126)$$

which are expressed in terms of $\hat{\mathbf{x}}$, $\hat{\mathbf{y}}$, and $\hat{\mathbf{z}}$. Using Eqs. (5.125) and (5.126), we have the vector ($\mathbf{A} \times \mathbf{B}$) as

$$(\mathbf{A} \times \mathbf{B}) = (A_x\hat{\mathbf{x}} + A_y\hat{\mathbf{y}} + A_z\hat{\mathbf{z}}) \times (B_x\hat{\mathbf{x}} + B_y\hat{\mathbf{y}} + B_z\hat{\mathbf{z}}) \quad (5.127)$$

so we get

$$(\mathbf{A} \times \mathbf{B}) = A_xB_x(\hat{\mathbf{x}} \times \hat{\mathbf{x}}) + A_xB_y(\hat{\mathbf{x}} \times \hat{\mathbf{y}}) + A_xB_z(\hat{\mathbf{x}} \times \hat{\mathbf{z}})$$
$$+ A_yB_x(\hat{\mathbf{y}} \times \hat{\mathbf{x}}) + A_yB_y(\hat{\mathbf{y}} \times \hat{\mathbf{y}}) + A_yB_z(\hat{\mathbf{y}} \times \hat{\mathbf{z}})$$
$$+ A_zB_x(\hat{\mathbf{z}} \times \hat{\mathbf{x}}) + A_zB_y(\hat{\mathbf{z}} \times \hat{\mathbf{y}}) + A_zB_z(\hat{\mathbf{z}} \times \hat{\mathbf{z}})$$

$$(5.128)$$

Substituting the results (5.120) to (5.123) into (5.127) gives

$$(\mathbf{A} \times \mathbf{B}) = A_xB_y\hat{\mathbf{z}} + A_xB_z(-\hat{\mathbf{y}}) + A_yB_x(-\hat{\mathbf{z}})$$
$$+ A_yB_z\hat{\mathbf{x}} + A_zB_x\hat{\mathbf{y}} + A_zB_y(-\hat{\mathbf{x}})$$

so the vector ($\mathbf{A} \times \mathbf{B}$) is given by

$$(\mathbf{A} \times \mathbf{B}) = (A_yB_z - A_zB_y)\hat{\mathbf{x}} + (A_zB_x - A_xB_z)\hat{\mathbf{y}}$$
$$+ (A_xB_y - A_yB_x)\hat{\mathbf{z}} \quad (5.129)$$

Equation (5.129) allows us to obtain the cross-product vector ($\mathbf{A} \times \mathbf{B}$) of any two vectors expressed in the forms (5.125) and (5.126).

As an example of the use of Eq. (5.129), let us find the vector product ($\mathbf{A} \times \mathbf{B}$) of

$$\mathbf{A} = \hat{\mathbf{x}} + \hat{\mathbf{y}} \qquad \mathbf{B} = \hat{\mathbf{x}} - \hat{\mathbf{y}} \qquad (5.130)$$

for which $A_x = 1$, $A_y = 1$, $A_z = 0$, $B_x = 1$, $B_y = -1$, and $B_z = 0$. Putting these values into (5.129) gives the result

$$(\mathbf{A} \times \mathbf{B}) = [(1)(0) - (0)(-1)]\hat{\mathbf{x}} + [(0)(1) - (1)(0)]\hat{\mathbf{y}}$$
$$+ [(1)(-1) - (1)(1)]\hat{\mathbf{z}}$$
$$(\mathbf{A} \times \mathbf{B}) = -2\hat{\mathbf{z}} = 2(-\hat{\mathbf{z}}) \qquad (5.131)$$

Equation (5.131) says that the cross product of the vectors ($\hat{\mathbf{x}} + \hat{\mathbf{y}}$) and ($\hat{\mathbf{x}} - \hat{\mathbf{y}}$) is a vector of length 2 along the negative z axis. Since both ($\hat{\mathbf{x}} + \hat{\mathbf{y}}$) and ($\hat{\mathbf{x}} - \hat{\mathbf{y}}$) lie in the xy plane, we expect from the definition that their cross product will be in the z direction because their cross product must be perpendicular to both vectors and hence perpendicular to the xy plane. As a check, we compute the magnitude of $(\mathbf{A} \times \mathbf{B})$ given by Eq. (5.131) from

$$|\mathbf{A} \times \mathbf{B}|^2 = (\mathbf{A} \times \mathbf{B}) \cdot (\mathbf{A} \times \mathbf{B})$$

$$= (-2\hat{z}) \cdot (-2\hat{z}) = 4(\hat{z} \cdot \hat{z}) = 4 \qquad (5.132)$$

where we are taking the *scalar* product of the vector $(\mathbf{A} \times \mathbf{B})$ with itself to find its magnitude. From Eq. (5.132), we see that $|\mathbf{A} \times \mathbf{B}| = 2$, as we already knew from Eq. (5.131).

One of the simplest and most common examples of the use of the cross product in physics is the Lorentz force exerted on a moving electrically charged particle in a magnetic field. If the charge on the particle is q, the velocity vector is $\mathbf{v}$, and the magnetic field vector is $\mathbf{B}$, then the (vector) force exerted on the particle is

$$\mathbf{F} = q(\mathbf{v} \times \mathbf{B}) \qquad (5.133)$$

Suppose the particle is moving along the positive x axis with speed v, so its velocity vector is $\mathbf{v} = v\hat{x}$, and the magnetic field is along the positive y axis, so

$$\mathbf{B} = B\hat{y} \qquad (5.134)$$

Let the charge q be a positive quantity. From Eq. (5.133), the Lorentz force $\mathbf{F}$ exerted on the particle by the magnetic field $\mathbf{B}$ is

$$\mathbf{F} = q(v\hat{x}) \times (B\hat{y}) = qvB(\hat{x} \times \hat{y}) = qvB\hat{z} \qquad (5.135)$$

on using Eq. (5.129) with Eq. (5.121). Equation (5.135) says that the Lorentz force in this situation is along the positive z axis and has a magnitude qvB. Figure 5.22 shows the vectors $\mathbf{v}$, $\mathbf{B}$, and $\mathbf{F}$ in this example.

Another example of the use of the cross product in physics is the concept of angular momentum, which is defined as follows. Given a single particle of linear momentum $\mathbf{p}$ and a fixed point O in space. Let $\mathbf{r}$ be the position vector from point O to the particle. Then the quantity

$$\mathbf{L} \equiv \mathbf{r} \times \mathbf{p} \qquad (5.136)$$

is defined as the angular momentum of the particle with respect to the point O. (Note that the spatial point O must be specified in order to define the position vector $\mathbf{r}$ in the definition.) Since the angular momentum $\mathbf{L}$ in Eq. (5.136) is defined by the vector product $(\mathbf{r} \times \mathbf{p})$, angular momentum is a vector quantity whose magnitude and direction are those of the cross product of the vectors $\mathbf{r}$ and $\mathbf{p}$, namely,

$$L = rp \sin \theta \qquad (5.137)$$

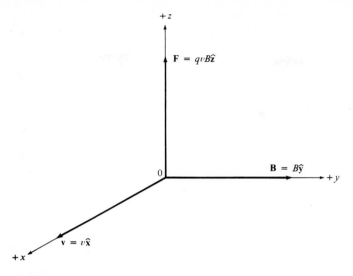

FIGURE 5.22
The Lorentz force $\mathbf{F} = qvB\hat{z}$ in the ($+z$) direction exerted on a particle of electric charge q (where q is positive) moving with speed v in the positive x direction in a magnetic field $\mathbf{B}$ in the positive y direction.

where θ is the angle between $\mathbf{r}$ and $\mathbf{p}$ and the direction of $\mathbf{L}$ is normal to both $\mathbf{r}$ and $\mathbf{p}$.

An example of angular momentum is afforded by a particle moving in a circle of radius R, as shown in Fig. 5.23. We want to calculate the angular momentum $\mathbf{L}$ of the particle using the definition (5.136). First we must choose the point with respect to which $\mathbf{L}$ is taken; we take the center O of the circle as a convenient (but not the only) choice. Relative to the center of the circular orbit, which we take, again for convenience, to lie in the xy plane, the position vector of the particle is

$$\mathbf{r} = x\hat{x} + y\hat{y} \tag{5.138}$$

Since the particle moves in a circle of radius R, the coordinates (x, y) of the particle in Eq. (5.138) are related by the equation

$$x^2 + y^2 = R^2 \tag{5.139}$$

of the circular orbit, so the magnitude of $\mathbf{r}$ is $r = R$.

Next, we need to know the linear momentum $\mathbf{p}$ of the particle. Suppose, in this example, that the particle is of mass m and moves with a tangential velocity $\mathbf{v}$ of constant magnitude v. Then

$$\mathbf{p} = m\mathbf{v} \tag{5.140}$$

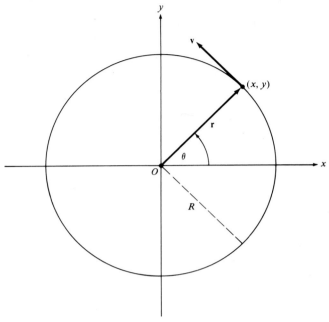

FIGURE 5.23
A particle of mass m moving in a circle of radius R with a tangential velocity vector $\mathbf{v}$ of constant magnitude v. The instantaneous position of the particle is the point of coordinates (x, y) and $\mathbf{r}$ is the position vector of the particle relative to the center O of the circular orbit in the xy plane.

is the linear momentum of the particle, so, from the definition (5.136), the angular momentum $\mathbf{L}$ is

$$\mathbf{L} = \mathbf{r} \times \mathbf{p} = (x\hat{\mathbf{x}} + y\hat{\mathbf{y}}) \times m\mathbf{v} \qquad (5.141)$$

In order to evaluate Eq. (5.141), we need an expression for the tangential velocity $\mathbf{v}$ in terms of the unit vectors $\hat{\mathbf{x}}$ and $\hat{\mathbf{y}}$ and the coordinates (x, y) of the particle. To find this expression, we recall from Eq. (5.105) that the unit vector

$$\hat{\mathbf{u}}_\theta \equiv (-\sin \theta)\hat{\mathbf{x}} + (\cos \theta)\hat{\mathbf{y}} \qquad (5.105)$$

is tangent to the circular orbit. Therefore, the tangential velocity $\mathbf{v}$ of the particle is given by

$$\mathbf{v} = v\hat{\mathbf{u}}_\theta = v\left[(-\sin \theta)\hat{\mathbf{x}} + (\cos \theta)\hat{\mathbf{y}}\right] \qquad (5.142)$$

Substituting Eq. (5.142) into the expression (5.141) for $\mathbf{L}$ gives

$$\mathbf{L} = (x\hat{\mathbf{x}} + y\hat{\mathbf{y}}) \times mv\left[(-\sin \theta)\hat{\mathbf{x}} + (\cos \theta)\hat{\mathbf{y}}\right] \qquad (5.143)$$

To evaluate Eq. (5.143), we can use Eqs. (5.121) to (5.124) for the cross products of the cartesian unit vectors, obtaining

$$\mathbf{L} = (mvx \cos \theta)(\hat{\mathbf{x}} \times \hat{\mathbf{y}}) + (-mvy \sin \theta)(\hat{\mathbf{y}} \times \hat{\mathbf{x}})$$

$$\mathbf{L} = mv[(x \cos \theta)\hat{\mathbf{z}} + (-y \sin \theta)(-\hat{\mathbf{z}})]$$

$$\mathbf{L} = mv(x \cos \theta + y \sin \theta)\hat{\mathbf{z}} \qquad (5.144)$$

Equation (5.144) gives the angular momentum vector $\mathbf{L}$ of a particle of mass m and constant tangential speed v in a circular orbit (relative to the center of the circle). Since the coordinates (x, y) of the particle are related by the equation

$$x^2 + y^2 = R^2 \qquad (5.145)$$

of the circle, and, further, from the geometry of Fig. 5.23,

$$\tan \theta = \frac{y}{x} \qquad (5.146)$$

we see that Eqs. (5.145) and (5.146) give the angle θ in terms of the coordinates x and y. From Eq. (5.144), we note that the angular momentum vector $\mathbf{L}$ is a scalar multiple of $\hat{\mathbf{z}}$, the unit vector in the z direction, so, in Fig. 5.23, the vector $\mathbf{L}$ is normal to the plane of the diagram. Finally, using the fact that $L^2 = \mathbf{L} \cdot \mathbf{L}$, one can calculate (see Exercise 5.18) the magnitude L of the angular momentum of the particle to be

$$L = mvR \qquad (5.147)$$

so the angular momentum vector of the particle is

$$\mathbf{L} = mvR\hat{\mathbf{z}} \qquad (5.148)$$

We conclude that the angular momentum vector $\mathbf{L}$ of the particle is of magnitude mvR and is directed perpendicular to the circular orbit in the xy plane.

The rather complicated expression (5.144) for the angular momentum $\mathbf{L}$ of a particle moving in a circle suggests that we use plane-polar coordinates instead of rectangular coordinates. To do this, we will need to know the cross product of the unit vectors $\hat{\mathbf{u}}_r$ and $\hat{\mathbf{u}}_\theta$, given by Eqs. (5.101) and (5.105). We have

$$\hat{\mathbf{u}}_r \times \hat{\mathbf{u}}_\theta = [(\cos \theta)\hat{\mathbf{x}} + (\sin \theta)\hat{\mathbf{y}}] \times [(-\sin \theta)\hat{\mathbf{x}} + (\cos \theta)\hat{\mathbf{y}}]$$

$$(5.149)$$

Again using the property that $(\hat{\mathbf{x}} \times \hat{\mathbf{x}}) = (\hat{\mathbf{y}} \times \hat{\mathbf{y}}) = \mathbf{0}$, Eq. (5.149) becomes

$$\hat{\mathbf{u}}_r \times \hat{\mathbf{u}}_\theta = \cos^2 \theta(\hat{\mathbf{x}} \times \hat{\mathbf{y}}) - \sin^2 \theta(\hat{\mathbf{y}} \times \hat{\mathbf{x}}) \qquad (5.150)$$

Using relations (5.121) and (5.122), this becomes

$$\hat{u}_r \times \hat{u}_\theta = (\cos^2 \theta + \sin^2 \theta)\,\hat{z} = \hat{z} \qquad (5.151)$$

Equation (5.151) tells us that the cross product of the unit vectors $\hat{u}_r$ and $\hat{u}_\theta$ is the unit vector $\hat{z}$ in the positive z direction.

We can now write, as can be seen from Fig. 5.23 and Eq. (5.115), the position vector **r** of the particle as

$$\mathbf{r} = R\hat{u}_r \qquad (5.152)$$

and the linear momentum $\mathbf{p} = m\mathbf{v}$ is given, using Eq. (5.142), by

$$\mathbf{p} = m\mathbf{v} = mv\,\hat{u}_\theta \qquad (5.153)$$

since the tangential velocity **v** is the speed v times the unit vector $\hat{u}_\theta$ which is tangent to the circular orbit and points in the direction of increasing angle θ. Using Eqs. (5.152) and (5.153), the angular momentum of the particle is

$$L \equiv \mathbf{r} \times \mathbf{p} = (R\hat{u}_r) \times (mv\,\hat{u}_\theta)$$

$$L = mvR(\hat{u}_r \times \hat{u}_\theta) = mvR\hat{z} \qquad (5.154)$$

on using Eq. (5.151). The result (5.154) is the same as the expression (5.148) found using rectangular coordinates but was much easier to obtain. From Eq. (5.154), the magnitude L is given by

$$L = (\mathbf{L} \cdot \mathbf{L})^{1/2} = \left[(mvR\hat{z}) \cdot (mvR\hat{z})\right]^{1/2}$$

$$L = \left[m^2v^2R^2(\hat{z} \cdot \hat{z})\right]^{1/2} = mvR \qquad (5.155)$$

the same expression as Eq. (5.147) but also much easier to obtain. This example shows how natural plane-polar coordinates are to use in cases of circular motion. We will use them again when we discuss circular motion in more detail.

EXERCISES

5.16. Given the vectors $\mathbf{A} = \hat{x} + \hat{z}$ and $\mathbf{B} = \hat{x} - \hat{z}$. (a) Calculate the magnitude and direction of $(\mathbf{A} \times \mathbf{B})$. (b) Describe in words the vector $(\mathbf{A} \times \mathbf{B})$. (c) The vector $(\mathbf{A} \times \mathbf{B})$ is normal to which of the coordinate planes in the rectangular coordinate system?

5.17. Show explicitly that $(\hat{u}_r \times \hat{z}) = -\hat{u}_\theta$.

5.18. Consider the example in the text in which the angular momentum **L** of a particle moving in a circle of radius R is given by Eq. (5.144) as

$$\mathbf{L} = mv(x \cos \theta + y \sin \theta)\hat{z} \qquad (5.144)$$

Using the scalar product of **L** with itself, show that its magnitude $L = mvR$, where $x^2 + y^2 = R^2$ is the equation of the circular orbit of the particle.

INTRODUCTION TO VECTOR CALCULUS

This section presents an introduction to some topics in vector calculus that students of physics frequently encounter near the beginning of their course. The topics discussed, vector derivatives and line integrals, are covered in some detail. The examples will be chosen from the elementary mechanics usually discussed in the first course in physics for scientists and engineers.

Consider, as shown in Fig. 5.24, a particle moving in a path which (although it is not necessary) we will take to be in the xy plane. The location of the particle will be specified by giving its position vector **r** relative to the origin 0 of the rectangular coordinate system. Since the

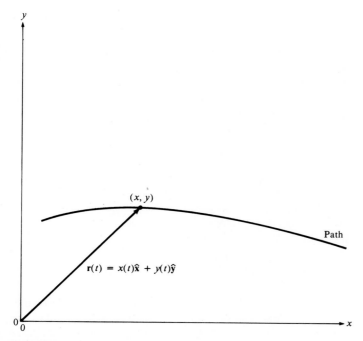

FIGURE 5.24
A particle moving in a two-dimensional path in the xy plane. The time-dependent position vector of the particle is $\mathbf{r}(t) = x(t)\hat{\mathbf{x}} + y(t)\hat{\mathbf{y}}$, where $x(t)$ and $y(t)$ are the time-dependent rectangular coordinates of the particle.

position of the moving particle is changing with time, position vector **r** will be a function **r**(*t*) of the time *t*. The two-dimensional position vector **r** is given by

$$\mathbf{r} = x\hat{\mathbf{x}} + y\hat{\mathbf{y}} \qquad (5.156)$$

where (*x*, *y*) are the instantaneous coordinates of the particle at some time *t*. Since the particle moves and its position changes with time, its coordinates (*x*, *y*) are also functions of time, so

$$x = x(t) \qquad y = y(t) \qquad (5.157)$$

and the position vector of the particle (5.156) is given by

$$\mathbf{r}(t) = x(t)\hat{\mathbf{x}} + y(t)\hat{\mathbf{y}} \qquad (5.158)$$

Equation (5.158) says that the position vector **r**(*t*) depends on the time *t* because the coordinates [*x*(*t*), *y*(*t*)] of the particle depend on the time.

Given the position vector **r**(*t*) of the particle, we define the instantaneous velocity **v**(*t*) of the particle by the equation

$$\mathbf{v}(t) \equiv \frac{d}{dt}\left[\mathbf{r}(t)\right] \qquad (5.159)$$

Equation (5.159) says that the velocity vector **v**(*t*) of the particle is the derivative, with respect to time, of the position vector **r**(*t*). In order to use Eq. (5.159), we must discuss the idea of the derivative of a vector. (In physics, we will often be interested in the derivatives of vectors with respect to time.) Since the derivative of a vector with respect to time is the rate of change of the vector with time, we ask ourselves in what ways a vector can change with time. Since a vector has both a magnitude and a direction, either the magnitude or the direction, or both, can change with time. We must, therefore, consider the possibility of changes in the magnitude and/or the direction of the vector when taking the derivative of the vector with time.

We define the derivative (*d***A**/*dt*) with respect to time *t* of a vector **A**(*t*), which is a function of time, by the equation

$$\frac{d\mathbf{A}(t)}{dt} \equiv \lim_{\Delta t \to 0}\left[\frac{\mathbf{A}(t + \Delta t) - \mathbf{A}(t)}{\Delta t}\right] \qquad (5.160)$$

Equation (5.160) is the analog of the usual definition of the derivative of a scalar function of one variable. In this equation **A**(*t* + Δ*t*) is the vector **A** at the time (*t* + Δ*t*) and **A**(*t*) is the vector **A** at the earlier time *t*. In general, the vector **A**(*t* + Δ*t*) will differ in both magnitude and direction from vector **A**(*t*), and we keep in mind that the difference [**A**(*t* + Δ*t*) − **A**(*t*)] is also a vector. Thus the right-hand side of Eq. (5.160) is a vector, and so the derivative [*d***A**(*t*)/*dt*] is also a vector.

We will discuss first the derivative of a vector, such as the cartesian unit vectors $\hat{\mathbf{x}}$, $\hat{\mathbf{y}}$, $\hat{\mathbf{z}}$, whose direction and magnitude are both constant. Clearly, these unit vectors cannot change either magnitude or direction with time, so we have

$$\frac{d}{dt}(\hat{\mathbf{x}}) = 0 \qquad \frac{d}{dt}(\hat{\mathbf{y}}) = 0 \qquad \frac{d}{dt}(\hat{\mathbf{z}}) = 0 \qquad (5.161)$$

for the time derivatives of the cartesian unit vector. Next, we consider the derivative of the product $k\mathbf{A}$ of a scalar k and a vector $\mathbf{A}$, where

$$\frac{d}{dt}[k\mathbf{A}] = k\frac{d\mathbf{A}}{dt} + \mathbf{A}\frac{dk}{dt} \qquad (5.162)$$

and where we have written Eq. (5.162) by analogy with the familiar rule for the derivative of a product. In Eq. (5.162), (dk/dt) is the derivative of the scalar k with respect to time and $(d\mathbf{A}/dt)$ is the derivative of the vector $\mathbf{A}$ with respect to time. We can use Eqs. (5.161) and (5.162) to determine the derivative $[d\mathbf{r}(t)/dt]$ by the time-dependent position vector $\mathbf{r}(t)$. Using Eq. (5.158) for $\mathbf{r}(t)$, we have

$$\frac{d}{dt}[\mathbf{r}(t)] = \frac{d}{dt}[x(t)\hat{\mathbf{x}} + y(t)\hat{\mathbf{y}}] \qquad (5.163)$$

where, since the functions $x(t)$ and $y(t)$ are scalars, we have from Eq. (5.162).

$$\frac{d\mathbf{r}(t)}{dt} = \frac{dx(t)}{dt}\hat{\mathbf{x}} + x(t)\frac{d\hat{\mathbf{x}}}{dt} + \frac{dy(t)}{dt}\hat{\mathbf{y}} + y(t)\frac{d\hat{\mathbf{y}}}{dt} \qquad (5.164)$$

However, the derivatives $(d\hat{\mathbf{x}}/dt) = 0$ and $(d\hat{\mathbf{y}}/dt) = 0$ from Eq. (5.161), so Eq. (5.164) becomes

$$\mathbf{v}(t) = \frac{d\mathbf{r}(t)}{dt} = \frac{dx(t)}{dt}\hat{\mathbf{x}} + \frac{dy(t)}{dt}\hat{\mathbf{y}} \qquad (5.165)$$

for the derivative of $\mathbf{r}(t)$ with respect to time, and where we have also used the definition (5.159) of the velocity vector $\mathbf{v}(t)$. Equation (5.165) gives the velocity vector $\mathbf{v}(t)$ in terms of the rates of change with time $[dx(t)/dt]$ and $[dy(t)/dt]$ of the time-dependent coordinates $[x(t), y(t)]$ of the moving particle. If we know the functions $x(t)$ and $y(t)$, we can compute their derivatives with respect to time and, using Eq. (5.165), find the velocity vector $\mathbf{v}(t)$. If we write the velocity vector $\mathbf{v}(t)$ in terms of time-dependent scalar components $v_x(t)$ and $v_y(t)$ in the x and y directions, Eq. (5.165) becomes

$$\mathbf{v}(t) = v_x(t)\hat{\mathbf{x}} + v_y(t)\hat{\mathbf{y}} \qquad (5.166)$$

where $v_x(t) \equiv [dx(t)/dt]$ and $v_y(t) \equiv [dy(t)/dt]$ are the rates of change with time of the coordinates $[x(t), y(t)]$ of the particle's position as it moves along its path. From Eq. (5.166), we can find the magnitude $v(t)$ of $\mathbf{v}(t)$ as

$$v(t) = [\mathbf{v}(t) \cdot \mathbf{v}(t)]^{1/2} = \left\{ [v_x(t)]^2 + [v_y(t)]^2 \right\}^{1/2} \quad (5.167)$$

giving the magnitude of $v(t)$ in terms of the components $v_x(t)$ and $v_y(t)$. Keep in mind that, since $v_x(t)$ and $v_y(t)$ will, in general, depend on time t, the magnitude $v(t)$ will also depend on the time.

So far, we have found the velocity vector $\mathbf{v}(t)$ in Eq. (5.165) and the magnitude $v(t)$ in Eq. (5.167). We now want to consider the *direction* of the velocity vector $\mathbf{v}(t) = d\mathbf{r}(t)/dt$ in relation to the path of the particle as it moves. We can find the direction of $\mathbf{v}(t)$ by using the definition (5.160), which gives us for the derivative of $\mathbf{r}(t)$,

$$\frac{d\mathbf{r}(t)}{dt} = \lim_{\Delta t \to 0} \left[\frac{\mathbf{r}(t + \Delta t) - \mathbf{r}(t)}{\Delta t} \right] \quad (5.168)$$

In Eq. (5.168), $\mathbf{r}(t + \Delta t)$ is the position vector of the particle at a point Q at time $(t + \Delta t)$ and $\mathbf{r}(t)$ is the position vector at a point P at the earlier time t. These position vectors are shown in Fig. 5.25, which also shows the difference vector $[\mathbf{r}(t + \Delta t) - \mathbf{r}(t)]$, whose magnitude $|\mathbf{r}(t + \Delta t) - \mathbf{r}(t)|$ is equal to the length of the chord $\overline{PQ}$. Now consider what happens in Fig. 5.25 as the magnitude of the time interval Δt becomes very small; we denote this by $\Delta t \to 0$. As $\Delta t \to 0$, point Q and point P are closer together, and we consider the quantity

$$\lim_{\Delta t \to 0} \frac{|\mathbf{r}(t + \Delta t) - \mathbf{r}(t)|}{\Delta s} = \lim_{\Delta t \to 0} \frac{|\overline{PQ}|}{\Delta s} \quad (5.169)$$

where Δs is the arc length (the distance along the particle's path) between points P and Q. Clearly, as $\Delta t \to 0$, both Δs and the magnitude $|\mathbf{r}(t + \Delta t) - \mathbf{r}(t)|$ become small, but their ratio in expression (5.169) does not necessarily become small because that ratio is the quotient of two small numbers. From Eq. (5.169) and Fig. 5.25, we can see, intuitively and geometrically, that two things happen as the time interval $\Delta t \to 0$. First, the chord length $\overline{PQ}$ and the arc length Δs approach the same magnitude, so the limit in Eq. (5.169) approaches the value unity. We write this result as

$$\lim_{\Delta t \to 0} \frac{|\mathbf{r}(t + \Delta t) - \mathbf{r}(t)|}{\Delta s} \equiv \left| \frac{d\mathbf{r}(t)}{ds} \right| = 1 \quad (5.170)$$

where the derivative $[d\mathbf{r}(t)/ds]$ is the rate of change of the position vector $\mathbf{r}(t)$ with respect to arc length s along the path of the particle. The

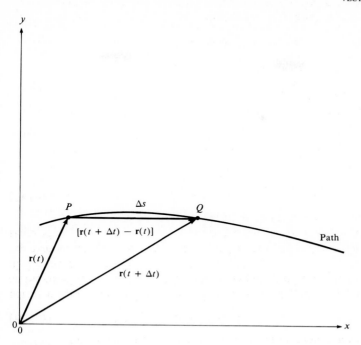

FIGURE 5.25
A particle·moving from point P to point Q along a path in the xy plane. At time t, the particle is at point P and its position vector is $\mathbf{r}(t)$. At the later time $(t + \Delta t)$, the particle is at point Q and its position vector is $\mathbf{r}(t + \Delta t)$. Also shown is vector $[\mathbf{r}(t + \Delta t) - \mathbf{r}(t)]$, whose magnitude is the length of the chord $\overline{PQ}$. The quantity Δs is the arc length, or distance along the path, between P and Q.

vector $[d\mathbf{r}(t)/ds]$, therefore, has magnitude unity. Second, the vector $[\mathbf{r}(t + \Delta t) - \mathbf{r}(t)]$ approaches the direction which is tangent to the path at point P (since point Q becomes the same as point P as $\Delta t \to 0$). Our overall conclusion is that the vector $(d\mathbf{r}/ds)$ is a vector of unit magnitude whose direction is the direction of the tangent to the path of the particle. We write this conclusion as

$$\frac{d\mathbf{r}(t)}{ds} = \hat{\mathbf{t}} \qquad (5.171)$$

where $\hat{\mathbf{t}}$ is the unit vector tangent to the path of the particle at the point P.

Given the result (5.171), we can use it to write the velocity vector $(d\mathbf{r}/dt)$ as

$$\frac{d\mathbf{r}}{dt} = \frac{d\mathbf{r}}{ds}\frac{ds}{dt} = \hat{\mathbf{t}}\frac{ds}{dt} \qquad (5.172)$$

where (ds/dt) is the rate of change of arc length s (along the path) with time, so the scalar (ds/dt) is the instantaneous speed $v(t)$ of the particle along its path. Using these results, we write the velocity vector $\mathbf{v}(t)$ in terms of the speed $v(t)$ as

$$\mathbf{v}(t) = \frac{d\mathbf{r}(t)}{dt} = v(t)\hat{\mathbf{t}} \qquad (5.173)$$

Equation (5.173) says that the velocity vector $\mathbf{v}(t)$ of the particle is equal to the scalar speed $v(t)$ of the particle along its path times the unit vector $\hat{\mathbf{t}}$ tangent to the path at that point. This result shows that the velocity vector $\mathbf{v}(t)$, defined by Eq. (5.159), is tangent to the path of the particle, and $\mathbf{v}(t)$ is thus called the *tangential velocity* of the particle. The vectors $\mathbf{r}(t)$ and $\mathbf{v}(t)$ are shown at one instant of time (one value of the time t) in Fig. 5.26. Note that the velocity vector $\mathbf{v}(t)$ is generally not perpendicular to the position vector $\mathbf{r}(t)$; however, for a circular path, $\mathbf{r}(t)$ and $\mathbf{v}(t)$ are perpendicular to each other.

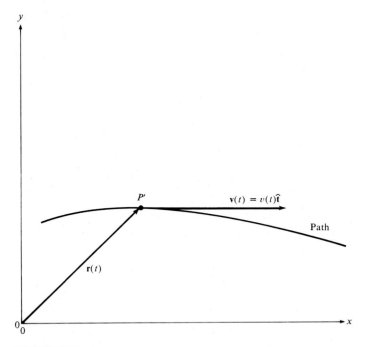

FIGURE 5.26
Instantaneous position P' of the particle, moving along its path, at time t, showing the instantaneous position vector $\mathbf{r}(t)$ and velocity vector $\mathbf{v}(t) = v(t)\hat{\mathbf{t}}$, where $v(t)$ is the instantaneous speed and $\hat{\mathbf{t}}$ is a unit vector tangent to the path.

As an example of the use of these results, suppose that the position vector $\mathbf{r}(t)$ of a certain moving particle is

$$\mathbf{r}(t) = (bt)\hat{\mathbf{x}} \qquad (5.174)$$

where b is a constant and t is the time. Equation (5.174) tells us that the position vector is a scalar multiple of the unit vector $\hat{\mathbf{x}}$, so $\mathbf{r}(t)$ lies along the x axis, meaning that the particle moves along the x axis and the magnitude

$$r = [\mathbf{r} \cdot \mathbf{r}]^{1/2} = bt \qquad (5.175)$$

of $\mathbf{r}$ varies with time. Then the velocity vector $\mathbf{v}$ of the particle is

$$\mathbf{v} = \frac{d}{dt}[\mathbf{r}(t)] = \frac{d}{dt}[bt]\hat{\mathbf{x}} = b\hat{\mathbf{x}} \qquad (5.176)$$

Comparing the velocity vector (5.176) with the form (5.173), we see that the speed v of the particle is equal to the constant b, and the tangent unit vector $\hat{\mathbf{t}}$ is tangent, in this case, to the x axis and so is the unit vector $\hat{\mathbf{x}}$ along the x axis.

As another example, consider a particle moving in the xy plane so that its coordinates at time t are

$$x(t) = R \cos \omega t \qquad y(t) = R \sin \omega t \qquad (5.177)$$

where R and ω are constants. From Eq. (5.158), the position vector of the particle, relative to the origin $(0, 0)$, is

$$\mathbf{r}(t) = (R \cos \omega t)\hat{\mathbf{x}} + (R \sin \omega t)\hat{\mathbf{y}} \qquad (5.178)$$

so the position vector of the particle depends on the time. The magnitude r of $\mathbf{r}(t)$ is

$$r = [\mathbf{r}(t) \cdot \mathbf{r}(t)]^{1/2} = (R^2 \cos^2 \omega t + R^2 \sin^2 \omega t)^{1/2} = R \quad (5.179)$$

and we see that $\mathbf{r}(t)$ has a constant magnitude equal to R. This means that the position vector, which depends on the time, has a constant length but changes its direction with time. Next, from Eq. (5.159), the velocity vector $\mathbf{v}(t)$ of the particle is

$$\mathbf{v}(t) = \frac{d}{dt}[\mathbf{r}(t)] = (-\omega R \sin \omega t)\hat{\mathbf{x}} + (\omega R \cos \omega t)\hat{\mathbf{y}} \quad (5.180)$$

so the velocity vector of the particle is a function of time. The magnitude v of $\mathbf{v}(t)$ is

$$v = (\mathbf{v} \cdot \mathbf{v})^{1/2} = (\omega^2 R^2 \sin^2 \omega t + \omega^2 R^2 \cos^2 \omega t)^{1/2} = \omega R \quad (5.181)$$

Since ω and R are constants, Eq. (5.181) tells us that the speed v of the particle is a constant and so is independent of the time. Since the magnitude of the velocity vector is independent of the time and, from Eq. (5.180), the vector $\mathbf{v}(t)$ depends on the time, the direction of $\mathbf{v}(t)$ must be changing with time as the particle moves. We conclude that both the position vector $\mathbf{r}(t)$ and the velocity vector $\mathbf{v}(t)$ of this moving particle are of constant magnitude, but their directions vary with time as the particle moves.

We can obtain information on the direction of $\mathbf{v}(t)$, relative to $\mathbf{r}(t)$, by calculating their scalar product, which is

$$\mathbf{v}(t) \cdot \mathbf{r}(t) = (-\omega R^2 \sin \omega t \cos \omega t + \omega R^2 \cos \omega t \sin \omega t) = 0$$

$$(5.182)$$

Equation (5.182) tells us that the scalar product $(\mathbf{v} \cdot \mathbf{r})$ is equal to zero for all values of the time, so the velocity vector $\mathbf{v}(t)$ is perpendicular to the position vector $\mathbf{r}(t)$, as the particle moves, even though the directions of $\mathbf{v}(t)$ and $\mathbf{r}(t)$ are both changing with time. Figure 5.27 shows the vectors at one instant of time and also shows (as a dashed line) part of the path of the particle. As discussed earlier, the velocity vector $\mathbf{v}(t)$ is tangent to the path as the particle moves.

Last, we can find the equation of the path of the particle from Eqs. (5.177), which we square and add to get

$$\left[x(t)\right]^2 + \left[y(t)\right]^2 = R^2 \cos^2 \omega t + R^2 \sin^2 \omega t = R^2 \quad (5.183)$$

Equation (5.183) says that the time-dependent coordinates $x(t)$ and $y(t)$ of the position of the moving particle satisfy the equation $x^2 + y^2 = R^2$, so the path of the particle is a circle of radius R with its center at the origin.

Returning to the general discussion, consider a particle moving with position vector $\mathbf{r}(t)$ and velocity vector $\mathbf{v}(t)$. Then the acceleration vector

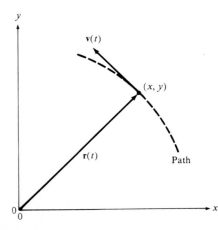

FIGURE 5.27
Position vector $\mathbf{r}(t)$ from Eq. (5.178) and velocity vector $\mathbf{v}(t)$ from Eq. (5.180) at one instant of time. The moving particle is at the point (x, y), where x and y are given by Eq. (5.177) at that instant and the vectors $\mathbf{v}$ and $\mathbf{r}$ are always perpendicular to each other as the particle moves.

$\mathbf{a}(t)$ of the moving particle is defined by

$$\mathbf{a}(t) \equiv \frac{d\mathbf{v}(t)}{dt} = \frac{d^2\mathbf{r}(t)}{dt^2} \qquad (5.184)$$

Thus the acceleration vector is the derivative with respect to time of the velocity vector and is also the second derivative with respect to time of the position vector. If we consider a particle moving in the xy plane, so that its time-dependent coordinates are $x(t)$ and $y(t)$, its position and velocity vectors are given by Eqs. (5.158) and (5.166) as

$$\mathbf{r}(t) = x(t)\hat{\mathbf{x}} + y(t)\hat{\mathbf{y}} \qquad \mathbf{v}(t) = v_x(t)\hat{\mathbf{x}} + v_y(t)\hat{\mathbf{y}} \qquad (5.185)$$

Applying the definition (5.184) of the acceleration vector gives

$$\mathbf{a}(t) = \left[\frac{dv_x(t)}{dt}\right]\hat{\mathbf{x}} + \left[\frac{dv_y(t)}{dt}\right]\hat{\mathbf{y}} \qquad (5.186)$$

and

$$\mathbf{a}(t) = \left[\frac{d^2x(t)}{dt^2}\right]\hat{\mathbf{x}} + \left[\frac{d^2y(t)}{dt^2}\right]\hat{\mathbf{y}} \qquad (5.187)$$

We can, from Eqs. (5.186) and (5.187), write the acceleration vector as

$$\mathbf{a}(t) = a_x(t)\hat{\mathbf{x}} + a_y(t)\hat{\mathbf{y}} \qquad (5.188)$$

where $a_x(t) = (dv_x/dt) = (d^2x/dt^2)$ and $a_y(t) = (dv_y/dt) = (d^2y/dt^2)$. If we know how the coordinates $x(t)$ and $y(t)$ of the moving particle depend on the time, we can calculate the components a_x and a_y in Eq. (5.188) and thereby obtain the acceleration vector $\mathbf{a}(t)$ of the particle.

We can find the acceleration vector $\mathbf{a}(t)$ of the moving particle in the example just discussed, for which the coordinates are given by Eq. (5.177) as

$$x(t) = R \cos \omega t \qquad y(t) = R \sin \omega t$$

We calculate

$$\frac{d^2x(t)}{dt^2} = -\omega^2 R \cos \omega t \qquad \frac{d^2v(t)}{dt^2} = -\omega^2 R \sin \omega t \qquad (5.189)$$

so, from Eq. (5.187), we have

$$\mathbf{a}(t) = (-\omega^2 R \cos \omega t)\hat{\mathbf{x}} + (-\omega^2 R \sin \omega t)\hat{\mathbf{y}} \qquad (5.190)$$

for the acceleration vector, which has a magnitude a of

$$a = (\mathbf{a} \cdot \mathbf{a})^{1/2} = (\omega^4 R^2 \cos^2 \omega t + \omega^4 R^2 \sin^2 \omega t)^{1/2} = \omega^2 R \qquad (5.191)$$

The magnitude a of the acceleration vector $\mathbf{a}(t)$ is, therefore, the constant $\omega^2 R$, so the direction of the vector $\mathbf{a}(t)$ is changing with time as the particle moves. To find the direction of $\mathbf{a}(t)$, we take its scalar product with the position vector $\mathbf{r}(t)$ of the particle, obtaining

$$\mathbf{a}(t) \cdot \mathbf{r}(t) = \left[(-\omega^2 R \cos \omega t)\hat{\mathbf{x}} + (-\omega^2 R \sin \omega t)\hat{\mathbf{y}} \right]$$
$$\cdot \left[(R \cos \omega t)\hat{\mathbf{x}} + (R \sin \omega t)\hat{\mathbf{y}} \right] \quad (5.192)$$

using the position vector of the particle given by Eq. (5.178). Equation (5.192) gives us

$$\mathbf{a}(t) \cdot \mathbf{r}(t) = -\omega^2 R^2 \cos^2 \omega t - \omega^2 R^2 \sin^2 \omega t = -\omega^2 R^2 \quad (5.193)$$

Using the form

$$\mathbf{a}(t) \cdot \mathbf{r}(t) = \left| \mathbf{a}(t) \right| \left| \mathbf{r}(t) \right| \cos\phi \quad (5.194)$$

for the scalar product, where ϕ is the angle between the vectors $\mathbf{a}(t)$ and $\mathbf{r}(t)$, we recall from Eqs. (5.179) and (5.191) that

$$\left| \mathbf{a}(t) \right| = \omega^2 R \qquad \left| \mathbf{r}(t) \right| = R \quad (5.195)$$

Substituting Eqs. (5.195) into Eq. (5.194) gives

$$\cos \phi = (-1) \quad (5.196)$$

so the angle ϕ is π radians (180°). We conclude that the acceleration vector $\mathbf{a}(t)$ of this particle is directed antiparallel to the position vector $\mathbf{r}(t)$. Since $\mathbf{r}(t)$ is directed outward from the origin toward the particle, the acceleration vector is directed inward from the particle toward the origin. Since, as shown above, this particle is moving in a circular path of radius R, the acceleration vector is pointing inward from the particle to the center of the circle. We conclude that the acceleration vector in this example has the constant magnitude $(\omega^2 R)$ and a direction that changes with time as the particle moves in a circle but the acceleration vector is always pointed from the particle toward the center of the circular orbit. The acceleration vector is shown in Fig. 5.28, which also shows the tangential velocity vector $\mathbf{v}(t)$.

We digress briefly to prove a useful theorem which states the following. Given a vector $\mathbf{A}(t)$ of constant magnitude A but changing direction as the variable t changes. Then the derivative $(d\mathbf{A}/dt)$ is a vector perpendicular to the vector $\mathbf{A}$. To prove this, we write two expressions for the derivative of the scalar product $(\mathbf{A} \cdot \mathbf{A})$ with respect to the variable t. We have

$$\frac{d}{dt}(\mathbf{A} \cdot \mathbf{A}) = \frac{d}{dt}(A^2) = 0 \quad (5.197)$$

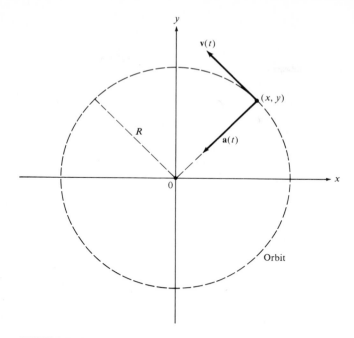

FIGURE 5.28
Particle whose coordinates are $x(t) = R \cos \omega t$, $y(t) = R \sin \omega t$ moving in a circle (of equation $x^2 + y^2 = R^2$) of radius R in the xy plane. The velocity vector $\mathbf{v}(t)$, given by Eq. (5.180), is tangent to the circular orbit centered at the origin 0, and the acceleration vector $\mathbf{a}(t)$, given by Eq. (5.190), is directed inward from the particle to the center 0 of the circle. The magnitudes are $v = \omega R$ and $a = \omega^2 R$.

since the magnitude A is a constant, and we also have

$$\frac{d}{dt}(\mathbf{A} \cdot \mathbf{A}) = \mathbf{A} \cdot \frac{d\mathbf{A}}{dt} + \frac{d\mathbf{A}}{dt} \cdot \mathbf{A} = 2\mathbf{A} \cdot \frac{d\mathbf{A}}{dt} \qquad (5.198)$$

For both Eqs. (5.197) and (5.198) to hold simultaneously, it must be true that

$$\mathbf{A} \cdot \frac{d\mathbf{A}}{dt} = 0 \qquad (5.199)$$

an equation which says, assuming $(d\mathbf{A}/dt)$ is not zero, that the vector $(d\mathbf{A}/dt)$ is perpendicular to the vector $\mathbf{A}$. We could have used the theorem in the example of circular motion just discussed, in which the particle's velocity vector $\mathbf{v}(t)$ was of constant magnitude (ωR) but of changing direction. The theorem says that the vector $(d\mathbf{v}/dt)$ is perpendicular to $\mathbf{v}$, so the acceleration vector $\mathbf{a} = (d\mathbf{v}/dt)$ is seen immediately to be perpendicular to the velocity vector **v** of the particle. We will use this theorem shortly in discussing the circular motion of a particle described by plane-polar coordinates.

Next, we again consider a particle moving in a circle of radius R lying in the xy plane, but now we will use plane-polar coordinates (r, θ) to describe the motion. Since the particle is moving in a circle of radius R, the polar coordinates of the particle are $[R, \theta(t)]$, where the angle $\theta(t)$ varies with time as the particle moves. The position vector **r** of the particle has a magnitude R and is in the direction outward from the center of the circle, so

$$\mathbf{r} = R\hat{\mathbf{u}}_r \qquad (5.200)$$

where $\hat{\mathbf{u}}_r$ is the unit vector in the direction of increasing polar coordinate r. The position vector **r** in Eq. (5.200) is shown in Fig. 5.29, and the unit vector $\hat{\mathbf{u}}_r$ is also shown. To find the velocity vector **v** of the particle, we

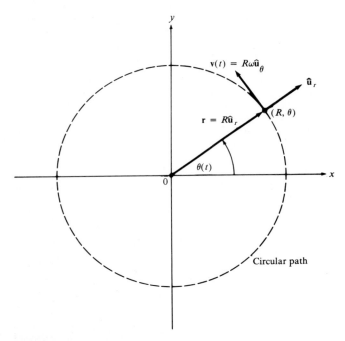

FIGURE 5.29
A particle located at the point of plane-polar coordinates (R, θ) as the particle moves in a circular path as the polar angle $\theta(t)$ varies with time. The position vector $\mathbf{r} = R\hat{\mathbf{u}}_r$ given by Eq. (5.200) and the unit vector $\hat{\mathbf{u}}_r$ are shown at one instant of time, as is the velocity vector $\mathbf{v}(t) = R\omega\hat{\mathbf{u}}_\theta$ given by Eq. (5.207).

use the definition (5.159) of **v**, and write, since R is a constant,

$$\mathbf{v}(t) = \frac{d\mathbf{r}}{dt} = R\frac{d\hat{\mathbf{u}}_r}{dt} \tag{5.201}$$

In Eq. (5.201), $(d\hat{\mathbf{u}}_r/dt)$ is the derivative, with respect to time, of the unit vector $\hat{\mathbf{u}}_r$ whose direction changes with time as the particle moves around its circular path. From the theorem just proved, we can see that the vector $(d\hat{\mathbf{u}}_r/dt)$ will be perpendicular to the unit vector $\hat{\mathbf{u}}_r$.

In order to obtain an expression for $(d\hat{\mathbf{u}}_r/dt)$, we use expression (5.101) for $\hat{\mathbf{u}}_r$, obtaining

$$\frac{d\hat{\mathbf{u}}_r}{dt} = \frac{d}{dt}\left[(\cos\theta)\hat{\mathbf{x}} + (\sin\theta)\hat{\mathbf{y}}\right]$$

$$= \left[\frac{d}{dt}(\cos\theta)\right]\hat{\mathbf{x}} + \left[\frac{d}{dt}(\sin\theta)\right]\hat{\mathbf{y}} \tag{5.202}$$

because the polar coordinate $\theta(t)$ is a function of time. Taking derivatives in Eq. (5.202) gives

$$\frac{d\hat{\mathbf{u}}_r}{dt} = \left[(-\sin\theta)\frac{d\theta}{dt}\right]\hat{\mathbf{x}} + \left[(\cos\theta)\frac{d\theta}{dt}\right]\hat{\mathbf{y}} \tag{5.203}$$

We now define the angular velocity ω of the particle by

$$\omega(t) \equiv \frac{d\theta(t)}{dt} \tag{5.204}$$

where, in the most general case, ω will be a function of $\omega(t)$ of the time. Substituting Eq. (5.204) in Eq. (5.203) gives

$$\frac{d\hat{\mathbf{u}}_r}{dt} = \omega\left[(-\sin\theta)\hat{\mathbf{x}} + (\cos\theta)\hat{\mathbf{y}}\right] = \omega\hat{\mathbf{u}}_\theta \tag{5.205}$$

on using expression (5.105) for the unit vector $\hat{\mathbf{u}}_\theta$ in the direction of increasing coordinate θ. Equation (5.205) says that the vector $(d\hat{\mathbf{u}}_r/dt)$ is of magnitude $\omega = (d\theta/dt)$ and is parallel to the unit vector $\hat{\mathbf{u}}_\theta$. Since we know from our earlier results that $\hat{\mathbf{u}}_\theta$ is perpendicular to $\hat{\mathbf{u}}_r$, the result (5.205) shows explicitly that the vector $(d\hat{\mathbf{u}}_r/dt)$ is perpendicular to the vector $\hat{\mathbf{u}}_r$. The fact that the vector $(d\hat{\mathbf{u}}_r/dt)$ depends on the time may be emphasized by writing Eq. (5.205) as

$$\frac{d\hat{\mathbf{u}}_r}{dt} = \left(\frac{d\theta}{dt}\right)\hat{\mathbf{u}}_\theta \tag{5.206}$$

because, since $\theta(t)$ depends on time t, the derivative $(d\theta/dt)$ will, in the most general case, depend on time also. Further, the unit vector $\hat{\mathbf{u}}_\theta$ itself depends, from Eq. (5.105), on the time through the time dependence of the polar angle θ. Combining Eq. (5.206) with expression (5.201) for the velocity vector $\mathbf{v}(t)$ gives the result

$$\mathbf{v}(t) = R\left(\frac{d\theta}{dt}\right)\hat{\mathbf{u}}_\theta = R\omega\hat{\mathbf{u}}_\theta \qquad (5.207)$$

for the particle moving in a circle of radius R. The velocity vector $\mathbf{v}(t)$ is also shown in Figure 5.29, and we see (as we already knew) that $\mathbf{v}$ is tangent to the circular path because $\hat{\mathbf{u}}_\theta$ is tangent to the circle.

Using Eq. (5.200) for the position vector $\mathbf{r}$ and Eq. (5.207) for the velocity vector $\mathbf{v}$, we can calculate $\mathbf{r}$ if we know R and calculate $\mathbf{v}$, at any instant of time t, if we know $\omega = (d\theta/dt)$ at that instant of time. The magnitudes are found, by taking scalar products, to be $r = R$ (the radius of the circle), and the speed v is

$$v = R\omega = R\left(\frac{d\theta}{dt}\right) \qquad (5.208)$$

Since R is a constant for circular motion, r is constant. The speed $v = R\omega$ will be constant in time only if the angular velocity ω is a constant. If ω is a function $\omega(t)$ of the time (which it may be), then the speed v will also depend on the time.

A common case of circular motion is that in which the angular velocity ω has a constant value. Then, from the definition (5.204), we have

$$\frac{d\theta(t)}{dt} = \omega = \text{constant} \qquad (5.209)$$

which can be integrated to give

$$\theta(t) = \omega t + \theta(0) \qquad (5.210)$$

where $\theta(0)$ is the value of the polar coordinate θ at the initial instant of time $t = 0$. While it is not necessary, it is convenient to choose $\theta(0) = 0$, which is equivalent to saying that the particle starts its circular motion at the point of polar coordinates $(R, 0)$ at time $t = 0$. With that choice, Eq. (5.210) becomes

$$\theta(t) = \omega t \qquad (5.211)$$

for the time dependence of the polar angle θ, so, in this case in which the angular velocity ω is constant, θ depends linearly on the time. With Eq. (5.211), we can use our earlier results to find the position and velocity vectors of the particle. From Eq. (5.200), we still have the position vector

$$\mathbf{r}(t) = R\hat{\mathbf{u}}_r \qquad (5.212)$$

and, from Eq. (5.207), the velocity vector is

$$\mathbf{v}(t) = R\left(\frac{d\theta}{dt}\right)\hat{\mathbf{u}}_\theta = R\omega\hat{\mathbf{u}}_\theta \tag{5.213}$$

where, in this example, $(d\theta/dt) = \omega$ is constant because ω is constant in Eq. (5.211). [Note that, if ω were *not* constant, the simple linear relation (5.211) between $\theta(t)$ and time t would not hold, and $(d\theta/dt)$ in the expression (5.213) for the velocity vector $\mathbf{v}$ would be more complicated.] As before, the magnitudes r and v are, from (5.212) and (5.213), $r = R$ and $v = R\omega$. We conclude that, in this case of constant angular velocity ω, the particle moves in a circle of radius R with constant speed $v = R\omega$.

Finally, we return to the general case of circular motion for which the angular velocity ω will not be constant and may be any function $\omega(t)$ of the time. We are interested in the acceleration vector $\mathbf{a}$ of the particle moving in a circle of radius R. From the definition (5.184) of acceleration and using Eq. (5.207), we have

$$\mathbf{a}(t) = \frac{d\mathbf{v}(t)}{dt} = R\frac{d}{dt}\left[\left(\frac{d\theta}{dt}\right)\hat{\mathbf{u}}_\theta\right]$$

so

$$\mathbf{a}(t) = R\left[\left(\frac{d^2\theta}{dt^2}\right)\hat{\mathbf{u}}_\theta + \left(\frac{d\theta}{dt}\right)\left(\frac{d\hat{\mathbf{u}}_\theta}{dt}\right)\right] \tag{5.214}$$

where $(d^2\theta/dt^2)$ and $(d\theta/dt)$ will both be nonzero in the most general case. To find $\mathbf{a}(t)$ from Eq. (5.214), we need to know $(d\hat{\mathbf{u}}_\theta/dt)$. Returning to the expression (5.108),

$$\hat{\mathbf{u}}_\theta = (-\sin\theta)\hat{\mathbf{x}} + (\cos\theta)\hat{\mathbf{y}} \tag{5.108}$$

we have, since $\theta(t)$ depends on the time,

$$\frac{d\hat{\mathbf{u}}_\theta}{dt} = (-\cos\theta)\frac{d\theta}{dt}\hat{\mathbf{x}} + (-\sin\theta)\frac{d\theta}{dt}\hat{\mathbf{y}}$$

$$= -\left(\frac{d\theta}{dt}\right)[(\cos\theta)\hat{\mathbf{x}} + (\sin\theta)\hat{\mathbf{y}}]$$

and

$$\frac{d\hat{\mathbf{u}}_\theta}{dt} = -\left(\frac{d\theta}{dt}\right)\hat{\mathbf{u}}_r = \frac{d\theta}{dt}(-\hat{\mathbf{u}}_r) \tag{5.215}$$

on comparison with the expression (5.107) for $\hat{\mathbf{u}}_r$. We see from Eq. (5.215) that $(d\hat{\mathbf{u}}_\theta/dt)$ equals $(d\theta/dt)$ times $(-\hat{\mathbf{u}}_r)$, which is in the direction of decreasing r, so $(d\hat{\mathbf{u}}_\theta/dt)$ points in the direction inward along the radius of the circle. With Eq. (5.215), the expression (5.214) for the acceleration vector becomes

$$\mathbf{a}(t) = R\left[\left(\frac{d^2\theta}{dt^2}\right)\hat{\mathbf{u}}_\theta - \left(\frac{d\theta}{dt}\right)^2\hat{\mathbf{u}}_r\right]$$

$$= R\left[\left(\frac{d^2\theta}{dt^2}\right)\hat{\mathbf{u}}_\theta + \left(\frac{d\theta}{dt}\right)^2(-\hat{\mathbf{u}}_r)\right] \qquad (5.216)$$

This equation says that $\mathbf{a}(t)$ is a vector with a component $R(d^2\theta/dt^2)$ parallel to $\hat{\mathbf{u}}_\theta$ and thus in the direction of increasing coordinate θ, and a component $R(d\theta/dt)^2$ parallel to $(-\hat{\mathbf{u}}_r)$ and thus in the direction of decreasing r.

Since the angular velocity $\omega \equiv (d\theta/dt)$, we define the angular acceleration α by

$$\alpha \equiv \frac{d\omega}{dt} = \frac{d^2\theta}{dt^2} \qquad (5.217)$$

Using this definition, the expression (5.216) for the acceleration vector $\mathbf{a}(t)$ can be written as

$$\mathbf{a}(t) = R\alpha\hat{\mathbf{u}}_\theta + R\omega^2(-\hat{\mathbf{u}}_r) \qquad (5.218)$$

Equation (5.218) tells us that the acceleration vector $\mathbf{a}(t)$ is the sum of two vector components. The first component, $R\alpha\hat{\mathbf{u}}_\theta$, is in the direction of increasing θ and so is tangent to the circular path. This component is called the *tangential component* of the acceleration $\mathbf{a}(t)$ of the particle. The second component, $R\omega^2(-\hat{\mathbf{u}}_r)$, is directed inward along the radius of the circular path and is called the *radial component* of $\mathbf{a}(t)$. Note that $\mathbf{a}(t)$ depends on the time t because, in the most general case, the angular acceleration α and the angular velocity ω can be functions of the time, and also the directions of the unit vectors $\hat{\mathbf{u}}_r$ and $\hat{\mathbf{u}}_\theta$ will always be changing with time as the particle moves. The vector $\mathbf{a}(t)$ and its components are shown in Fig. 5.30.

Returning to the example in which we have constant angular velocity ω, for which, from Eq. (5.211) $\theta = \omega t$, and the angular acceleration $\alpha = (d^2\theta/dt^2) = 0$ and $(d\theta/dt) = \omega$, a constant, in this case. Then Eq. (5.218) gives the acceleration vector $\mathbf{a}(t)$ as

$$\mathbf{a}(t) = R\omega^2(-\hat{\mathbf{u}}_r) \qquad (5.219)$$

Equation (5.219) says that, if the angular velocity ω is constant so that the angular acceleration is zero, then the acceleration vector $\mathbf{a}(t)$ of the particle is directed inward along the radius of the circle and there is no tangential component of the acceleration. This radial component $R\omega^2(-\hat{\mathbf{u}}_r)$ is the familiar centripetal acceleration of circular motion.

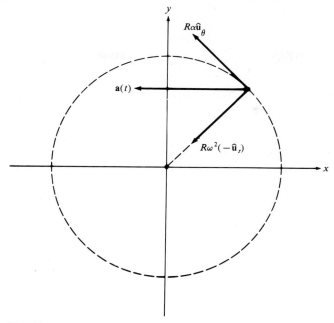

FIGURE 5.30
Particle moving in a circular path of radius R with acceleration vector $\mathbf{a}(t)$ given by Eq. (5.218). The vector $R\alpha\hat{\mathbf{u}}_\theta$ is the tangential component of $\mathbf{a}(t)$, and the vector $R\omega^2(-\hat{\mathbf{u}}_r)$ is the radial component of $\mathbf{a}(t)$; the two components are perpendicular to each other.

Finally, it should be pointed out that, in order to determine the acceleration vector $\mathbf{a}(t)$ in Eq. (5.218) when the angular velocity is not constant, we must know the functional dependence $\theta(t)$ of the coordinate θ on the time so that we can calculate the angular acceleration α and angular velocity ω in the expression for $\mathbf{a}(t)$.

Having discussed the derivative of a vector, we consider next one kind of vector integral, called a *line integral*. Line integrals are used frequently in physics to treat, among other topics, the work done by a force in moving a body along a curved path in space.

Consider first a curve C in space, where the vector

$$\mathbf{r} = x\hat{\mathbf{x}} + y\hat{\mathbf{y}} + z\hat{\mathbf{z}} \tag{5.220}$$

is the position vector (relative to an origin O) of the point $P_1(x, y, z)$, of coordinates (x, y, z) on the curve C. Thus the vector $\mathbf{r}$ given by Eq. (5.220) is the vector from the origin O to the point $P_1(x, y, z)$ on the curve C. We now take the differential of both sides of Eq. (5.220), which gives us

$$d\mathbf{r} = (dx)\hat{\mathbf{x}} + (dy)\hat{\mathbf{y}} + (dz)\hat{\mathbf{z}} \qquad (5.221)$$

In Eq. (5.221), we interpret $d\mathbf{r}$ as a differential vector of infinitesimal length whose scalar components are the differentials dx, dy, and dz of the rectangular coordinate variables x, y, and z. The magnitude dr, where

$$dr = (d\mathbf{r} \cdot d\mathbf{r})^{1/2} = \left[(dx)^2 + (dy)^2 + (dz)^2 \right]^{1/2} \qquad (5.222)$$

is an infinitesimal scalar quantity. We may also think of the vector $d\mathbf{r}$ as the infinitesimal vector from a point P_1, of coordinates (x, y, z), on curve C, to a second nearby point P_2 of coordinates $([x + dx], [y + dy], [z + dz])$ on curve C. This is shown in Fig. 5.31, from which we see that the vector

$$\mathbf{r} + d\mathbf{r} = (x + dx)\hat{\mathbf{x}} + (y + dy)\hat{\mathbf{y}} + (z + dz)\hat{\mathbf{z}} \qquad (5.223)$$

is the position vector (from origin O) to point P_2. We often refer to $d\mathbf{r}$ as a *differential position vector*.

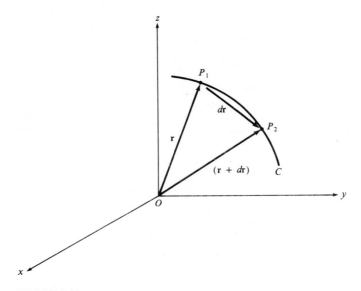

FIGURE 5.31
Curve C, showing points P_1, of coordinates (x, y, z) and P_2, of coordinates $([x + dx], [y + dy], [z + dz])$ on the curve. The vector $\mathbf{r} = x\hat{\mathbf{x}} + y\hat{\mathbf{y}} + z\hat{\mathbf{z}}$ is the position vector from the origin O to point P_1, the vector $d\mathbf{r} = (dx)\hat{\mathbf{x}} + (dy)\hat{\mathbf{y}} + (dx)\hat{\mathbf{z}}$ is the infinitesimal vector from P_1 to P_2, and the vector $(\mathbf{r} + d\mathbf{r}) = (x + dx)\hat{\mathbf{x}} + (y + dy)\hat{\mathbf{y}} + (z + dz)\hat{\mathbf{z}}$ is the position vector from the origin O to P_2. The scalar distance dr from P_1 to P_2 is equal to $[(dx)^2 + (dy)^2 + (dz)^2]^{1/2}$.

We now recall, from Eq. (5.171), that

$$\frac{d\mathbf{r}}{ds} = \hat{\mathbf{t}} \tag{5.171}$$

where $(d\mathbf{r}/ds)$ is the derivative of the position vector $\mathbf{r}$, given by Eq. (5.220), with respect to arc length s along a curve C and $\hat{\mathbf{t}}$ is a unit vector tangent to the curve C. Multiplying both sides of Eq. (5.171) by the differential ds gives us

$$d\mathbf{r} = (ds)\hat{\mathbf{t}} \tag{5.224}$$

Equation (5.224) says that the infinitesimal differential position vector $d\mathbf{r}$ is equal to the unit tangent vector $\hat{\mathbf{t}}$ times the scalar differential ds of arc length. These quantities are shown in Fig. 5.32, which for simplicity is two-dimensional. We conclude that, if $\mathbf{r}$ is the position vector (5.220) to a point P on a curve C, then the differential vector $d\mathbf{r}$, given by Eq. (5.224), is a vector tangent to curve C at point P, and its magnitude dr is equal to the differential ds of arc length at point P.

Given the curve C and the differential position vector $d\mathbf{r}$, we consider next a vector $\mathbf{A}$ which has a different value at each point in space.

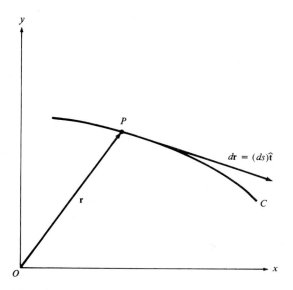

FIGURE 5.32
Curve C, showing the position vector $\mathbf{r}$ from origin O to point P on the curve. The differential vector $d\mathbf{r} = (ds)\hat{\mathbf{t}}$ is tangent to curve C at point P since $\hat{\mathbf{t}}$ is a tangent unit vector, and the magnitude dr is equal to ds, the differential of arc length at P.

In particular, the vector **A** will have a different value at each point of the curve C, so, if (x, y, z) are the coordinates of a point P of the curve, the vector **A** will depend on the coordinates (x, y, z). From the definition (5.220), the position vector **r** of point P depends on the coordinates (x, y, z) of P. We can, therefore, say that vector **A** will depend on the position vector **r**, and write

$$\mathbf{A} = \mathbf{A}(\mathbf{r}) \qquad (5.225)$$

Equation (5.225) says that **A** is a vector which is a function of the position vector **r**, and hence of the coordinates (x, y, z) of the point P at which **A** is evaluated. An example is

$$\mathbf{A} = (xy)\hat{\mathbf{z}}$$

which says that the vector **A** is in the $(+z)$ direction and its magnitude is equal to xy, where (x, y) are the coordinates of the point at which **A** is evaluated. Note that this vector function of a *vector* is not the same as a vector which is a function of a *scalar*, an example of which might be a force vector $\mathbf{F}(t)$ which is a function of the time t, a scalar.

With these results, we return to the curve C in space and, at any point P of the curve, form the scalar product

$$\mathbf{A}(\mathbf{r}) \cdot d\mathbf{r} \qquad (5.226)$$

In Eq. (5.226), $\mathbf{A}(\mathbf{r})$ is a vector which is a function of the position of point P on curve C [**r** is the position vector (5.220) of point P relative to the chosen origin] and $d\mathbf{r}$ is the differential position vector given by Eqs. (5.221) and (5.224). We can see the meaning of the scalar product (5.226) by using Eq. (5.224) for the differential vector $d\mathbf{r}$, obtaining

$$\mathbf{A}(\mathbf{r}) \cdot d\mathbf{r} = \mathbf{A}(\mathbf{r}) \cdot (ds)\hat{\mathbf{t}} = \left[\mathbf{A}(\mathbf{r}) \cdot \hat{\mathbf{t}}\right] ds \qquad (5.227)$$

From the definition of the scalar product, we can see from Eq. (5.227) that $[\mathbf{A}(\mathbf{r}) \cdot \hat{\mathbf{t}}]$ is the component of the vector $\mathbf{A}(\mathbf{r})$ along the tangential unit vector $\hat{\mathbf{t}}$, at point P. Therefore, from Eq. (5.227), the quantity $[\mathbf{A}(\mathbf{r}) \cdot d\mathbf{r}]$ is equal to the tangential component of $\mathbf{A}(\mathbf{r})$ times the differential ds of arc length s at point P. It should be emphasized that the quantity $[\mathbf{A}(\mathbf{r}) \cdot d\mathbf{r}]$ given in Eq. (5.227) will have a different value at different points P of the curve C because, as seen from Fig. 5.33, the position vector **r** is different at different points P, and so, therefore, are the vectors $\mathbf{A}(\mathbf{r})$ and $d\mathbf{r}$.

We can now define the line integral of a vector function $\mathbf{A}(\mathbf{r})$ along a curve C as follows. Given the vector function $\mathbf{A}(\mathbf{r})$ of the position vector **r** of point P on curve C, as discussed above. At every point P of the curve, we form the quantity $[\mathbf{A}(\mathbf{r}) \cdot d\mathbf{r}]$ given by Eq. (5.227). We

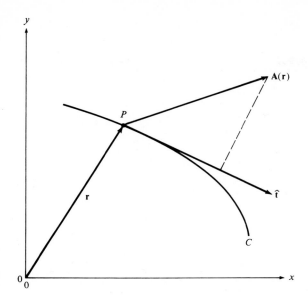

FIGURE 5.33
Curve C, showing, at point P, the position vector $\mathbf{r}$ and the vector $\mathbf{A}(\mathbf{r})$ at P. The unit vector $\hat{\mathbf{t}}$ is tangent to the curve at P, and $[\mathbf{A}(\mathbf{r}) \cdot \hat{\mathbf{t}}]$ is the component of $\mathbf{A}(\mathbf{r})$ along $\hat{\mathbf{t}}$, so, from Eq. (5.227), $[\mathbf{A}(\mathbf{r}) \cdot d\mathbf{r}]$ is that component times the differential ds of arc length s at point P.

then sum or "add up" all the values of $[A(\mathbf{r}) \cdot d\mathbf{r}]$ for all the points P along the given curve C, and obtain the integral

$$\int_C \mathbf{A}(\mathbf{r}) \cdot d\mathbf{r} \qquad (5.228)$$

which is called the *line integral* of the vector function $\mathbf{A}(\mathbf{r})$ along the curve C. Usually one takes the line integral (5.228) between specified points of curve C. It should also be clear that, for a given vector function $\mathbf{A}(\mathbf{r})$, the line integral (5.228) will be different for different curves C.

Let's consider a simple example of a line integral, in which the vector function $\mathbf{A} = (xy)\hat{\mathbf{y}}$ and the curve C is the parabola $x = y^2$ (in the xy plane) between the points $(0, 0)$ and $(4, 2)$. The vector $\mathbf{A}$ clearly depends on the point of the curve C at which $\mathbf{A}$ is evaluated. The differential position vector $d\mathbf{r}$ is given by Eq. (5.221), so the scalar product (5.226) is

$$\mathbf{A} \cdot d\mathbf{r} = \left[(xy)\hat{\mathbf{y}}\right] \cdot \left[(dx)\hat{\mathbf{x}} + (dy)\hat{\mathbf{y}} + (dz)\hat{\mathbf{z}}\right] = xy\, dy \quad (5.229)$$

The line integral (5.228) is given by

$$\int_C \mathbf{A} \cdot d\mathbf{r} = \int_C xy \, dy \qquad (5.230)$$

where the curve C is the parabola $x = y^2$ between the points $(0, 0)$ and $(4, 2)$. The fact that the line integral (5.230) is along the curve $x = y^2$ means that the values of x and y in the line integral must be such that $x = y^2$. Substituting $x = y^2$ in the integral (5.230) gives

$$\int_C \mathbf{A} \cdot d\mathbf{r} = \int_0^2 y^3 \, dy = \left[\tfrac{1}{4}y^4\right]_0^2 = 4 \qquad (5.231)$$

where the limits are $y = 0$ and $y = 2$ in Eq. (5.231) because we are taking the line integral along the curve $x = y^2$ from the point $(x = 0, y = 0)$ to the point $(x = 4, y = 2)$. As shown in Exercise 5.22, the line integral in Eq. (5.230) depends on the curve C. If, instead of the parabola $x = y^2$ between the points $(0, 0)$ and $(4, 2)$, the curve is the straight line $2y = x$ between the same points, then the line integral (5.230) has a different value.

One of the important applications of the line integral to physics is in calculating the work done by a force in moving a body along a curved path. Consider the curve C in Fig. 5.34 which, although not necessary, is two-dimensional and in the xy plane. Any point P on the curve is located by the position vector $\mathbf{r}$ relative to the origin 0. A particle at point P experiences a force $\mathbf{F}(\mathbf{r})$, where the vector $\mathbf{F}(\mathbf{r})$ may be different at different points P, so $\mathbf{F}(\mathbf{r})$ depends on the location of P. At point P, the particle moves a differential or infinitesimal distance ds along the curve C, where s is the arc length. The infinitesimal displacement of the particle at P due to the force $\mathbf{F}(\mathbf{r})$ is the vector $d\mathbf{r}$, where, from Eq. (5.224),

$$d\mathbf{r} = (ds)\hat{\mathbf{t}} \qquad (5.232)$$

and where $\hat{\mathbf{t}}$ is the unit vector tangent to curve C at point P. From the definition (5.66), the infinitesimal amount of work dW done by the force $\mathbf{F}(\mathbf{r})$ in moving the particle through the displacement $d\mathbf{r}$ is

$$dW = \mathbf{F}(\mathbf{r}) \cdot d\mathbf{r} \qquad (5.233)$$

From Eq. (5.233) and Fig. 5.34, we see that the infinitesimal amount of work dW will be different at different points P of the curve because the force vector $\mathbf{F}(\mathbf{r})$ and the displacement vector $d\mathbf{r}$ are different at different points. Suppose the particle starts at point P_0 on the curve and ends up at point P_1. We can calculate the total amount of work W done by the force in moving the particle between points P_0 and P_1 by summing all of the

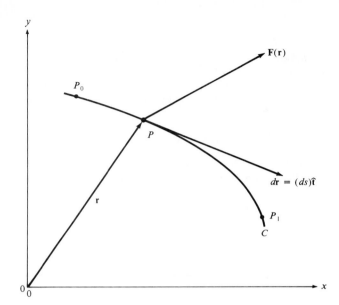

FIGURE 5.34
Curve C in the xy plane, showing the position vector $\mathbf{r}$ of a point P on the curve. The vector $\mathbf{F}(\mathbf{r})$ is the force exerted on a particle at P; the particle moves along curve C from point P_0 to point P_1. The displacement vector of the particle at P is $d\mathbf{r}$.

infinitesimal elements of work dW given by Eq. (5.233) as

$$W = \int_C dW = \int_C \mathbf{F}(\mathbf{r}) \cdot d\mathbf{r} = \int_C \left[\mathbf{F}(\mathbf{r}) \cdot \hat{\mathbf{t}}\right] ds \quad (5.234)$$

The integral in Eq. (5.234) is the line integral of $\mathbf{F}(\mathbf{r})$ along the curve C because each dW given by Eq. (5.233) is evaluated at a point P of the curve. In order to evaluate the line integral in Eq. (5.234), we must, of course, know the curve C and the way in which the force $\mathbf{F}$ depends on the position of point P on the curve.

As an example, consider a particle moving along the line $y = x$ (in the xy plane) from $(0, 0)$ to $(1, 1)$ under the influence of the force $\mathbf{F} = (F_0 x)\hat{\mathbf{y}}$, where F_0 is a constant. The force $\mathbf{F}$ is seen to have a constant direction [the $(+y)$ direction] but a magnitude $(F_0 x)$ which depends on the x coordinate of the particle as it moves along the line $y = x$. We want to calculate the work W done by the force $\mathbf{F}$ in moving the particle from the origin $(0, 0)$ to the point $(1, 1)$. We need to find the infinitesimal displacement vector $d\mathbf{r}$ of the particle at any point of the curve C, which in this case is the straight line $y = x$. From Eq. (5.221), since $z = 0$ in

We use Eq. (5.242) to find the differentials dx and dy as

$$dx = -L \sin \theta \, d\theta \qquad dy = L \cos \theta \, d\theta \qquad (5.243)$$

so the differential position vector $d\mathbf{r}$ is, in this case,

$$d\mathbf{r} = L[(-\sin \theta)\hat{\mathbf{x}} + (\cos \theta)\hat{\mathbf{y}}] d\theta = (L \, d\theta)\hat{\mathbf{u}}_\theta \qquad (5.244)$$

on using the expression (5.105) for the unit vector $\hat{\mathbf{u}}_\theta$ in the tangential direction. Using Eq. (5.239) for $\mathbf{F}$ and Eq. (5.244) for $d\mathbf{r}$, we have

$$\mathbf{F} \cdot d\mathbf{r} = FL \, d\theta \qquad (5.245)$$

since $(\hat{\mathbf{u}}_\theta \cdot \hat{\mathbf{u}}_\theta) = 1$. Then, from Eq. (5.234), the work W done by the force $\mathbf{F}$ is

$$W = \int_C \mathbf{F} \cdot d\mathbf{r} = \int_C FL \, d\theta = FL \int_C d\theta \qquad (5.246)$$

where the line integral is along the curve C that is the circular path of the particle. Note that we have really already specified the curve C when we wrote down Eqs. (5.242) connecting the coordinates (x, y) with the polar coordinates (L, θ) of the circle of radius L since Eq. (5.242) leads to

$$x^2 + y^2 = L^2 \qquad (5.247)$$

the equation of a circle of radius L. We are told that the particle moves one revolution around the circle, so the variable of integration θ in Eq. (5.246) varies from $\theta = 0$ to $\theta = 2\pi$. The work done is, therefore,

$$W = FL \int_0^{2\pi} d\theta = 2\pi FL \qquad (5.248)$$

by the force $\mathbf{F}$ on the mass in moving the mass one revolution around the circular path of radius L.

Many other topics in vector calculus are used frequently in physics. However, these are beyond the scope of this brief introduction to the subject. For further reading on vector analysis, written with applications in mind, I suggest *Advanced Calculus for Applications*, 2d ed., by F. B. Hildebrand, Prentice-Hall, 1976, chap. 6.

EXERCISES

5.19. Given the two-dimensional position vector $\mathbf{r}(t) = x(t)\hat{\mathbf{x}} + y(t)\hat{\mathbf{y}}$ of a moving particle in Eq. (5.158), and the velocity vector $\mathbf{v}(t) = [dx(t)/dt]\hat{\mathbf{x}} + [dy(t)/dt]\hat{\mathbf{y}}$ in Eq. (5.165), where $\mathbf{v}(t)$ is tangent to the path of the particle. Show that for $\mathbf{v}(t)$ to be always normal to $\mathbf{r}(t)$, the path of the particle must be a circle. Do this as follows. First, use the scalar product to determine the condition that must hold if $\mathbf{v}(t)$ is to be normal to $\mathbf{r}(t)$. Second, integrate this condition and obtain the equation of the path of the particle when $\mathbf{v}(t)$ and $\mathbf{r}(t)$ are perpendicular to each other.

5.20. Consider a particle moving in a circle of radius A so that its polar coordinate θ varies with time as $\theta(t) = bt^2$, where b is a constant. (a) Find the position vector $\mathbf{r}$ of the particle, using unit vectors in plane-polar coordinates. Does $\mathbf{r}$ depend on the time? (b) Find the velocity vector $\mathbf{v}$ of the particle. (c) Find the speed v of the particle. (d) Do the magnitude of $\mathbf{v}$, the direction of $\mathbf{v}$, both, or neither, depend on the time? Explain. (e) Find the acceleration $\mathbf{a}$ of the particle. Does $\mathbf{a}$ depend on the time? (f) Describe how the magnitudes of the tangential and radial components of $\mathbf{a}$ vary with time. (g) Calculate the magnitude a of the acceleration. Does a depend on the time? (h) In this motion, is the angular velocity constant? Is the angular acceleration constant?

5.21. A particle is constrained to move along the line $y = 2x + 1$ (in the xy plane) such that its x coordinate varies with time t as $x(t) = 2t$. (a) Write down the position vector $\mathbf{r}(t)$ of the particle as a function of time. (b) Calculate $\mathbf{r}(1)$, the position vector of the particle when the time $t = 1$ second. Make a sketch showing the vector $\mathbf{r}(1)$. (c) What is the position of the particle when $t = 1$ second? (d) Find the velocity vector $\mathbf{v}$ of the particle. (e) Does $\mathbf{v}$ depend on the time? Calculate the speed v.

5.22. Evaluate the line integral of $\mathbf{A} = (xy)\hat{\mathbf{y}}$ along the straight line $y = (x/2)$ from the point $(0, 0)$ to the point $(x = 4, y = 2)$. Compare your answer with the line integral of the same vector $\mathbf{A}$ between the same points of the different curve $x = y^2$ done as an example in the text.

5.23. A particle moves along the parabola $y = x^2$, in the xy plane, acted on by a force $\mathbf{F}$ in the x direction whose magnitude $F = axy$, where a is a constant. The force moves the particle from the origin $(0, 0)$ to the point $(2, 4)$. Calculate the total work done on the particle by the force by evaluating the appropriate line integral.

SOLUTIONS
TO THE
EXERCISES

1.1. Adding $(-2x)$ to both sides of the equation gives

$$2x + 6 = 10$$

Adding (-6) to both sides gives

$$2x = 4$$

Dividing both sides by 2 gives the answer $x = 2$.

1.2. Adding $(+y)$ to both sides of the equation gives

$$y = 2x$$

thereby giving y in terms of x. Since we have only one equation in the two unknowns x and y, we cannot solve for separate values of x and y.

1.3.

$$z = \frac{-b \pm (b^2 - 4ac)^{1/2}}{2a} \quad \text{with} \quad a = 1, b = -1, c = -2$$

so

$$z = \frac{1 \pm (9)^{1/2}}{2} = \frac{1 \pm 3}{2}$$

giving $z_1 = 2$, $z_2 = (-1)$.

1.4. Adding the first and third equations gives

$$2x + z = 10 \tag{S.1}$$

Multiplying the second equation by (-2) gives

$$-2x + 4z = 20$$

Adding these equations yields

$$5z = 30$$

$$z = 6$$

Substituting $z = 6$ into Eq. (S.1) gives

$$2x + 6 = 10$$

$$x = 2$$

Finally, substituting $x = 2$ into the first of the original equations gives us

$$4 - y = 0$$

$$y = 4$$

completing the solution for x, y, and z.

1.5. (a) From Eq. (1.43), $\sin(\theta - \phi) = \sin\theta\cos\phi - \cos\theta\sin\phi$. If $\theta = 0$, we have

$$\sin(-\phi) = \sin 0 \cos\phi - \cos 0 \sin\phi$$

Since $\sin 0 = 0$, $\cos 0 = 1$,

$$\sin(-\phi) = -\sin\phi$$

(b) From Eq. (1.44), $\cos(\theta - \phi) = \cos\theta\cos\phi + \sin\theta\sin\phi$. If $\theta = 0$, we have

$$\cos(-\phi) = \cos 0 \cos\phi + \sin 0 \sin\phi$$

so

$$\cos(-\phi) = \cos\phi$$

1.6. Since $x = \tan^{-1} 1$, $\tan x = 1$, $x = 45°$.

1.7.
$$\sec\theta = (1 + \tan^2\theta)^{1/2}$$

$$\sec^2\theta = 1 + \tan^2\theta = 1 + \frac{\sin^2\theta}{\cos^2\theta}$$

$$\frac{1}{\cos^2\theta} = \frac{\cos^2\theta + \sin^2\theta}{\cos^2\theta} = \frac{1}{\cos^2\theta}$$

1.8. For an equilateral triangle, all of the sides have the same length, which we will call a. Substituting a for each side in Eqs. (1.64) to (1.66) gives

$$a^2 = a^2 + a^2 - 2a^2\cos\gamma = 2a^2(1 - \cos\gamma)$$

$$a^2 = a^2 + a^2 - 2a^2\cos\beta = 2a^2(1 - \cos\beta)$$

$$a^2 = a^2 + a^2 - 2a^2\cos\alpha = 2a^2(1 - \cos\alpha)$$

These equations reduce to $\cos \alpha = (1/2)$; $\cos \beta = (1/2)$; $\cos \gamma = (1/2)$, so $\alpha = \beta = \gamma = 60°$.

2.1. Since the expression $w = 7u^2 + 6u + 3$ gives w as a function of u, w is the dependent variable and u is the independent variable. Thus, assigning a value to u (for example, $u = 2$) determines the value of w. If $u = 2$, $w = 43$.

2.2. We can solve Eq. (2.1), $y = x^2$, for x in terms of y, obtaining

$$x = \pm\sqrt{y}$$

In this relation, the dependent variable x is a function of the independent variable y. Note that x is a many (i.e., two)-valued function of y since two values of the dependent variable x correspond to each value of the independent variable y.

2.3. The functional relation between C and r is $C = 2\pi r$. In this relation, C is the dependent variable and r is the independent variable.

2.4. Since $f(x) = 3x^2 + 2$, we have
(a) $f(2) = 3 \cdot (2)^2 + 2 = 12 + 2 = 14$;
(b) $f(0) = 3 \cdot (0)^2 + 2 = 0 + 2 = 2$;
(c) $f(-1) = 3 \cdot (-1)^2 + 2 = 3 + 2 = 5$.

2.5. Since $y(x, t) = A \sin(kx - \omega t)$, where A, k, and ω are constants, the dependent variable y is a function of the *two* independent variables x and t. Then (a) $y(0, 0)$ is obtained by substituting $x = 0$, $t = 0$ in the expression for $y(x, t)$, giving

$$y(0, 0) = A \sin(k \cdot 0 - \omega \cdot 0) = A \sin(0) = 0$$

(b) $y(0, t)$ is obtained by setting $x = 0$, giving

$$y(0, t) = A \sin(k \cdot 0 - \omega t)$$

$$= A \sin(0 - \omega t) = A \sin(-\omega t) = -A \sin \omega t$$

so $y(0, t)$ is itself a function of the variable t and is not just a number as was $y(0, 0) = 0$ in part (a) above; (c) $y(x, 0)$ is obtained by setting $t = 0$, giving

$$y(x, 0) = A \sin(kx - \omega \cdot 0) = A \sin(kx - 0) = A \sin kx$$

2.6. If we replace the variable x in $f(x)$ by the new variable $(x - a)$, we get $f(x - a)$. Since in this problem

$$f(x) = (1 - x^2)^{1/2}$$

$$f(x - a) = \left(1 - [x - a]^2\right)^{1/2} = \left(1 - [x^2 - 2ax + a^2]\right)^{1/2}$$

so

$$f(x - a) = (1 - x^2 + 2ax - a^2)^{1/2}$$

2.7. (a) $f(x) = x - 2x^2$

x	0	0.05	0.10	0.15	0.20	0.25	0.30	0.35	0.40	0.45	0.50
$f(x)$	0	0.045	0.080	0.105	0.120	0.125	0.120	0.105	0.080	0.045	0

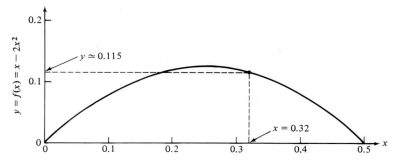

FIGURE S.1
Graph of $f(x) = x - 2x^2$ for $0 \leq x \leq 0.5$.

(b) The curve is shown in Fig. S.1.
(c) This curve is a parabola whose axis is parallel to the y axis. (d) From the curve, $y \cong 0.115$ when $x = 0.32$. (e) From the curve, $y = 0$ when $x = 0$ and also when $x = 0.5$, in agreement with setting $y = 0$ in the equation

$$y = x - 2x^2$$

If $y = 0$, we have

$$0 = x - 2x^2$$
$$0 = x(1 - 2x)$$

leading to the solutions $x = 0$ and $x = (1/2) = 0.5$.

2.8. (a) Since the equation of a straight line of slope m and y intercept $(0, b)$ is given by Eq. (2.39) as $y = mx + b$, $m = 2$ since the slope is given as equal to 2. Since the line passes through the origin $(0, 0)$, its y intercept is zero, so $b = 0$. Thus the equation of the required straight line is $y = 2x$; since the slope $m = \tan \theta$, where θ is the angle made by the line with the x axis,

$$\tan \theta = 2$$
$$\theta = \tan^{-1} 2$$
$$\theta = 63.4° = 1.11 \text{ radians}$$

(c) The graph is shown in Fig. S.2.

2.9. (a) We begin by calculating a table of values of

$$y = f(x - a) = \left[1 - (x - a)^2\right]^{1/2}$$

for the value $a = 0$ of the constant a. If $a = 0$, the function f becomes

$$y = f(x - 0) = f(x) = (1 - x^2)^{1/2}$$

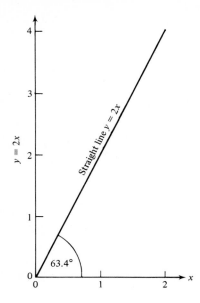

FIGURE S.2

Graph of $y = f(x) = 2x$ for $0 \le x \le 2$.

We use, as requested, values of x from $x = 1$ to $x = -1$ in intervals of 0.2; we consider only positive values of y:

x	1.0	0.8	0.6	0.4	0.2	0	−0.2	−0.4	−0.6	−0.8	−1.0
y	0	0.6	0.8	0.92	0.98	1	0.98	0.92	0.8	0.6	0

The graph of $y = f(x - a)$ for $a = 0$ is shown in Fig. S.3.

(b) We now repeat the graphing procedure for $a = 4$. If $a = 4$, then the function $f(x - a)$ is

$$y = f(x - 4) = \left[1 - (x - 4)^2\right]^{1/2}$$

We make the table, as requested, for values of x between 3 and 5, at intervals of 0.2; again considering only positive values of y:

x	3.0	3.2	3.4	3.6	3.8	4.0	4.2	4.4	4.6	4.8	5.0
y	0	0.6	0.8	0.92	0.98	1	0.98	0.92	0.8	0.6	0

The graph of $f(x - a)$ for $a = 4$ is also shown in Fig. S.3. Considering the graph of $f(x - a)$ for $a = 0$, we see that the graph of

$$y = f(x - a) = (1 - x^2)^{1/2}$$

is a semicircle with its center at $x = 0$. Similarly, for $a = 4$, the graph of

$$y = f(x - a) = \left[1 - (x - 4)^2\right]^{1/2}$$

is a semicircle with its center at $x = 4$. More generally, the graph of

$$f(x - a) = \left[1 - (x - a)^2\right]^{1/2}$$

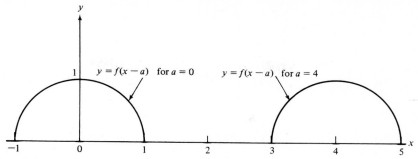

FIGURE S.3
Graph of $y = f(x - a) = [1 - (x - a)^2]^{1/2}$ for $a = 0$ and for $a = 4$.

is a semicircle with its center at $x = a$ since we are considering only positive values of y.

2.10. Since 2π radians $= 360°$, π radians $= 180°$, and we have
(a) $(\pi/8)$ radian $= (180/8)° = 22.5°$;
(b) $(3\pi/4)$ radians $= (3 \cdot 180/4)° = 135°$;
(c) 3π radians $= (3 \cdot 180)° = 540°$;
(d) $(31\pi/32)$ radians $= (31 \cdot 180/32)° = 174.38°$.

2.11. We calculate the values of $\cos x$ for $0 \le x \le 4\pi$ in multiples of $(\pi/8)$ radian:
(a)

x	0	$\pi/8$	$2\pi/8$	$3\pi/8$	$4\pi/8$	$5\pi/8$	$6\pi/8$	$7\pi/8$
$\cos x$	1	0.924	0.707	0.383	0	-0.383	-0.707	-0.924

x	$8\pi/8$	$9\pi/8$	$10\pi/8$	$11\pi/8$	$12\pi/8$	$13\pi/8$	$14\pi/8$	$15\pi/8$	$16\pi/8$
$\cos x$	-1	-0.924	-0.707	-0.383	0	0.383	0.707	0.924	1

x	$17\pi/8$	$18\pi/8$	$19\pi/8$	$20\pi/8$	$21\pi/8$	$22\pi/8$	$23\pi/8$
$\cos x$	0.924	0.707	0.383	0	-0.383	-0.707	-0.924

x	$24\pi/8$	$25\pi/8$	$26\pi/8$	$27\pi/8$	$28\pi/8$	$29\pi/8$	$30\pi/8$	$31\pi/8$	$32\pi/8$
$\cos x$	-1	-0.924	-0.707	-0.383	0	0.383	0.707	0.924	1

(b) We make the graph of $\cos x$ as a function of x shown in Fig. S.4; each interval on the x axis is equal to $(\pi/8)$ radian.
(c) From the graph, the maximum value of $\cos x$ is 1; the minimum value is -1. (d) We can see from the graph that the function $\cos x$ repeats itself (i.e., goes from 1 to -1 and back to 1) when x goes from zero to $(16\pi/8)$ radians. Hence $\cos x$ is periodic, with period $(16\pi/8)$ radians $= 2\pi$ radians. (e) The period is 2π radians. (f) There are two cycles of $\cos x$ on the graph. The first cycle is for values of x between $x = 0$ and $x = (16\pi/8)$; the second is for values of x between $x = (16\pi/8)$ and $x = (32\pi/8)$ radians. (g) The cosine of $(39\pi/16)$ radians $= \cos(19.5\pi/8)$. From the graph $\cos(19.5\pi/8) \cong 0.18$. The precise value is 0.195.

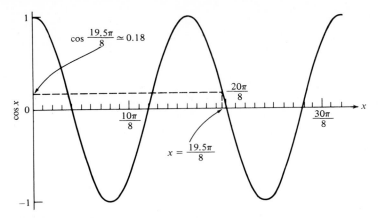

FIGURE S.4
Graph of cos x as a function of x for $0 \leq x \leq (32\pi/8)$. Each interval on the x axis is $(\pi/8)$ radian.

2.12. Since the equation of the straight line in rectangular coordinates is $y = mx + b$, on substituting $x = r \cos \theta$ and $y = r \sin \theta$, we obtain

$$r \sin \theta = mr \cos \theta + b \qquad r(\sin \theta - m \cos \theta) = b$$

Next, we express the polar coordinate θ in terms of x and y as

$$\theta = \tan^{-1}\left(\frac{y}{x}\right)$$

leading to the expression

$$r = \frac{b}{\sin\left[\tan^{-1}(y/x)\right] - m \cos\left[\tan^{-1}(y/x)\right]}$$

for r in terms of x and y. These two last equations give the polar coordinates (r, θ) of a point on the line $y = mx + b$ in terms of the rectangular coordinates (x, y) of that point. Clearly, the complexity of these expressions shows that polar coordinates are not particularly convenient here.

3.1. Since $f(x) = x^3$, we have

$$f(x + \Delta x) = (x + \Delta x)^3 = x^3 + 3x^2(\Delta x) + 3x(\Delta x)^2 + (\Delta x)^3$$

$$f(x + \Delta x) - f(x) = 3x^2(\Delta x) + 3x(\Delta x)^2 + (\Delta x)^3$$

$$[f(x + \Delta x) - f(x)]/(\Delta x) = 3x^2 + 3x(\Delta x) + (\Delta x)^2$$

Taking the limit as $\Delta x \to 0$ gives us

$$f'(x) = \lim_{\Delta x \to 0} \left[3x^2 + 3x(\Delta x) + (\Delta x)^2\right] = 3x^2$$

so the derivative of $f(x) = x^3$ is $f'(x) = 3x^2$.

3.2. Since $f(x) = (1/x)$, we have $f(x + \Delta x) = [1/(x + \Delta x)]$ and thus

$$f(x + \Delta x) - f(x) = \frac{1}{x + \Delta x} - \frac{1}{x} = \frac{x - (x + \Delta x)}{x(x + \Delta x)} = \frac{-\Delta x}{x(x + \Delta x)}$$

Then

$$\frac{f(x + \Delta x) - f(x)}{\Delta x} = \frac{1}{\Delta x}\left[\frac{-\Delta x}{x(x + \Delta x)}\right] = \frac{-1}{x(x + \Delta x)}$$

Taking the limit as $\Delta x \to 0$ gives us

$$f'(x) = \lim_{\Delta x \to 0}\left[\frac{-1}{x(x + \Delta x)}\right] = \frac{-1}{x(x)} = \frac{-1}{x^2}$$

so the derivative of $f(x) = (1/x)$ is $f'(x) = -1/(x^2)$.

3.3. Using the product rule in Eq. (3.40) with $u(x) = e^x$ and $v(x) = \sin x$, we have

$$\frac{d}{dx}[e^x \sin x] = e^x \frac{d}{dx}(\sin x) + (\sin x)\frac{d}{dx}(e^x)$$

$$= e^x \cos x + (\sin x)e^x$$

$$= e^x(\sin x + \cos x)$$

3.4. Using the quotient rule in Eq. (3.42) with $u(x) = \cos x$ and $v(x) = \sin x$, we have

$$\frac{d}{dx}\left[\frac{\cos x}{\sin x}\right] = \frac{1}{\sin^2 x}\left[(\sin x)\frac{d}{dx}(\cos x) - (\cos x)\frac{d}{dx}(\sin x)\right]$$

$$= \frac{1}{\sin^2 x}[(\sin x)(-\sin x) - (\cos x)(\cos x)]$$

$$= \frac{-(\sin^2 x + \cos^2 x)}{\sin^2 x} = \frac{-1}{\sin^2 x} = -\csc^2 x$$

so we have shown that

$$\frac{d}{dx}[\cot x] = -\csc^2 x$$

3.5. To calculate the derivative of x^3, we see that x^3 is x^n with $n = 3$, so Eq. (3.35) becomes

$$\frac{d}{dx}[x^3] = 3x^{3-1} = 3x^2$$

To differentiate $(1/x) = x^{-1}$, we have $n = -1$, so Eq. (3.35) is

$$\frac{d}{dx}[x^{-1}] = (-1)x^{-1-1} = -x^{-2} = \frac{-1}{x^2}$$

These results are the same as those obtained in Exercises 3.1 and 3.2.

3.6. Since $y(x) = e^{-2x^2}$, we have $y(x) = g(u) = e^u$ and $u(x) = -2x^2$ so, by the chain rule, either in the form (3.67) or the form (3.49), we have

$$y'(x) = g'(u) u'(x) = (e^u) (-4x) = (-4x) e^{-2x^2}$$

3.7. Using the chain rule again, we have $y(x) = u^4 = g(u)$ and $u(x) = (x^2 + 3x - 2)$, so

$$y'(x) = g'(u) u'(x) = (4u^3) (2x + 3) = 4(x^2 + 3x - 2)^3 (2x + 3)$$

3.8. In this problem, we will have to use the chain rule twice. First

$$y(x) = g(u) = \sin u \qquad u(x) = e^{x^2}$$

$$y'(x) = g'(u) u'(x) = (\cos u) u'(x) = \left[\cos (e^{x^2})\right] u'(x) \quad \text{(S.2)}$$

Next, we have to find the derivative $u'(x)$, where

$$u'(x) = \frac{d}{dx} [e^{x^2}]$$

by using the chain rule. Just as in Exercise 3.6 above, we say that

$$u(x) = g(v) = e^v \qquad v(x) = x^2$$

$$u'(x) = g'(v) v'(x) = (e^v) (2x) = 2xe^{x^2} \quad \text{(S.3)}$$

Combining the results (S.2) and (S.3) above, we obtain

$$y'(x) = \left[\cos (e^{x^2})\right] (2xe^{x^2})$$

so our final answer is

$$y'(x) = \frac{d}{dx} \left[\sin (e^{x^2})\right] = 2xe^{x^2} \cos (e^{x^2})$$

3.9. From Exercise 3.3 above, we had the result that, for the function $f(x) = e^x \sin x$, the derivative $f'(x)$ is

$$f'(x) = e^x(\cos x + \sin x)$$

To find $f''(x)$, we differentiate $f'(x)$, obtaining

$$f''(x) = \frac{d}{dx} [f'(x)] = \frac{d}{dx} [e^x(\cos x + \sin x)]$$

$$= e^x \frac{d}{dx} (\cos x + \sin x) + (\cos x + \sin x) \frac{d}{dx} (e^x)$$

$$= e^x(-\sin x + \cos x) + (\cos x + \sin x) (e^x)$$

$$= -e^x \sin x + e^x \cos x + e^x \cos x + e^x \sin x$$

$$= e^x \cos x + e^x \cos x = 2e^x \cos x$$

$$f''(x) = 2e^x \cos x$$

3.10. Since $y = f(x) = 6x + 2$, and $x_1 = 1.00$, $(x_1 + \Delta x) = 1.01$, $\Delta x = 0.01$, we have

$$f(x_1) = f(1) = 6(1) + 2 = 8.00$$

$$f(x_1 + \Delta x) = f(1.01) = 6(1.01) + 2 = 8.06$$

(a) $\Delta y = f(x_1 + \Delta x) - f(x_1) = 8.06 - 8.00 = 0.06$

$$\frac{\Delta y}{\Delta x} = \frac{0.06}{0.01} = 6 = \text{average rate of change of } y \text{ with respect to } x \text{ for } x \text{ between } 1.00 \text{ and } 1.01$$

(b) Since $\Delta y = 6(\Delta x)$, $\Delta y = 6(0.01) = 0.06$ when $\Delta x = 0.01$. The change Δy in y is $\Delta y = 0.06$ when x changes from 1.00 to 1.01.

3.11. We are given that $f(x) = x^3$, so (a) $f'(x) = 3x^2$ is the instantaneous rate of change of x^3 with respect to x; (b) when $x = 1$, $f'(1) = 3(1)^2 = 3$ is the value of the rate of change.

3.12. (a) Since s is directly proportional to t^3, with constant of proportionality B, the equation giving s as a function of t is $s = Bt^3$. (b) The rate of change of s with respect to time t is

$$\frac{ds}{dt} = \frac{d}{dt}[Bt^3] = 3Bt^2$$

(c) Since velocity v is the rate of change of distance with respect to time,

$$v = \frac{ds}{dt} = 3Bt^2$$

giving the velocity v as a function of time.

3.13. (a) Since $s = 2.4t^2$, the rate of change of distance s with respect to time is

$$\frac{ds}{dt} = 4.8t$$

(b) Yes, (ds/dt) does vary with (is directly proportional to) time. (c) Velocity v is the rate of change of distance with respect to time, so

$$v = \frac{ds}{dt} = 4.8t$$

When $t = 1$ second (that is, 1 second after the block begins to move), $v = 4.8(1) = 4.8$ meters per second.

3.14. (a) Since $C = 2\pi r$, the rate of change of C with respect to r is given by

$$\frac{dC}{dr} = \frac{d}{dr}[2\pi r] = 2\pi$$

where (dC/dr) is the rate of change of C with respect to r. (b) This rate of change is the change in the circumference C (in meters) per meter of change in the radius r. The rate of change (dC/dr) is equal to 2π, meaning that C changes by 2π ($= 6.28$) meters for a change of 1 meter in r. Note that, in this case, the rate of change (dC/dr) does *not* depend on the value of the radius r.

3.15. We found in part (c) of Exercise 3.12 that the velocity $v = 3Bt^2$. Since the acceleration is the rate of change (dv/dt) of the velocity with respect to time, we have

$$a = \frac{dv}{dt} = \frac{d}{dt}[3Bt^2] = 6Bt$$

since B is a constant. This acceleration a is *not* constant with time (as it is for a vertically falling body without air resistance).

3.16. Using the notation employed in the text, let

$$y = g(u) = 6 \cos u$$

$$u = f(x) = 6x^4$$

Then

$$\frac{dy}{dx} = \left(\frac{dy}{du}\right)\left(\frac{du}{dx}\right) = (-6 \sin u)(24x^3)$$

$$= (-144x^3) \sin (6x^4)$$

Multiplying both sides of this equation by the differential dx gives

$$dy = [(-144x^3) \sin (6x^4)]\, dx$$

for the required differential dy.

3.17. Since $A = \pi r^2$, we can take the differential dA as

$$dA = \pi(2r)\, dr = (2\pi)\, r\, dr$$

where dr is the differential of r. Dividing both sides of the expression for dA by dt, the differential of time t, gives

$$\frac{dA}{dt} = (2\pi)\, r\, \frac{dr}{dt}$$

This equation says that the rate of change (dA/dt) of the area with respect to time equals the constant 2π times the radius r times (dr/dt), the rate of change of the radius with respect to time. Note that the rate of change (dA/dt) depends on *both* r and (dr/dt).

3.18. Since distance dx equals the rate v times the time dt, we have $dx = v\, dt$. This equation says that the particle moves the infinitesimal distance dx in the infinitesimal time dt while traveling at the constant velocity v.

3.19. (a) Since $a = (dv/dt)$, we can multiply both sides of this equation by the differential dt, obtaining

$$a\, dt = \left(\frac{dv}{dt}\right) dt = dv$$

so our result is

$$dv = a\,dt$$

(b) The meaning of our result is as follows. If a particle or body moves with constant acceleration a for the infinitesimal length of time dt, its velocity v will change by the very small amount dv.

3.20. Using $dy = f'(x)\,dx = (3x^2)\,dx$ with $dx = 0.00001$, we evaluate $f'(x) = 3x^2$ for $x = 2.000005$, so we have

$$f'(2.000005) = 3(2.000005)^2 = 3(4.00002) = 12.00006 \cong 12$$

so

$$dy \cong (12)(0.00001) = 0.00012$$

3.21. (a) From the information given,

$$dQ = mc\,dT$$

giving dQ in terms of m, c, and dT, where dQ is the infinitesimal amount of heat necessary to raise the temperature of the mass m by a very small amount dT. (b) Dividing both sides of the equation for dQ by dT gives

$$mc = \frac{dQ}{dT} \quad \text{or} \quad c = \frac{1}{m}\frac{dQ}{dT}$$

as the equation defining the specific heat c.

3.22. (a) Since $f(x) = x^2 + 2$, $f'(x) = 2x$, and $f'(5) = 10$, so $\tan\theta = 10$ is the slope of the geometric tangent at $x = 5$. (b) The angle θ, where $\tan\theta = 10$, is the angle the geometric tangent makes with the x axis. Then $\theta = \tan^{-1} 10 = 84.3°$. (c) The slope of the curve at any point is the slope of the geometric tangent at that point. At $x = 2$, the slope of the geometric tangent, and hence of the curve, is $f'(2) = 2(2) = 4$.

3.23. (a) The graph is shown in Fig. S.5. The values of s and t are calculated from $s = 2t^3$.

s	0	0.002	0.016	0.054	0.128	0.250	0.432	0.686	1.024	1.458	2.000	2.662
t	0	0.1	0.2	0.3	0.4	0.5	0.6	0.7	0.8	0.9	1.0	1.1

s	3.456	4.394	5.488	6.750	8.192	9.826	11.664	13.718	16.000
t	1.2	1.3	1.4	1.5	1.6	1.7	1.8	1.9	2.0

where s is in meters and t is in seconds. (b) The slope is given by (ds/dt) evaluated at $t = 1$ second, so

$$\text{Slope} = \left(\frac{ds}{dt}\right)_{t=1} = (6t^2)_{t=1} = 6 \text{ meters per second}$$

(c) The velocity v is the time rate of change of distance, so

$$v = \frac{ds}{dt} = 6t^2$$

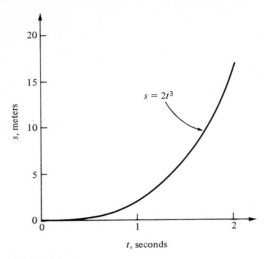

FIGURE S.5
Graph of $s = 2t^3$ for $0 \leq t \leq 2$ seconds.

From this equation, we calculate values of v and t as follows:

v	0	0.06	0.24	0.54	0.96	1.50	2.16	2.94	3.84	4.86
t	0	0.1	0.2	0.3	0.4	0.5	0.6	0.7	0.8	0.9

v	6.00	7.26	8.64	10.14	11.76	13.50
t	1.0	1.1	1.2	1.3	1.4	1.5

v	15.36	17.34	19.44	21.66	24.00
t	1.6	1.7	1.8	1.9	2.0

The values of v are in meters per second and t is in seconds. The graph of v as a function of t is shown in Fig. S.6. This curve is a parabola whose equation is $v = 6t^2$. (d) The slope of the curve $v = 6t^2$ is given by the derivative (dv/dt), where

$$\frac{dv}{dt} = 12t$$

When $t = 1$ second,

$$\text{Slope} = \left(\frac{dv}{dt}\right)_{t=1} = (12t)_{t=1} = 12 \text{ (meters per second) per second}$$

(e) The acceleration a is the rate of change of velocity with respect to time, so

$$a = \frac{dv}{dt} = 12t$$

The graph of a as a function of t is shown in Fig. S.7.

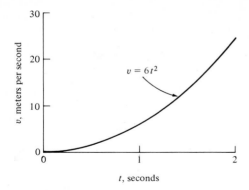

FIGURE S.6
Graph of $v = 6t^2$ for $0 \leq t \leq 2$ seconds.

This "curve" is the straight line whose equation is $a = 12t$. (f) The acceleration a is *not* constant. From the graph in part (e), we see that $a = 12t$ increases linearly with increasing time.

3.24. (a) To find the value of x at which $\sin x$ has its first maximum, we first find the first derivative $f'(x)$ and set it equal to zero. Thus

$$f'(x) = \frac{d}{dx}(\sin x) = \cos x = 0$$

For what values of x does $\cos x = 0$? The values are the critical points

$$x = \frac{\pi}{2} = 90° \qquad x = \frac{3\pi}{2} = 270° \qquad \ldots$$

Thus $f(x) = \sin x$ has its first critical point at $x = (\pi/2)$ radians. Since we know from the graph of $\sin x$ that (for $x \geq 0$), $\sin x$ *increases* as x

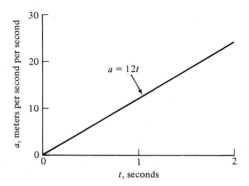

FIGURE S.7
Graph of $a = 12t$ for $0 \leq t \leq 2$ seconds.

increases from zero, the first critical point $x = (\pi/2)$ is a maximum. (b) In the same way, we see that the first minimum in sin x is at the second critical point $x = (3\pi/2)$ radians. (c) To check, we apply the second derivative test, where

$$f''(x) = \frac{d}{dx}(\cos x) = -\sin x$$

When $x = (\pi/2), f''(\pi/2) = -\sin(\pi/2) = -1$ so the second derivative is *negative* at the critical point $x = (\pi/2)$, meaning this is a *maximum*. When $x = (3\pi/2)$,

$$f''\left(\frac{3\pi}{2}\right) = -\sin\left(\frac{3\pi}{2}\right) = -(-1) = +1$$

so the second derivative is *positive* at the critical point $x = (3\pi/2)$, meaning that this is a *minimum*.

3.25. (a) Since the vertical height y is given by

$$y = (v_0 \sin \theta)t - 4.9t^2$$

we want to find the value of t for which y is a maximum. We take the derivative (dy/dt) and set it equal to zero:

$$\frac{dy}{dt} = (v_0 \sin \theta) - 9.8t = 0$$

where we keep in mind that v_0 and θ are constants which are fixed permanently at the initial instant of time $t = 0$. Solving for t, we get

$$t = \frac{v_0 \sin \theta}{9.8}$$

as the time at which y is a maximum. (We know we are dealing with a maximum value of y, and not a minimum, from the physics of the situation; that is, y increases as the ball moves, y reaches a maximum, and then y decreases until the ball hits the ground.) If we knew the particular values of v_0 and θ, we could calculate the value of t explicitly. The equation for t above holds for all values of v_0 and θ. (b) We want to know the horizontal distance x moved by the ball when the vertical height y is a maximum, so we want to know x when $t = (v_0 \sin \theta/9.8)$ seconds. Since x is given as a function of time by

$$x = (v_0 \cos \theta)t$$

we simply substitute $t = (v_0 \sin \theta/9.8)$ into the expression for x as a function of t, obtaining

$$x = (v_0 \cos \theta)\left(\frac{v_0 \sin \theta}{9.8}\right) = \frac{v_0^2 \sin \theta \cos \theta}{9.8}$$

This is the value of x when y is a maximum.

3.26. (a) $x_1^2 + x_2^2 + x_3^2 + x_4^2 = \sum\limits_{i=1}^{4} x_i^2$

(b) $1 + y + y^2 + y^3 + y^4 + y^5 = \sum\limits_{i=0}^{5} y^i$ (since $y^0 = 1$)

(c) $1^2 + 2^2 + 3^2 = \sum\limits_{k=1}^{3} k^2$

3.27. (a) If $f(x) = \ln x$, then $d(\ln x)/dx = x^{-1}$, $d^2(\ln x)/dx^2 = (-x^{-2})$, $d^3(\ln x)/dx^3 = 2x^{-3}$, and so forth, so

$$\frac{d^n(\ln x)}{dx^n} = (-1)^{n+1}(n-1)!\,x^{-n}$$

Thus all of the derivatives of $\ln x$ are infinite at $x = 0$.

(b) From Eq. (3.216) or (3.217),

$$f(x) = f(a) + \sum\limits_{n=1}^{\infty} \frac{1}{n!} f^{(n)}(a)(x-a)^n$$

Using the expression for $f^{(n)}(a)$ when $f(x) = \ln x$, we obtain

$$\ln x = \ln a + \sum\limits_{n=1}^{\infty} \frac{(-1)^{n+1}}{n} a^{-n}(x-a)^n$$

Since we are expanding about the point $x = 1$, we have $a = 1$, and, using $\ln 1 = 0$, we get

$$\ln x = \sum\limits_{n=1}^{\infty} \frac{(-1)^{n+1}}{n}(x-1)^n$$

$$= (x-1) - \frac{1}{2}(x-1)^2 + \frac{1}{3}(x-1)^3 - \cdots$$

3.28. (a) Since this is a Maclaurin's series, $a = 0$, and Eq. (3.216) gives the first four terms as

$$f(x) = f(0) + f'(0)x + \frac{1}{2}f''(0)x^2 + \frac{1}{6}f'''(0)x^3$$

Since $f(x) = \sin x$, $f'(x) = \cos x$, $f''(x) = -\sin x$, $f'''(x) = -\cos x$, and $f(0) = 0$, $f'(0) = 1$, $f''(0) = 0$, $f'''(0) = (-1)$, the series is

$$\sin x = x - \frac{1}{6}x^3$$

(b) Using the series above for $\sin x$, if $x = 1.0$ radian,

$$\sin 1.0 = 1.0 - \frac{1}{6} = 0.8333$$

The exact value, to four figures, is $\sin 1.0 = 0.8415$.

(c) If $x = 0.5$ radian, the series gives

$$\sin 0.5 = 0.5 - \frac{1}{6}(0.5)^3 = 0.4792$$

The exact value, to four figures, is $\sin 0.5 = 0.4794$. We see that the two-term series for $\sin x$ is a better approximation for the smaller value of $x = 0.5$ radian.

3.29. (a) Since this is again a Maclaurin's series, $a = 0$ and Eq. (3.216) gives us again

$$f(x) = f(0) + f'(0)x + \frac{1}{2}f''(0)x^2 + \frac{1}{6}f'''(0)x^3$$

Since $f(x) = \cos x, f'(x) = -\sin x, f''(x) = -\cos x, f'''(x) = \sin x$, and $f(0) = 1, f'(0) = 0, f''(0) = -1, f'''(0) = 0$, the series is thus

$$\cos x = 1 - \frac{1}{2}x^2$$

(b) Using the two-term series for $\cos x$, we get, with $x = 1.0$ radian,

$$\cos 1.0 = 1 - 0.5 = 0.5000$$

The exact value, to four figures, is $\cos 1.0 = 0.5403$.
(c) If $x = 0.5$ radian, the series gives

$$\cos 0.5 = 1 - \frac{1}{2}(0.5)^2 = 0.8750$$

The exact value is $\cos 0.5 = 0.8776$, and, again, the series is a better approximation for $\cos x$ for the smaller value of x.

4.1. Use the substitution $u = 3x$, so $du = 3\, dx$, and the integral becomes

$$\frac{1}{3}\int \cos u \, du = \frac{1}{3}(\sin u) = \frac{1}{3}\sin 3x$$

so our answer is

$$\int \cos 3x \, dx = \frac{1}{3}\sin 3x + C$$

4.2. Use the substitution $u = (x - a)$, so $du = dx$ and the integral becomes

$$\int u^2 \, du = \frac{1}{3}u^3 = \frac{1}{3}(x - a)^3$$

and our answer is

$$\int (x - a)^2 \, dx = \frac{1}{3}(x - a)^3 + C$$

SOLUTIONS TO THE EXERCISES **219**

4.3. Use the substitution $u = x^2$, so $du = 2x\,dx$, $(1/2)\,du = x\,dx$ and the integral becomes

$$\frac{1}{2}\int e^{-u}\,du = \frac{-1}{2}e^{-u} = \frac{-1}{2}e^{-x^2}$$

so our answer is

$$\int xe^{-x^2}\,dx = \frac{-1}{2}e^{-x^2} + C$$

4.4. Use $u = x$, $dv = \cos x\,dx$, so $du = dx$ and

$$v = \int dv = \int \cos x\,dx = \sin x + C'$$
$$uv = x(\sin x + C') = x\sin x + C'x$$

and

$$\int u\,dv = \int x\cos x\,dx = uv - \int v\,du$$
$$= x\sin x + C'x - \int(\sin x + C')\,dx$$
$$= x\sin x + C'x + \int(-\sin x)\,dx - \int C'\,dx$$
$$= x\sin x + C'x + \cos x - C'x = x\sin x + \cos x$$

(Note that the constant C' drops out and could have been ignored from the start.) Our answer is therefore

$$\int x\cos x\,dx = x\sin x + \cos x + C$$

4.5. Use $u = x$, $du = dx$, $dv = e^x\,dx$, so $v = \int dv = \int e^x\,dx = e^x$, where, just as in 4.4 above, we ignore any constant of integration in the integration of dv to get v. Then

$$\int xe^x\,dx = \int u\,dv = uv - \int v\,du = xe^x - \int e^x\,dx = xe^x - e^x$$

and our final answer is

$$\int xe^x\,dx = xe^x - e^x + C = (x-1)e^x + C$$

4.6. The velocity v is the rate of change of distance s with respect to time, so

$$v = \frac{ds}{dt} = V$$

where V is a constant. Multiplying by the differential dt gives $ds = V\,dt$.

To get s we integrate over the variable t, obtaining

$$s = \int ds = \int V \, dt = V \int dt = Vt + C$$

so

$$s(t) = Vt + C$$

To determine the constant C, we know that $s = 100$ when $t = 0$, so $s(0) = 100$. Putting $t = 0$ in the equation for $s(t)$ gives $s(0) = C$, so the constant $C = 100$ meters, and the complete equation for the distance $s(t)$ as a function of time is

$$s(t) = Vt + 100 \text{ meters}$$

where s is in meters when t is in seconds.

4.7. Since $(dy/dx) = 6 - 2x$ we have $dy = (6 - 2x) \, dx$ so

$$y = \int dy = \int (6 - 2x) \, dx = 6x - x^2 + C$$
$$y(x) = 6x - x^2 + C$$

Since $y = 9$ when $x = 3$, we have

$$9 = 6(3) - (3)^2 + C = 18 - 9 + C$$
$$C = 0$$

In this case the constant of integration has the value zero, and the function $y(x)$ is

$$y(x) = 6x - x^2$$

This function is the parabola shown in Fig. 3.17.

4.8. Again we are given the value of the acceleration, which is constant with the value zero. Then, if v is the velocity and setting $A = 0$ in Eq. (4.55), we get

$$\frac{dv}{dt} = 0$$

so

$$dv = 0 \cdot dt$$
$$v = \int dv = \int 0 \cdot dt$$

What is the integral of zero, or, in other words, what function has zero as its derivative? The answer is that a constant has zero as its derivative, so we have for the velocity

$$v(t) = C$$

where C is a constant. The initial condition given in the problem is that $v = 100$ meters per second when $t = 0$, so

$$v(0) = 100 \text{ meters per second}$$

Since $v(t) = C$, meaning that the velocity is *constant* and does not change with time, it is also true that

$$v(0) = C$$

so the value of the constant C is $C = 100$ meters per second. The complete equation for $v(t)$ is therefore

$$v(t) = 100 \text{ meters per second}$$

an equation which says that the velocity is constant with the value 100 meters per second (and thus the acceleration is zero because the velocity is not changing with time). Note that this equation tells us how v behaves with time in that it tells us that v is *independent* of time.

4.9. Here the function $F(x) = \int \sin x \, dx = -\cos x$, so

$$\int_0^\pi \sin x \, dx = [-\cos x]_0^\pi = -[\cos \pi - \cos 0] = -[-1 - 1] = 2$$

4.10. In this problem the function $F(x)$ is given by

$$F(x) = \int x^2 \, dx = (1/3)x^3$$

so

$$\int_0^2 x^2 \, dx = \left[\frac{1}{3}x^3\right]_0^2 = \frac{1}{3}[2^3 - 0^3] = \frac{8}{3}$$

4.11. Here the function $F(x)$ is given by $F(x) = \int e^{-x} \, dx = -e^{-x}$, so

$$\int_0^\infty e^{-x} \, dx = [-e^{-x}]_0^\infty = -\left[\frac{1}{e^x}\right]_0^\infty = -\left[\frac{1}{e^\infty} - \frac{1}{e^0}\right]$$

$$= -\left[\frac{1}{\infty} - 1\right] = 1$$

4.12. Here the function $F(x) = \int (x - a)^2 \, dx$, which was found in Exercise 4.2 to be

$$\int (x - a)^2 \, dx = \frac{1}{3}(x - a)^3$$

so

$$\int_0^a (x - a)^2 \, dx = \left[\frac{1}{3}(x - a)^3\right]_0^a = \frac{1}{3}[(a - a)^3 - (0 - a)^3] = \frac{1}{3}a^3$$

4.13. In this case the function $F(x)$ is $F(x) = \int x^{-2}\, dx = -x^{-1}$, so

$$\int_{\infty}^{b} x^{-2}\, dx = -\left[\frac{1}{x}\right]_{\infty}^{b} = -\left[\frac{1}{b} - \frac{1}{\infty}\right] = -\frac{1}{b}$$

4.14. In this example, the function

$$F(x) = \int \frac{x\, dx}{(d^2 + x^2)^{1/2}}$$

We make the substitution $(d^2 + x^2) = u$, so $du = 2x\, dx$, $x\, dx = (1/2)\, du$, and the integral becomes

$$\int \frac{x\, dx}{(d^2 + x^2)^{1/2}} = \frac{1}{2} \int \frac{du}{u^{1/2}} = \frac{1}{2}(2u^{1/2}) = u^{1/2} = (d^2 + x^2)^{1/2}$$

Then the definite integral is

$$\int_{0}^{a} \frac{x\, dx}{(d^2 + x^2)^{1/2}} = \left[(d^2 + x^2)^{1/2}\right]_{0}^{a} = (d^2 + a^2)^{1/2} - d$$

4.15. The area A between the curve $f(x) = 2x + 1$ and the x axis between $x = 1$ and $x = 2$ is

$$A = \int_{1}^{2} (2x + 1)\, dx = \left[x^2 + x\right]_{1}^{2} = [2^2 + 2 - 1^2 - 1] = 4$$

4.16. In Eq. (4.101),

$$A \equiv \int_{a}^{b} f(x)\, dx = \text{area between } f(x) \text{ and } x \text{ axis between } x = a \text{ and } x = b$$

$$A_1 \equiv \int_{a}^{c} f(x)\, dx = \text{area between } f(x) \text{ and } x \text{ axis between } x = a \text{ and } x = c$$

$$A_2 \equiv \int_{c}^{b} f(x)\, dx = \text{area between } f(x) \text{ and } x \text{ axis between } x = c \text{ and } x = b$$

Hence Eq. (4.101) says that area $A = $ area $A_1 + $ area A_2.

4.17. Since $p = p(V) = CV^{-1}$, the area A is

$$A = \int_{V_1}^{V_2} p(V)\, dV = \int_{V_1}^{V_2} \frac{C}{V}\, dV = C \int_{V_1}^{V_2} \frac{dV}{V}$$

$$= C[\ln V]_{V_1}^{V_2} = C[\ln V_2 - \ln V_1] = C \ln\left(\frac{V_2}{V_1}\right)$$

Since $V_2 > V_1$, $(V_2/V_1) > 1$, $\ln(V_2/V_1) > 0$, and $A > 0$.

4.18. Figure S.8 shows the x axis with the interval $a \leq x \leq b$. Also shown is an element of length dx located at a point x. We want to calculate L, the

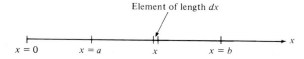

FIGURE S.8
The x axis, showing an element of length dx located at the point x between $x = a$ and $x = b$.

distance from $x = a$ to $x = b$. We find L by adding up (integrating) all the elements of length dx between $x = a$ and $x = b$, so we have

$$L = \int dx = \int_a^b dx$$

Here the variable of integration is x and the lower and upper limits of the integral are a and b, respectively. Then

$$L = \int_a^b dx = [x]_a^b = (b - a)$$

the answer we would have expected from the results of analytic geometry.

4.19. Figure S.9 shows the straight line $f(x) = x$ and the shaded strip is an element of area dA, where $dA = x\, dx$ since the width of the strip is dx and its height is $f(x) = x$. Note that the area $dA = x\, dx$ depends on x. The total area A is obtained by integrating all of the elements dA, so

$$A = \int dA = \int_0^a x\, dx = \left[\frac{x^2}{2}\right]_0^a = \left(\frac{a^2}{2} - 0\right) = \frac{a^2}{2}$$

where the variable of integration is x and x varies from $x = 0$ to $x = a$, so those are the limits of the definite integral.

4.20. The top view of the pipe is shown in Fig. S.10. The volume element dV is a thin cylindrical shell a distance r from the axis, which is normal to the plane of the paper and passes through the center O of the pipe. Then $dV = 2\pi L r\, dr$ because L is the length of the pipe (the height of the cylinder). The element of mass dm is $dm = \rho\, dV = 2\pi \rho L r\, dr$. The moment of inertia

$$I = \int r^2\, dm = 2\pi \rho L \int_{R_1}^{R_2} r^3\, dr = 2\pi \rho L \left[\frac{r^4}{4}\right]_{R_1}^{R_2}$$

because the variable of integration r varies from $r = R_1$ to $r = R_2$. Then

$$I = \frac{\pi \rho L}{2} (R_2^4 - R_1^4) = \frac{\pi \rho L}{2} (R_2^2 + R_1^2)(R_2^2 - R_1^2)$$

Note that $\pi L(R_2^2 - R_1^2)$ is the volume of the solid part of the pipe, so

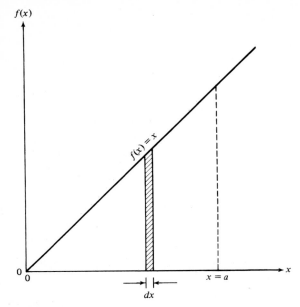

FIGURE S.9
Graph of $f(x) = x$ for $0 \le x \le a$, showing a strip (shaded) of width dx and area $dA = x \, dx$.

$\pi \rho L (R_2^2 - R_1^2) = M$, the mass of the pipe. Thus

$$I = \frac{1}{2} M(R_1^2 + R_2^2)$$

is the required moment of inertia.

4.21. The geometry is as shown in Fig. S.11. The distance r from the element of charge dq to point P is $r = (a^2 + d^2)^{1/2}$. The charge element $dq = \lambda \, ds = \lambda a \, d\theta$ on using Eq. (4.183). The element of electrostatic potential

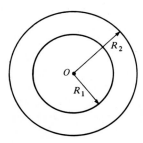

FIGURE S.10
End view of a hollow circularly cylindrical "pipe" of inner radius R_1 and outer radius R_2.

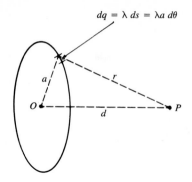

FIGURE S.11

Circular loop of radius a, showing an element of charge dq located a distance r from point P. The point P is a perpendicular distance d from the center O of the circle.

at point P due to the element of charge dq is

$$dV = \frac{1}{4\pi\epsilon_0} \frac{dq}{r} = \frac{1}{4\pi\epsilon_0} \frac{\lambda a \, d\theta}{\left(a^2 + d^2\right)^{1/2}}$$

where λ, a, d are all constants. The total electrostatic potential at point P is

$$V = \int dV = \frac{1}{4\pi\epsilon_0} \frac{\lambda a}{\left(a^2 + d^2\right)^{1/2}} \int d\theta$$

where the variable of integration θ varies from $\theta = 0$ to $\theta = 2\pi$ on going around the circular loop. Then

$$V = \frac{1}{4\pi\epsilon_0} \frac{\lambda a}{\left(a^2 + d^2\right)^{1/2}} \int_0^{2\pi} d\theta = \frac{2\pi\lambda a}{4\pi\epsilon_0 \left(a^2 + d^2\right)^{1/2}} = \frac{\lambda a}{2\epsilon_0 \left(a^2 + d^2\right)^{1/2}}$$

so V depends on λ, a, and d. Note that, if $d \to 0$, we get $V = (\lambda/2\epsilon_0)$, in agreement with our previous result in Eq. (4.185) for the electrostatic potential at the center O of the circular loop.

4.22. To evaluate $\int \cos^2 \omega t \, dt$ we substitute $u = \omega t$, $du = \omega \, dt$, so

$$\int \cos^2 \omega t \, dt = \frac{1}{\omega} \int \cos^2 u \, du = \frac{1}{\omega}\left[\frac{u}{2} + \frac{\sin 2u}{4}\right] = \frac{1}{\omega}\left[\frac{\omega t}{2} + \frac{\sin 2\omega t}{4}\right]$$

on using a table of integrals. Then

$$\frac{1}{2\pi/\omega} \int_0^{2\pi/\omega} \cos^2 \omega t \, dt = \frac{\omega}{2\pi} \frac{1}{\omega}\left[\frac{\omega t}{2} + \frac{\sin 2\omega t}{4}\right]_0^{2\pi/\omega}$$

$$= \frac{1}{2\pi}\left[\frac{2\pi}{2} + \frac{\sin 4\pi}{4}\right] = \frac{1}{2}$$

5.1. (a) Force is a vector; force is also the name of the scalar magnitude of this vector; the vector is written **F**, and so its scalar magnitude is written F; (b) density; pressure.

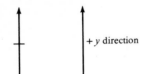

+ *y* direction

FIGURE S.12
An arrow 2 centimeters long representing a vector velocity
of 10 meters per second in the (+*y*) direction. The scale is
1 centimeter, which equals a speed of 5 meters per second.

5.2. Taking upward in the plane of the paper as the positive *y* axis as shown in Fig. S.12, and using a scale of 1 centimeter of length equals a speed of 5 meters per second, the required vector velocity is represented by a vertical arrow 2 centimeters in length pointing upward.

5.3. (a) Draw vectors $\mathbf{v}_1$ and $\mathbf{v}_2$ using a scale of 1 centimeter equals a speed of 1 meter per second. Take the *x* and *y* axes as shown in Fig. S.13. Then $\mathbf{v}_1$ is an arrow 4 centimeters long in the (+*x*) direction and $\mathbf{v}_2$ is an arrow 3 centimeters long in the (+*y*) direction, as shown in Fig. S.13. Placing the "tail" of $\mathbf{v}_2$ at the "tip" of $\mathbf{v}_1$, we get the sum vector $\mathbf{v} = \mathbf{v}_1 + \mathbf{v}_2$ graphically as shown in the drawing. Measuring the length of the sum vector gives its magnitude as $|\mathbf{v}| = 5$ centimeters. (b) Calling θ the angle made by $\mathbf{v}$ with the positive *x* axis, we measure θ to be approximately 37°. We can *calculate* the angle θ from $\theta = \tan^{-1}(3/4) = \tan^{-1}(0.75) = 36.9°$.

5.4. Using the same *x* and *y* axes as in Fig. S.13, Fig. S.14 shows the vectors $\mathbf{A}$, $\mathbf{B}$, and $(-\mathbf{B})$, using a scale of 1 centimeter equals 2 meters. (a) Vector sum $(\mathbf{A} + \mathbf{B})$: the length of the arrow is approximately 2.7 centimeters, corresponding to a magnitude $|(\mathbf{A} + \mathbf{B})| \cong 5.4$ meters. The angle between $(\mathbf{A} + \mathbf{B})$ and the positive *x* axis is about 112°. (b) The vector $(\mathbf{A} - \mathbf{B})$ has a length of approximately 2.7 centimeters, again corresponding to a magnitude $|(\mathbf{A} - \mathbf{B})| \cong 5.4$ meters. The angle between vector $(\mathbf{A} - \mathbf{B})$ and the positive *x* axis is about 68°.

5.5. The vector $\mathbf{C}$ and its components $\mathbf{C}_x$ and $\mathbf{C}_y$, where $\mathbf{C} = \mathbf{C}_x + \mathbf{C}_y$, are shown in Fig. S.15. The angle between $\mathbf{C}$ and the positive *x* axis is $(\pi/6)$ radian, or 30°, so the angle between $\mathbf{C}$ and its *x* component $\mathbf{C}_x$ is also 30°,

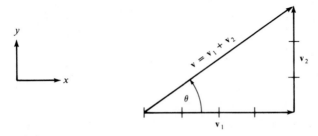

FIGURE S.13
The *x* and *y* axes as used in Exercise 5.3, and the graphical sum $\mathbf{v} = \mathbf{v}_1 + \mathbf{v}_2$.

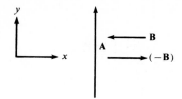

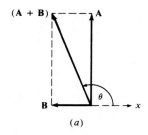

(a)

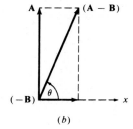

(b)

FIGURE S.14
(a) Graphical determination of (**A** + **B**) in Exercise 5.4; (b) graphical determination of (**A** − **B**).

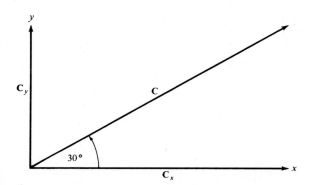

FIGURE S.15
The vector **C** = **C**$_x$ + **C**$_y$ in Exercise 5.5. The magnitude |**C**| = 100 units.

as shown in the figure. (a) From trigonometry, the magnitudes C_x, C_y, and C are related by

$$\frac{C_x}{C} = \cos 30° = 0.866 \qquad \frac{C_y}{C} = \sin 30° = 0.500$$

Since $C = 100$ units, we have

$$C_x = 86.6 \text{ units} \qquad C_y = 50.0 \text{ units}$$

(b) Writing $\mathbf{C}$ in the form $\mathbf{C} = C_x\hat{\mathbf{x}} + C_y\hat{\mathbf{y}}$, we obtain

$$\mathbf{C} = (86.6)\hat{\mathbf{x}} + (50.0)\hat{\mathbf{y}}$$

in terms of the rectangular coordinate unit vectors $\hat{\mathbf{x}}$ and $\hat{\mathbf{y}}$.

5.6. The vectors $\mathbf{v}$, $\mathbf{v}_x$, and $\mathbf{v}_y$, where $\mathbf{v} = \mathbf{v}_x + \mathbf{v}_y$, are shown in Fig. S.16. The angle between vectors $\mathbf{v}$ and $\mathbf{v}_x$ is $(\pi/4)$ radian, or 45°, and the magnitude $v = 100$ meters per second. (a) From trigonometry, we have

$$\frac{v_x}{v} = \cos 45° = 0.707 \qquad \frac{v_y}{v} = \sin 45° = 0.707$$

Since $v = 100$ meters per second, the scalar components v_x and v_y are

$$v_x = 70.7 \text{ meters per second}$$

$$v_y = 70.7 \text{ meters per second}$$

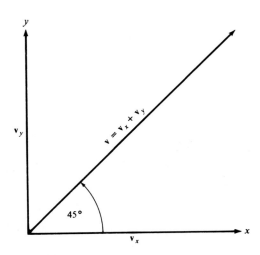

FIGURE S.16
Vectors $\mathbf{v}$, $\mathbf{v}_x$, and $\mathbf{v}_y$ in Exercise 5.6, where $\mathbf{v} = \mathbf{v}_x + \mathbf{v}_y = v_x\hat{\mathbf{x}} + v_y\hat{\mathbf{y}}$.

(b) Since $\mathbf{v} = v_x\hat{\mathbf{x}} + v_y\hat{\mathbf{y}}$, we have

$$\mathbf{v} = (70.7)\hat{\mathbf{x}} + (70.7)\hat{\mathbf{y}} = (70.7)(\hat{\mathbf{x}} + \hat{\mathbf{y}})$$

(c) To make a check, where $v^2 = (100)^2 = 10^4$,

$$v_x^2 + v_y^2 = (70.7)^2 + (70.7)^2 = 5000 + 5000 = 10^4$$

explicitly demonstrating that $v^2 = v_x^2 + v_y^2$.

5.7. Given $\mathbf{A} = 5\hat{\mathbf{x}} + 3\hat{\mathbf{y}}$ and $\mathbf{B} = -\hat{\mathbf{x}} - 2\hat{\mathbf{y}}$, so the scalar components of $\mathbf{A}$ and $\mathbf{B}$ are $A_x = 5$, $A_y = 3$, $B_x = -1$, and $B_y = -2$. Then

(a) $(\mathbf{A} + \mathbf{B}) = (A_x + B_x)\hat{\mathbf{x}} + (A_y + B_y)\hat{\mathbf{y}} = 4\hat{\mathbf{x}} + \hat{\mathbf{y}}$
(b) $(\mathbf{A} - \mathbf{B}) = (A_x - B_x)\hat{\mathbf{x}} + (A_y - B_y)\hat{\mathbf{y}} = 6\hat{\mathbf{x}} + 5\hat{\mathbf{y}}$
(c) $(\mathbf{A} + \mathbf{B}) + (\mathbf{A} - \mathbf{B}) = (4\hat{\mathbf{x}} + \hat{\mathbf{y}}) + (6\hat{\mathbf{x}} + 5\hat{\mathbf{y}}) = 10\hat{\mathbf{x}} + 6\hat{\mathbf{y}} = 2\mathbf{A}$
(d) Figure S.17 shows the vectors $(\mathbf{A} + \mathbf{B})$ and $(\mathbf{A} - \mathbf{B})$.

5.8. The position vector $\mathbf{r}$ of a point P, of rectangular coordinates (x, y), relative to the origin $(0, 0)$, is $\mathbf{r} = x\hat{\mathbf{x}} + y\hat{\mathbf{y}}$, so here $\mathbf{r} = 5\hat{\mathbf{x}} + 4\hat{\mathbf{y}}$ is the position vector from $(0, 0)$ to the point $(5, 4)$.

5.9. Given vectors $\mathbf{A} = \hat{\mathbf{x}} + \hat{\mathbf{y}}$ and $\mathbf{B} = \hat{\mathbf{x}} - \hat{\mathbf{y}}$. Then (a) $(\mathbf{A} \cdot \mathbf{B}) = (\hat{\mathbf{x}} + \hat{\mathbf{y}}) \cdot (\hat{\mathbf{x}} - \hat{\mathbf{y}}) = (1)(1) + (1)(-1) = 0$. (b) Since $(\mathbf{A} \cdot \mathbf{B}) = AB \cos \phi$, where ϕ is the angle between vectors $\mathbf{A}$ and $\mathbf{B}$, part (a) tells us that $\cos \phi = 0$, so $\phi = (\pi/2)$ radians, or $90°$. This result shows that the vectors $\mathbf{A}$ and $\mathbf{B}$ are

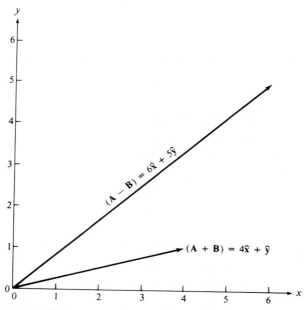

FIGURE S.17
Vectors $(\mathbf{A} + \mathbf{B}) = 4\hat{\mathbf{x}} + \hat{\mathbf{y}}$ and $(\mathbf{A} - \mathbf{B}) = 6\hat{\mathbf{x}} + 5\hat{\mathbf{y}}$ in Exercise 5.7.